633.202

GRASSLAND MANAGEMENT IN THE 'ENVIRONMENTALLY SENSITIVE AREAS'

Occasional Symposium No. 32 British Grassland Society, 199

KT-140-768

Proceedings of the British Grassland Society Conference held at the University of Lancaster, 23-25 September 1997.

LACKHAM LRC

WITHDRAWN

Edited by
R.D. SHELDRICK, OBE
Hon. Research Associate
Institute of Grassland and Environmental Research
North Wyke Research Station
OKEHAMPTON
Devon
EX20 2SB
UK

LACKHAM
COLLEGE
LIBRARY

i

OCCASIONAL SYMPOSIUM NO. 32

British Grassland Society

All rights reserved. No part of this publication may be reproduced, stored in a retrieval system, or transmitted, in any form or by any means, electronic, mechanical, photocopying, recording or otherwise, without the prior permission of the copyright owner.

Acknowledgements and disclaimer
This Conference was organised by a committee under the chairmanship of Dr J.H. McAdam. BGS gratefully acknowledges all those individuals and organisations who gave time to ensure the success of the Conference.

Occasional reference is made in this publication to trade names and proprietary products. No endorsement or criticism of named products is intended nor is any criticism implied of similar products which are not mentioned.

British Library Cataloguing-in-Publication Data available.

1997
ISBN 0 905944 54 2
ISSN 0572 7022

Copyright British Grassland Society

Cover photograph by F.I. Sant, B.Sc., LMPA

Printed by Arrowhead Books Ltd., 14 Portman Road, Reading, RG30 1LZ

CONTENTS

SESSION 3B: SCIENCE INTO PRACTICE - APPLICATION

SESSION 4: THE FUTURE

SESSION 1

POLICY ISSUES

Chairman: Angus Golightly
Jealotts Hill Research Station,
Bracknell

Environmental Policy in the European Context

KAREN MITCHELL

IEEP London, Dean Bradley House, 52 Horseferry Road, London, SWIP 2AG

ABSTRACT

Agricultural production is the dominant use of grassland in Europe hence the Common Agricultural Policy has a strong influence on grassland management. However, as well as the agri-environment Regulation 2078/92 which was adopted as an accompanying measure to the mainstream CAP support measures on their reform in 1992, there are a variety of other European environmental policies which influence the management of grassland. Of particular importance are the Birds and Habitats Directives which together provide for the establishment of a network of protected areas known as Natura 2000, and the Nitrates Directive. These policies form the main focus of this presentation.

EU AGRI-ENVIRONMENT REGULATION 2078/92

This Regulation, adopted as an environmental accompaniment to the 1992 reforms of the CAP, obliges Member States to establish aid schemes, so-called agri-environment measures, under which farmers are offered payments in return for complying with certain management practices. Measures may be devised and operated by national, regional or even local authorities. About 117 programmes, some containing several different schemes, have been approved by the European Commission. The schemes cover a wide range of objectives including reduced consumption of fertilisers and pesticides; organic farming; extensification of crop and livestock production; conversion of arable to extensive grassland; long-term set-aside of farmland for environmental purposes; management of abandoned land; farmer training; the rearing of rare livestock breeds; and the improvement and maintenance of natural values on agricultural land through management agreements.

FEOGA expenditure for the period 1993-97 was expected to be in the region of ECU 4.3 billion but is likely to be lower than this in practice. Indications are that the majority of the schemes apply to grasslands. Twenty year set-aside schemes, potentially an important means of recreating habitats, do not appear to be widespread or to have a high take-up rate.

NATURA 2000

The Natura 2000 network, composed of areas protected either under the habitats Directive (Council Directive 92/43 on the conservation of natural habitats and wild fauna and flora) or the Birds Directive (79/409 on the protection of wild birds), is due to be in place by June 2004. The network will cover all 15 Member States. The two categories of protected area within the network are:

- Special Areas of Conservation (SACs) designated under the Habitats Directive. The Directive lists 253 habitat types and 434 plant and 200 animal species of Community interest, of which a number are given 'priority' status because they are at the greatest risk of disappearing. Each Member State should have submitted a list of areas containing the habitat types and species specified in the Directive to the European Commission by June 1995. So far, only a few have done so. The Commission is responsible for compiling a list of areas for the whole Union by mid-1998. Member States must then designate all the agreed areas within six years. Due to the severe delays in the process which have already occurred, this timetable is likely to slip.
- Special Protection Areas (SPAs) designated under the Birds Directive which requires Member States to take appropriate measures to maintain populations of all wild bird species. SPAs should have been designated by the Member States within two years of the application of the Directive, but most authorities have failed to comply with this timetable.

Member States are obliged to establish measures to conserve the areas designated under the habitats Directive. Appropriate measures include schemes in which payments are made to farmers to follow management plans. Once established, the Natura 2000 network could cover a considerable area of land, including significant tracts of farmland.

THE EU NITRATES DIRECTIVE

The Nitrates Directive (Council Directive 91/676 concerning the protection of waters against pollution caused by nitrates from agricultural sources) adopted in December 1991, seeks to reduce or prevent the pollution of water caused by the application and storage of inorganic fertiliser and manure on farmland. It is intended both to safeguard drinking water supplies and to prevent wider ecological damage caused by the eutrophication of freshwater and marine waters.

Member States were obliged to identify 'vulnerable zones' which are areas of land which drain into waters susceptible to nitrate pollution by December 1993. By December 1995, Action Programmes relating to these vulnerable zones were to be established and implemented by December 1999 at the latest. The Action Programmes are to include a number of mandatory measures, such as:

- periods when the application of certain fertilisers is prohibited;
- limits on the quantities of fertilisers applied;
- a limit on the application of nitrogen in livestock manure per hectare initially equivalent to 210 kg N, falling to 170 kg after four years (these limits may be varied subject to approval from the European Commission);
- conditions relating to the storage capacity on farms for livestock manure;
- a code of good agricultural practice (which also may be implemented in areas other than vulnerable zones on a voluntary basis).

3

A number of Member States already had national policies targeting nitrate pollution prior to adoption of the Directive, particularly the northern Member States where the impact of intensive agriculture on water quality is especially strong *e.g.* Denmark and the Netherlands. In some Member States, additional measures, such as incentive payments to farmers to reduce nitrogen use, are being used.

UK Policy for ESAs

D. COATES

Head of Environment Group, Ministry of Agriculture Fisheries and Food,
17 Smith Square, London SW1P 3JR.

ABSTRACT

Government policy for agriculture and the environment seeks to balance the interests of efficient food production and the countryside through a range of instruments which include regulation, advice and incentives. The Environmentally Sensitive Area (ESA) Scheme is the oldest UK agri-environment incentive scheme and was introduced in 1987. It now forms part of the UK's implementation of EC Regulation 2078/92 which required all Member States of the EU to introduce zonal agri-environmental programmes. Key features of the ESA Scheme are that payments are only made for activities additional to the "good practice" or regulatory baseline; the use of 10 year voluntary contracts; and flat rate payments which are subject to regular review. ESAs are designated in areas of national importance, and the requirements are developed individually to meet local requirements.

The English ESA Scheme has been successively expanded in terms of numbers of areas, from 5 in 1987 to 22 in 1994. Evaluations based on an extensive monitoring programme have concluded that the scheme has been largely successful in achieving its objectives, and provides good value for money to the taxpayer. Grassland management is a central part of the ESA scheme, for wildlife, landscape and archeological objectives.

Recent reviews have identified a need for greater flexibility in some areas of the scheme, to tailor agreements to the needs of individual sites and concentrate more on the "outputs" to be achieved. Increased emphasis is also placed in the delivery of biodiversity priorities. The UK Biodiversity Action Plan published in 1995 and proposals for reform of the Common Agricultural Policy will be influential in shaping the future of ESAs and other agri-environment schemes.

THE POLICY CONTEXT OF ESAs

Government policy for agriculture and the environment seeks to balance the demand for efficiently produced food with the demand for the countryside to be protected. Indeed a duty to balance such factors is imposed on the Minister of Agriculture, Fisheries and Food by Section 17 of the Agriculture Act 1986. Farmers and other land managers have a major role in caring for the countryside, and Government policy assists them to reconcile agricultural and environmental needs through a combination of guidance, protection measures and incentives.

The Environmentally Sensitive Areas (ESA) scheme is the oldest of a series of measures now operated by the UK Government under which incentive payments are made to farmers and other land managers in return for land management practices directed at the conservation of the rural environment. The origin of such policies as adopted by the UK in the early 1980s, and more recently by other Member States of the European Union, was as part of the Government's response to public concern about the effects of technological progress, involving improved farm machinery new cultivation techniques and land drainage, the operation of support regimes and other Government policies designed to increase agricultural efficiency. These factors were contributing to losses of habitats (such as permanent grassland and hedges) and changes to landscape which were widely perceived as damaging.

Such policies, termed "agri-environment" implying the integration of agricultural and environmental aspects, are one element in the range of Government policies designed to protect and enhance the rural environment. A second major area of activity is protection through regulatory restrictions, such as on the avoidance of pollution (controls on the safe storage of farm animal and other wastes and the safe use of pesticides), planning designations (particularly those operating in areas of high landscape value such as the National Parks), conservation designations such as SSSIs and sites designated under the EU Birds and Habitats and Species Directives and proposed hedgerow regulations. Cross-compliance measures introduced to control over-grazing on semi-natural vegetation and environmental conditions applied to set aside land, for example to prohibit mowing during the bird nesting season, could be described as quasi-regulatory policies.

Advice on environmentally appropriate practices is also regarded by the Government as an important way of influencing behaviour of land managers. MAFF publishes a series of Codes of Good Agricultural Practice for the Protection of Soil, Air and Water. These will shortly be updated and relaunched in order to increase farmers' awareness of them. Finally, MAFF funds a programme of free conservation advice which is provided by ADAS and FWAG to farmers, and participates in the LEAF initiative providing environmental audit and demonstration farms using sustainable agricultural techniques such as Integrated Crop Management.

The choice of policy tool depends on the circumstances and the issues being addressed. Land managers will not normally be funded to carry out activities which would be expected of them in any case, such as following Good Agricultural Practice. Regulation is used to ensure compliance with such expectations where necessary. Incentives such as those offered under the agri-environment schemes are used where the environmental goals sought go beyond those that can reasonably be expected of farmers to carry out of their own accord.

ORIGIN AND DEVELOPMENT OF ESAs

The pilot ESA covering the Halvergate marshes was developed under the title of the Broads Grazing Marshes Conservation Scheme. This operated in 1985 and 1986, and was replaced in 1987 by the Broads ESA, one of the first ESAs launched in 1987 following the passage of 1986 Agriculture Act. Section 18 of this Act gave the Minister of Agriculture, Fisheries and Food the power to designate and make payments in areas of national environmental significance in England following consultation with the Department of Environment, the Countryside Commission and the (then) Nature Conservancy Council. The Act itself followed the EC Regulation 797/85 (EC, 1985) which permitted Member States to make payments to farmers in designated areas of high conservation value in order to encourage farming practices of benefit to the environment. ESAs were also introduced in Scotland, Wales and Northern Ireland by the relevant Agriculture Departments. The general principle of the scheme is the same in these countries, although the mechanism has been adapted to deal with local conditions and environmental priorities.

The protection of grassland has always been a central objective of the ESA scheme, and in the first five ESAs the protection of species-rich and wet grassland are prominent objectives. Unlike some agri-environment policies which are directed at single environmental objectives, the ESA scheme was conceived as multi-functional, with landscape, wildlife conservation and historic/archaeological objectives. Experience has shown that is normally possible to design incentive measures which can integrate these fundamental objectives into a coherent scheme, with little conflict between the objectives being pursued. The conservation of permanent grassland is a good example of this, since protecting and enhancing permanent grassland will often benefit both landscape and wildlife, with the added bonus of protecting buried archaeological remains.

The early experience of the ESA scheme was encouraging. Following monitoring and evaluation of the first 10 ESAs launched in 1987 and 1988 it was concluded that they had been largely successful in their aim of protecting the designated areas. The schemes were relaunched in 1992 and 1993 with revised objectives, which included a greater emphasis on restoration and enhancement. New options (or tiers) were introduced, and boundary extensions made. Two further sets of ESAs were launched in England in 1993 and 1994, which brought the total designated area to over a million hectares which cover roughly 10% of agricultural land in England. Payments to farmers in English ESAs were about £28 million in 1996/7, on 8,200 agreements covering some 434,000 hectares. Current public expenditure plans envisage an increase in ESA payments to some £43 million in 1999/00.

The CAP reforms of 1992 included a number of accompanying measures as part of the main reforms which moved support away from being linked directly to production and to introduce supply controls (quotas) on output. One of these was Regulation 2078/92 (EC 1992), which obliged Member States to introduce a zonal programme of agri-environmental measures. In responding to this requirement, MAFF introduced a number of measures including the Habitats Scheme for salt marshes, waterside and former set-aside land and the Moorland and Organic Aid Schemes. The Countryside Stewardship scheme which had been introduced as a pilot by the Countryside Commission in 1991 was transferred to MAFF in 1996, following the passage of enabling measures in the 1995 Environment Act.

The experience of operating ESAs provided a basis for the development of these further schemes. Many of the basic elements - 10 year contracts, flat rate payments in return with compliance with management prescriptions and guidelines, regular payment reviews - have been adopted in these more recent schemes. The largest of these is Countryside Stewardship which was introduced in 1991 and is available throughout England - not just within designated areas. The environmental priorities for Stewardship are similar to ESAs and aim to make conservation part of farming and land management practice by offering payments for changes in management practices which will improve the natural heritage of the countryside. The objectives are to:

- sustain the beauty and diversity of the countryside;
- improve and extend wildlife habitats;
- conserve archaeological sites and historic features; improve opportunities for countryside enjoyment;
- restore neglected features;
- create new habitats and landscapes.

Currently there are over 5,200 agreements covering in excess of 92,000 ha with a further 1320 agreements entering the scheme this year.

Although Stewardship is available throughout England the scheme is targeted at priority landscapes and features including chalk and limestone grassland, waterside land, old meadows and pastures, the coast, lowland heath, the uplands, historic landscapes and features, countryside around towns, old orchards, field margins on arable land, field boundaries - including hedges, walls, banks, ditches and dikes and new access.

Payments to Countryside Stewardship agreement holders were over £11 million in 1996/7. Under MAFF's current public expenditure plans we envisage an increase in payments to about £28 million in 1999/00.

RECENT DEVELOPMENTS IN ESA POLICY

The development of the ESA scheme is carried out within a review cycle, in which each ESA is reviewed at five-yearly intervals and decisions taken about its future. To inform these reviews a range of information is collected and consultations carried out with a wide range of organisations. MAFF has also established a system of consultation for agri-environment schemes generally, consisting of a National Agri-Environment Steering Group containing the national statutory advisory bodies, and a National Agri-Environment Forum with a wider membership including NGOs. These arrangements are supported at regional level by Regional Agri-Environment Consultation Groups, and separate liaison groups in each ESA.

The review programme under the ESA scheme is informed by an extensive environmental monitoring programme, costing £2.2 million when review work was at its peak in 1996/97. This work enables the success of the scheme to be evaluated against the detailed environmental objectives which have been published for each ESA (MAFF, 1996a). A wide range of research is also undertaken in support of the ESA and Countryside Stewardship schemes, which amounted to £1.75 million in 1996/7. Finally, economic research into the ESA policy has been carried out. For example, a contingent valuation cost-benefit analysis conducted in 1993 showed that the South Downs and Somerset Levels and Moors ESAs represented good value for money: the benefits of the South Downs ESA were shown to be at least five times the cost of payments to farmers in the scheme; in the Somerset Levels and Moors the benefits were at least twice the cost (Willis and Garrod, 1993).

The most recent opportunity to review the operation of the ESA scheme was in 1996, when a major review of the first five ESAs launched in 1987 was carried out. The results of environmental and economic evaluations were published during the review (MAFF, 1996b and ADAS, 1996) and five consultation documents were issued in October 1996 setting out MAFF's proposals for the future of these ESAs. The outcome of the review was announced in February 1997 by the Minister of Agriculture Fisheries and Food.

The evaluation confirmed that the ESA scheme was delivering positive environmental benefits which would not have been achieved in its absence. In particular, the economic evaluation (ADAS, 1996) demonstrated that farmers were incurring significant opportunity costs through their participation in the ESA. It also showed that whilst most farmers were committed to this scheme in the long term and saw the ESA as a valuable means of environmental protection, many of the practices encouraged by the ESA scheme would not be continued in its absence.

The environmental monitoring work, and the related R&D identified a need for greater flexibility in some areas of the scheme. MAFF considers that the ESA mechanism of area-based payments made in return for compliance with standard prescriptions offers substantial benefits in terms of administrative efficiency, and has advantages for farmers who can clearly see that they are receiving equality of treatment. Regulation 2078/92 under which the ESA scheme is approved is also based on this principle. However, MAFF has identified that there is a need in some respects for greater flexibility, and the tailoring of agreements to the environmental requirements of an individual site. A more flexible approach can also help identify how farmers can best deliver environmental benefits within the context of their own farming operations, since it can involve concentrating more on the "outputs" required, rather than solely on the "inputs" such as stocking densities.

Two examples of this are the measures adopted in the Pennine Dales and South Downs ESAs to draw up individual grazing management plans to take account of site specific management requirements; and the introduction of flexibility in relation to water levels in the Somerset Levels and Moors ESA, to enable the water regime of sites to be adjusted to take account of botanical communities' water level requirements.

MAFF has also increased the designated area of four out of the five Stage I ESAs by a total of 16,700 hectares. A substantial proportion of this increase is permanent grassland and rough grazing, notably in the Pennine Dales, Broads and Somerset Levels and Moors ESAs. This expansion has made a significant contribution to national biodiversity priorities, for example in response to the Biodiversity Action Plans for grazing marshes which envisages the extension of positive management to an additional 5,000 hectares of grazing marsh beyond that currently targeted by the ESA programme (DoE 1995). It is likely that similar changes may be introduced following the review of Stage II and III ESAs in 1997/98.

FUTURE DEVELOPMENTS

The Biodiversity Convention, signed in Rio de Janeiro in June 1992, committed Governments to conserve and enhance biological diversity. The UK, Biodiversity Action Plan was published in January 1994 and following this a Biodiversity Steering Group was established involving representatives drawn from Government and non-Government, including MAFF. The Steering Group Report published in 1995 contains a series of Action Plans for both species and habitats and more are in preparation. As a partner in the UK Biodiversity Action Plan, MAFF is committed to working for the delivery of biodiversity priorities, including habitat and species Action Plans. ESAs, alongside other agri-environment schemes such as Countryside Stewardship, are an important delivery mechanism for biodiversity priorities. Even where MAFF schemes are not specifically identified as a delivery mechanism for individual Action Plans, there may be scope for the ESA and other schemes to play a useful contribution.

The structure and role of agri-environment schemes will also need to take account of developments in agricultural policy. In 1997 we find ourselves in a period of preparation, between the implementation of the GATT Uruguay Round which was associated with the 1992 reforms of the CAP, and a new round of negotiations under the World Trade Organisation likely to start in 1999. Preparations for these negotiations have already begun, based in the European Union and elsewhere. Developments in agricultural support policy within the EU and world-wide will have implications for the English countryside and thus for the objectives and mechanism of the ESA scheme. A conference in Cork in November 1996 provided an opportunity for both Governments and NGOs to put forward their views on the future shape of rural policy. The conference concluded with a declaration calling for an integrated rural policy, taking account of both environmental and economic objectives. It seems likely that future developments in this area could have a significant role in shaping the future of ESAs and other agri-environment schemes.

The future of agri-environment policy in the United Kingdom, therefore must be seen as part of a wider debate. Whilst the principle of Government purchase of environmental goods from farmers and land managers on behalf of the taxpayer has been established, and now constitutes a significant thread in Government rural policy, the future development of ESA and other agri-environment policies is intimately connected to the wider economic policies and constraints.

REFERENCES
ADAS (1996) Economic evaluation of Stage I ESAs: follow up study report on the South Downs, Somerset Levels and Moors, Pennine Dales, West Penwith and Broads ESAs. Available on the Environment page on MAFF's Internet site (http://www.open.gov.uk/maffhome.htm).

DoE (1995) Biodiversity; the UK Steering Group Report, London HMSO 1995

EC (1985) Regulation 797/85; EC Official Journal ref: L93 30/3/85

EC (1992) Regulation 2078/92; EC Official Journal ref: L215 30/07/92

MAFF (1996a) Memorandum of evidence on Environmentally Sensitive Areas and other schemes under the Agri-Environment Regulation; House of Commons Select Committee on Agriculture Second Report; Vol II, HC 45 II. HMSO 1997.

MAFF (1996b) ADAS reports to MAFF on environmental monitoring in the South Downs, Somerset Levels and Moors, Pennine Dales, West Penwith and Broads ESAs; MAFF Publications 1996.

WILLIS and GARROD (1993) Valuation of the South Downs and Somerset Levels and Moors Environmentally Sensitive Areas Landscapes by the General Public. Research Report to MAFF. Department of Agricultural Economics and Food Marketing, University of Newcastle upon Tyne.

Annex A

CURRENT ENVIRONMENTALLY SENSITIVE AREAS IN ENGLAND

Name	Date First Designated	Latest Renewal Date	Total Area Designated
STAGE I			
The Broads	1987	1997	35,820
Somerset Levels and Moors	1987	1997	27,717
Pennine Dales	1987	1997	46,371
West Penwith	1987	1997	7,180
South Downs	1987	1997	69,377
STAGE I TOTAL AREA (HECTARES)			186,465
STAGE II			
Breckland	1988	1993	94,032
North Peak	1988	1993	54, 875
Clun	1988	1993	21,365
Suffolk River Valleys	1988	1993	43,780
Test Valley	1988	1993	4,800
STAGE II TOTAL AREA (HECTARES)			218,852
STAGE III			
Avon Valley	1993		5,200
Exmoor	1993		81,000
Lake District	1993		245,200
North Kent Marshes	1993		14,700
South Wessex Downs	1993		45,900
South West Peak	1993		33,900
STAGE III TOTAL AREA (HECTARES)			425,900
STAGE IV			
Cotswold Hills	1994		84,669
Dartmoor	1994		100,777
Blackdown Hills	1994		39,325
Essex Coast	1994		27,006
Shropshire Hills	1994		38,514
Upper Thames Tributaries	1994		27,700
STAGE IV TOTAL AREA (HECTARES)			317,991
ENGLAND TOTAL AREA (HECTARES)			**1,149,208**

LANDSCAPE AND CONSERVATION ISSUES

Chairman: Peter Costigan
Chief Scientists Group
Ministry of Agriculture, Fisheries and Food

Grasslands: the Historical Context

J. SHEAIL

Institute of Terrestrial Ecology, Monks Wood, Huntingdon, Cambridgeshire PE17 2LS

ABSTRACT

Through a selection of old farming and natural-history texts, the paper identifies the more salient elements of grassland management since the sixteenth century, with particular reference to the establishment of new grasslands and the influence of ecology.

INTRODUCTION

Although the emphasis of this Conference is on the present and future, it is assumed, at least implicitly, that there should be an historical underpinning in place. Both the Environmentally Sensitive Areas and Countryside Stewardship Schemes require an historical dimension. Landowners, farmers and the community at large are enjoined to conserve, manage and re-create valued landscapes and habitats. Each of the six environmental objectives of the Countryside Stewardship Scheme recognises the essentially dynamic qualities of the countryside - the ability to lose, sustain and develop fresh attributes. In fulfilling the objectives of the schemes, it is no exaggeration to say that a knowledge of the past is a key to competent and successful management of the countryside in the future.

Printed and manuscript sources, and an informed interpretation of the evidence that survives in the countryside itself, help to reconstruct in our minds the state of grasslands in the past. They help to explain how those of the present-day evolved. It is a task that involves more than simply describing when and where grasslands developed. The challenge is to explain how and why change came about, and the significance of the end product. In short, we need to get into the mind of the landowner, farmer and their 'expert' advisers. How conscious were they of the varying quality of their grasslands? What steps were taken to manipulate species composition? How adept were they in establishing new grasslands?

PAST GRASSLANDS

Broad descriptions of grasslands may be found in old agricultural texts and natural-histories. In his 'Rural Economy of the West of England', published in 1796, the agricultural commentator, William Marshall, described the herbage of South Sedgemoor in Somerset as

> "singularly fine: apparently the Dogstail (*Cynosurus cristatus*), Raygrass, and White Clover; with however, some plots of thistles, on the drier parts, and stripes of silver weed (*Potentilla anserina*) on the sides of the drains, and more swampy places" (Marshall, 1796).

Land of the first quality, it was fit for 'every purpose of permanent grassland'.

14

Whilst our historical sources might use such familiar words as 'pasture' and 'meadow', and species names that are recognisable today, the swards were for the most part very different. Among the clues is the frequent reference to the anthill as a serious agricultural nuisance. According to Walter Blith, the author of 'The English Improver' of 1649, anthills had become the "great enemies to the grazier" in old grassland. "Infinite great pastures all over the kingdome are so over-runne". Bearing little or no grass, but "a little wild time and speary harsh grasse" that cattle would eat only when hungry, "one fourth part of the clear fruit of that land" might be lost (Blith, 1649). And writing of pastures in the late nineteenth century, the naturalist, Richard Jefferies, described how the anthills were often so close to one another that one could walk some 20 to 30 yards without touching proper ground (Jefferies, 1879).

Writers emphasised the wide variety of conditions both within and between the different parts of the country. In the Somerset Moors, West Sedgemoor was famed for the grazing of young stock, bullocks and horses, whereas a form of shifting cultivation was practised over large parts of nearby King's Sedgemoor, whereby the surface vegetation was pared and burned, and a few crops of wheat, oats and potatoes or beans taken. Everywhere the character and productivity of the Moors closely reflected the incidence of local husbandry practices. Whilst the soils of the higher levels contained the most 'proof', many of the grasslands on the thinner soils along the rivers produced a higher-quality cheese for as long as winter flooding continued to sustain fertility. So as to ensure that sufficient sediment was deposited, a system of artificial warping was adopted at Glastonbury between the higher level of the Brue and lower level. By means of hatches, or small sluices, formed in the bank of the higher river, the winter floodwaters, thick with sediment, were directed onto the meadows where they were retained for as long as it took for the sediment to be deposited (Acland and Sturge, 1851; Clark, 1854).

Some writers strove to explain what farmers had for long observed. In 'The Surveiors Dialogue', John Norden wrote of how the

> "land is like the body: if it bee not fed with nutriture, and comforted and adorned with the most expedient commodities, it will pine away, and become forlorne, as the minde that hath no rest or recreation, waxeth lumpish and heavy" (Norden, 1610).

By the late seventeenth century, there is increasing evidence of grasslands being systematically cultivated, fertilised and sown with seeds (Lane, 1980). In a volume of 1747, William Ellis set out three ways of enjoying "a meadow ground in the highest perfection". The most obvious way was by creating water-meadows, the second by broadcasting common hay seeds in February on "old decayed meadows", and the third by converting arable land to "a delicate thick planted profitable meadow" (Ellis, 1747). In his 'Hints to Gentlemen of Landed Property', Nathaniel Kent wrote, in 1793, of how "the first, and most easy, and the greatest of all improvements" to meadow and pasture land was by flooding (Kent, 1793). William Marshall described in 1798 how the entire surface of the floodplain of the river Avon, below Salisbury, was thrown into convex beds, about 10 yards wide. Whilst the natural herbage was short and of a harsh nature, that of the watered ground was soft, long, and apparently of rich quality, comprising "raygrass, the meadow poa, the marsh and other bent grasses, and the meadow fescues". On the sides of the trenches and ditches, "the flote fescue, reed canary grass (*Phalaris arundinacea*) and the water poa (*Poa aquatica*)" were common. The common dock appeared to be the only common weed (Marshall, 1798).

Such ventures in resource engineering may have wrecked what was there before. Almost certainly the irrigated lands contained a smaller range of species than the previous naturally-flooded meadows. The deeper green and greater density of those water meadows nevertheless attracted the considerable attention of those authors, who wrote for the increasing number of Victorian readers, content to explore the countryside from the armchair. In his volume, 'Wild England of To-day and the Wild Life in it', Cornish described how the river Itchen in Hampshire flowed "like a vein of warm life through the cold body of the hills", even in the coldest weather. Although "ribbed across with multitudinous channels of white and crackling ice", the watermeadows remained green, and were crowded with

> "plovers and redwings, snipe and water-hens, sea-gulls, field-fares and missel thrushes, pipits and larks, and all the soft billed birds in search of food" (Cornish, 1895).

From a review of agricultural texts and journals, Angus and Owen Davies (1996) concluded that the grassland landscape remained for the most part floristically-rich until at least the late nineteenth century. If the naturalist made inventories of their composition so as to distinguish the locally and nationally rare, the author of a letter to the *Journal of the Bath and West of England Agricultural Society* had another purpose in mind in 1853, in pressing the Society's Council to organise the listing of plants in every locality according to their Linnaean and common names, with details based on "actual experiment or observation" as to whether livestock would eat them. Such knowledge would provide "the best and most effective means" of eradicating the majority from which the grazier derived no benefit (Cotterell, 1853). But if that was the aspiration of the improver-farmer, it is difficult to discern whether it was economics or some other factor that deterred the more 'traditional' farmer from controlling the species composition of pastures more closely. One can only speculate as to whether such 'non-improving' farmers simply lacked the basic botanical knowledge and agricultural education, or whether they took the presence of such rich mixtures as evidence of the land being 'in good heart'? In some cases, the mixtures may have been consciously preserved for the health of the livestock (Davies and Davies, 1996). It is only a little less hazardous to generalise as to the changing extent of grasslands. Throughout the late eighteenth and early nineteenth centuries much of the higher chalk downland acquired the name of 'bakelands'. Arthur Young described, in the *Annals of Agriculture* for 1795 how the maiden down in the Stockbridge area of Hampshire had been broken up by paring-and-burning the turf in readiness for tillage. One could not fail to see the effect, 'the original down now left is very trifling'. One or two cereal crops might be taken, before the land was laid down to rye-grass and rested. In other instances, as many crops as possible were taken, before the ground was left to 'tumbledown' to whatever vegetation might establish itself (Young, 1795). The agricultural historian has expended much energy distinguishing the respective roles of changes in fiscal policy (and most obviously the repeal of the Corn Laws) and that of innovation in husbandry methods, in stimulating the so-called period of High Farming in the mid-nineteenth century. The increasing use of crushed bones and guano may have later encouraged 'a more regular system of culture' on the higher downlands. Barns and yards appeared in larger number. Even so, much of the land reverted to grassland following the marked fall in cereal prices as increasing volumes of relatively cheap imported grain arrived from the Americas from the 1870s onwards (Perren, 1995).

Evidence of that phase of abandonment of tillage land is preserved in the annual statistics of the Board of Agriculture from 1866 onwards, official inquiries and the farming press and, in some instances, the landscape itself. Permanent grassland made up 43.8% of the total area of crops and grassland in England and Wales between 1866 and 1875, 48% (1876-85), 53% (1886-95), 56% (1896-1905) and 58% (1906-15) (Ministry of Agriculture, 1968). The impact on grassland quality may have been twofold. Management may have become more intensive where, say, dairying found a ready market in nearby towns or railheads. Where, however, supplementary feeds reduced the farmer's dependence on grass as a source of energy and proteins for livestock, the herbage might become even coarser. The rough-grazing and scrub symbol become noticeably more prominent in the revisions of the large-scale Ordnance Survey maps published at the turn of the century (Duffey et al., 1974).

Where such grassland communities have been preserved from modern agriculture, as in the extensive military training areas of Wiltshire, a mosaic of swards of different conjectured ages can be discerned. For some parts of the mosaic, there is no evidence of past cultivation. For a much greater area, there are records of the land being cultivated at some point in the last century. Of the six sward-types identified on Porton Down in Wiltshire, in the early 1970s, five could be related to differences in past land use (Wells et al., 1976).

ON LAYING DOWN PERMANENT PASTURES

The historical record is both incomplete and distorted. In his 'Treatise on Watermeadows', Boswell wrote, in 1801, of how those with the most relevant knowledge had little opportunity, let alone incentive, to set down their opinions (Boswell, 1801). There was, however, no mistaking the motive of William Curtis in writing his book, 'Practical Observations on the British Grasses best adapted to the Laying Down, or Improving of Meadows and Pastures', published in 1789. It was to boost sales of his packets of seed mixtures. A botanical writer and lecturer, Curtis (1790) set up a garden at Brompton, from which he could supply seeds for retail. As well as describing the further 27 species that warranted attention. He had no doubt,

> "but at some future time, it will be as common to sow a meadow with a composition somewhat like this, as it now is to sow a field of wheat or barley."

Other commentators were less sanguine. The President of the Board of Agriculture, Sir John Sinclair, described the conversion of old tillage to permanent pasture as one of the most difficult operations (Sinclair, 1818). The author of the Board's report for Leicestershire, published in 1809, recounted how local custom and the covenants of leases strongly discouraged the breaking up of grass land. The principal graziers and breeders believed it would take up to forty years for "rich, old feeding land", once ploughed, to be restored to its former fertility and nutritive state. Because of the way the fibrous roots of the best grasses struck "imperceptible small shoots", many feet into the earth, the grasslands rarely suffered in hot, dry summers. Once broken up, "this deep communication is cut off", and many years must elapse before it could be restored (Pitt, 1809).

In his study, 'Hortus Gramineus Woburnensis', published in 1824, the gardener to the Duke of Bedford, George Sinclair, argued that many of the difficulties and long delays arose from the farmer's failure to sow the most productive grass species, suited to the soil of the new pastures. In choosing a mixture, the farmer should take account of nutritive quality, early growth, reproductive power, permanency in the soil, and the ease with which plants could be propagated from seed. No species excelled in all these qualities. When establishing a new sward, the aim should be to select species which would, when taken together, provide a constant supply of rich succulent herbage. To Sinclair (1824), it seemed extraordinary that the farmer should leave it to nature to establish such productive grassland. Since "the whole art of cultivating plants is nothing more than assisting Nature in the provision of the growth of vegetables", it was an obvious step for farmers to help nature in "clothing the soil with its natural perennial grasses" and, by doing so, ensure that it took only 3 or 4 years, rather than the 8, 10 or 20 years required by nature.

The most powerful stimulus to improvements in grassland husbandry was most likely to come from market forces. In 1875, the *Journal of the Royal Agricultural Society* published 55 reports from different parts of England and Wales on "the laying down of permanent pasture and the increase in the length of time arable land was left under artificial grasses", compiled in response to a questionnaire distributed by the Society. In an introduction to the reports, the editors commented on how, for many years, it had become apparent to farmers that the conversion of arable land to pasture would enable them to benefit from the rise in meat prices at a time when corn prices were static. There would also be considerable savings in labour and machinery costs (Evans and Bowstead, 1875). These considerations became ever more pressing when cereal prices fell dramatically during the 1870s.

The most widely-read prescription for laying down pastures appeared in the *Journal* in 1882, written by an estate owner in Kent. In emphasising the need to select and sow the right species, it called for considerable improvements in the purity of mixtures being provided by the commercial seed trade (Laune, 1882). The seed merchants themselves became an increasingly important source of advice to farmers. A notable example was William Toogood's book, 'Pasture and Pasture Plants'. According to him, plants should be chosen that would form a complete sward and yield "the greatest possible, most certain and sustained annual produce of palatable food for a desired period". Judicious mixtures of grasses and leguminous plants would not only suppress weeds, but utilise the different strata of the soil more profitably and fully than when sown singly. They were less likely to cause partial chemical exhaustion of the land by using one element too quickly. Experience indicated that mixtures were less sensitive to adverse external factors than species sown singly. Where a species was injured, there was a greater chance of another filling its space (Toogood, 1897).

Whilst no one denied the importance of selecting seed mixtures carefully, several commentators emphasised how this would not in itself ensure that the grasslands contained the optimal proportions of each species in later years. From his trials at Clifton Park in Roxburghshire, Robert Elliott concluded that soil and climatic factors were likely to be so variable as to preclude any general rules being laid down for the establishment of pasture (Elliott, 1943). It was impossible to predict precisely how much space would be eventually occupied by any particular species. The rivalry in the newly-sown sward was so keen, and the chances of competitors so evenly balanced, that a heavy fall of rain at one time might prejudice one type of grassland, and a similar fall a fortnight later might cause quite another to develop (Everitt, 1897).

THE INFLUENCE OF THE ENVIRONMENT

An understanding of the relationships between vegetation cover and the physical and chemical properties of the soil began to emerge in the late nineteenth century. William Fream compared the botanical composition of turves from 25 rich, old pastures in England and Ireland, which had been transplanted and grown side by side in their original soils (Fream, 1888). Manurial experiments on grasslands were pioneered at the Rothamsted Experimental Station from 1856 onwards (Lawes, 1889), and taken up by the Royal Agricultural College at Cirencester in 1888, and at the Cockle Park Experimental Station after 1896. It remains far from clear how quickly research findings were translated into everyday farming-practice. Certainly Lawes and Gilbert, at Rothamsted, seem to have been assiduous in disseminating their work, Lawes writing in 1851, "I consider my investigations so much in the light of public property and am so anxious that they should be of service to the scientific work that I do not care how much my figures are circulated" (Williams, 1993).

During trials on grass and clover mixtures at Cockle Park, Douglas Gilchrist had recognised the great superiority of wild White clover over the commercial strains in use (Pawson, 1960). Soon after his appointment in 1912 to Aberystwyth as an Adviser in Agricultural Botany, R.G. Stapledon began to collaborate with T. J. Jenkin in identifying ways of promoting the development of indigenous plants in established swards. Early trials indicated that the most effective way of encouraging the spread and colonisation of such plants was to 'disturb' that pasture by 'reasonably heavy grazing'. In order to identify which of the treatments studied on the trial plots might be applied to particular tracts of farmland, a systematic method was required for classifying grasslands (Stapledon and Jenkin, 1916).

It was here that Stapledon drew insight and inspiration from the early development of ecology or, more precisely, the British Vegetation Committee. During a year in Cambridge in 1909-10, taking an agricultural diploma, he took every opportunity to gatecrash lectures and joined the field excursions of the ecologists, C.E. Moss and A.G. Tansley (Sheail, 1986). He completed a vegetation map at the scale of 1:10560 for over 100,000 acres of north Cardiganshire in 1913. He was struck not only by the variety of plant communities recorded, but by the evidence to suggest that large tracts of heath, bracken, gorse and bog were only of recent origin. In some parts, the vegetation covered plough ridges, dating perhaps from the Napoleonic Wars. Under Stapledon's direction, the mapping of grasslands of Wales proceeded at a scale of 1:63360, and often 1:10560, based on the premise that each grassland type represented "a complex community of a number of different species representing a number of different growth forms and physiological relationships towards the habitat" (Stapledon, 1933). It was only possible to undertake such surveys, and the detailed studies made, for example, of the Cocksfoot (*Dactylis glomerata*), where the eventual agricultural benefit might warrant the cost of the facilities required. Stapledon (1928) hoped ecologists would soon be able to obtain sufficient financial backing for a research station of their own. Only then would it be possible "to elucidate with reasonable assurance the fundamental problems connected with the distribution, acclimatization and evolution of plants".

GRASSLAND ECOLOGY AND WILDLIFE MANAGEMENT

Initially at least, the period of post-war reconstruction offered outstanding opportunities, in as much as the State extended unprecedented levels of material support not only for agriculture and forestry but for a third force in the countryside, the protection of amenity and wildlife, and promotion of outdoor recreation. But if the State wished to encourage each of these activities, it offered little incentive for them to pool their intellectual resources. Ministers, and most strikingly Lord Hailsham as Minister for Science, forbade scientists of the Nature Conservancy from engaging in research that might be construed as having agricultural application. It meant the Conservancy's pioneering studies as to the optimal way of managing grasslands for nature-conservation purposes had to be largely confined to National Nature Reserves (Sheail, 1996).

Even if the sensibilities of the different research institutions had allowed a more liberal attitude to be taken towards cross-sectoral research, the scope for applying knowledge gained of the management, rehabilitation, restoration and creation of grasslands for conservation purposes in the wider countryside would have been severely limited. Such was the scale and rapidity of habitat destruction, caused by cultivation and the heavy use of fertilisers and pesticides, that there would have been little chance to make use of it. New grasslands were however formed for non-agricultural purposes, as part of the rehabilitation of derelict land or for amenity purposes in country parks, new towns or the verges of motorways. The standard Department of Environment mixture for major road verges specified highly-productive cultivars, like S23 perennial ryegrass and S59 red fescue. Whilst meeting its immediate objective, such dense sward made colonisation by other plants difficult. The fast-growing species also required more frequent cutting. Supported by the Nature Conservancy Council, the Institute of Terrestrial Ecology at Monks Wood drew on many years of research into the management of existing grasslands for nature-conservation purposes in developing, from 1978 onwards, techniques for establishing *de novo* colourful and attractive grasslands using mixtures of native grasses and broad-leaved herbs.

In articles in the 'Gardener's Chronical and Horticultural Trader's Journal', proceedings of the Recreation Ecology Research Group, and a booklet, 'Creating Attractive Grasslands using Native Plant Species' (published by the Nature Conservancy Council), Wells (1981a, b and c) and Wells, Bell and Frost (1981) recounted ways in which such attractive grasslands might be created either from direct seeding into prepared seed beds, or by transplanting plants grown from seed in a glasshouse into rows in the field. A nurse crop might provide an immediate vegetation cover, both for aesthetic reasons and to minimise soil erosion. Like others before him, Wells prescribed a fine tilth for the seed bed, with a firm, even surface free from annual and perennial weeds. Experience indicated that wild-flower mixtures did best on soils of low fertility. They could compete much better with many of the grasses. Results from the first 7 years of a trial on chalk soils (where the sward was cut at least once a year) indicated that, as the grassland gradually settled down, the one or two prominent species of the first 3 years after sowing gave way to a much broader range of species. Conservation bodies were soon alarmed lest the increasing use of wild-flower seed, mostly imported from the Netherlands and Germany, might contaminate introduced strains. Whilst believing the evidence was slight, Wells asserted there were other good reasons for using the seed of native species. Guidance was given as to the timing and methods of collecting the seed, and its handling and germination. Wells was confident that, within 5 years, it should be possible to produce commercially enough seed from native stock to meet demand in Britain.

The breaking down of the barrier between agricultural and environmental research occurred remarkably quickly. The President of the British Ecological Society, in August 1984, wrote of how one of the most serious defects in applied ecology was "the seemingly unbridgeable gap between conservation and agriculture". Less than two years later, his successor was able to describe research sponsored explicitly to reconcile the interests of conservation, agriculture and forestry (Sheail, 1987). Credit for the change in circumstances is commonly accorded to a report, 'Agricultural and Environmental Research', of the House of Lords' Select Committee on Science and Technology, published in 1984. But the Committee itself was responding to two kinds of pressure. Besides the evidence put forward by environmental scientists, there was, much more importantly, increasing public resentment at what was perceived to be the considerable damage caused to the countryside by modern farming methods. Not only were they subsidised, but many of the foodstuffs were now in surplus under the European Community's Common Agricultural Policy (Select Committee, 1984).

In time, the Agriculture Act of 1986 may well be seen, with the Agriculture Act of 1947 and National Parks and Access to the Countryside Act of 1949, as an important milestone in the management of the countryside. For the first time, the Act required the Agricultural Ministers "to have regard to and endeavour to achieve a reasonable balance" between

> "the promotion and maintenance of a stable and efficient agricultural industry; the economic and social interest of rural areas; the conservation and enhancement of the natural beauty and amenity of the countryside (including its flora and fauna and geological and physiographical features) and any feature of archaeological interest there; and the promotion of the enjoyment of the countryside by the public."

Whilst the proportion of the agriculture budget transferred to countryside management schemes has been relatively small, it has represented a very significant injection of resources. There is now at least the possibility of 'pump priming' monies being used to promote a more integrated approach to agriculture and the environment, not least in the research field (Sheail, 1995).

In a sense, Agricultural Ministers found themselves in a position analogous to that of the Nature Conservancy in 1949. Their powers to manage the countryside had raced ahead of their capacity to provide perhaps the most relevant prescriptions of how that might be achieved. Under the aegis of the Ministry of Agriculture, and in the context of the ESAs, inter-disciplinary research programmes have been instituted since 1991, involving scientists, for example, in ADAS, the BBSRC Institute of Grassland and Environmental Research and Silsoe Research Institute, NERC Institute of Terrestrial Ecology, and Silsoe College of the University of Cranfield. In a sense, these studies are endeavouring to bring the kind of scientific rigour to conservation management that Stapledon and his generation had begun to develop for the agricultural use of grasslands. In a fundamental way, the task is even more daunting. The aim is not to produce a crop of few species, but the maintenance and creation of a species-rich community of plants and animals - what ecologists might call an ecosystem.

The scale and significance of that challenge forms the subject matter of this Conference.

REFERENCES
ACLAND T.D. and STURGE W. (1851) *The Farming of Somerset*. London, Murray, 56-8.
BLITH W. (1649) *The English Improver*. London, Wright.
BOSWELL G. (1801) *A Treatise on Watering Meadows*. London, Almon.
CLARK J.A. (1854) On the Bridgewater and other Levels of Somersetshire, *Journal of the Bath and West of England Society*, 2, 99-128.
CORNISH C.J. (1895) *Wild England of To-day and the Wild Life in it*. London, Sealey, 258-60.
COTTERELL J.H. (1854) Proposal for obtaining information respecting wildplants. *Journal of the Bath and West of England Agricultural Society*, 2, 230-1.
CURTIS W. (1790) *Practical Observations on the British Grasses Best Adapted to the Laying Down*. London, Author.

DAVIES A. and O. (1996) English agriculturalists' attitudes towards grassland vegetation, 1780-1914: an ecological perspective. *Landscape History*, 18, 71-80.

DUFFEY E., MORRIS M.G., SHEAIL J., WARD L.K., WELLS D.A. and WELLS T.C.E. (1974) *Grassland Ecology and Wildlife Management*. London, Chapman and Hall, 1-40.

ELLIOTT R. (1943) *The Clifton Park System of Farming and Laying Down to Grass*. London, Faber.

ELLIS W. (1747) *The Farmer's Instructor*. London, Hodges, 130-7.

EVANS M. and BOWSTEAD T. (1875) Report on laying down land to permanent pasture. *Journal of the Royal Agricultural Society*, 11, 442-509.

EVERITT N. (1897) *Practical Notes on Grasses and Grass Growing*. London, Jarrold, 43-51.

FREAM W. (1888) The herbage of old grass lands. *Journal of the Royal Agricultural Society*, 24, 415-47

JEFFERIES R. (1879) *Wild Life in a Southern County*. reprinted 1949 Lutterworth, Lutterworth Press, 292-4.

KENT N. (1793) *Hints to Gentlemen of Landed Property*. Dodsley, London, 51-8.

LANE C. (1980) The development of pastures and meadows during the sixteenth and seventeenth centuries. *Agricultural History Review*, 28, 18-30.

LAUNE F. de (1882) On laying down land to permanent grass, *Journal of the Royal Agricultural Society*, 43, 229-64.

LAWES J.B. (1889) The history of a field newly laid down to permanent pasture. *Journal of the Royal Agricultural Society*, 25, 1-24.

MARSHALL W. (1796) *The Rural Economy of the West of England.*. London: Nicol, Volume 2, 181.

MARSHALL W. (1798) *The Rural Economy of the Southern Counties*. London, Nicol, Volume 2, 333-5.

MINISTRY OF AGRICULTURE, FISHERIES AND FOOD (1968) *A Century of Agricultural Statistics*. London, HMSO.

NORDEN J. (1610) *The Surveiors Dialogue*. London, Busby, 163-7.

PAWSON H.C. (1960) *Cockle Park Farm*. Oxford, Clarendon.

PERREN R. (1995) *Agriculture in Depression 1870-1940*. Cambridge, University Press.

PITT W. (1809) *A General View of the Agriculture of the County of Leicester*. London, Nicol, 157-8.

SELECT COMMITTEE ON SCIENCE AND TECHNOLOGY (1984) *Fourth Report. Agricultural and Environmental Research*. London, HMSO, HL 161.

SHEAIL J. (1986) Grassland management and the early development of British ecology. *British Journal for the History of Science*, 19, 283-99.

SHEAIL J. (1987) *Seventy-five Years in Ecology: the British Ecological Society*. Oxford, Blackwell Scientific, 254-5.

SHEAIL J. (1995) Nature protection, ecologists and the farming context: a UK historical perspective. *Journal of Rural Studies*, 11, 79-88.

SHEAIL J. (1996) From aspiration to implementation - the establishment of the first National Nature Reserves in Britain. *Landscape Research*, 21, 37-54.

SINCLAIR G. (1824) *Hortus Gramineus Woburnensis*. London, Ridgeway.

SINCLAIR J. (1818) *Essays on Agriculture*. London, Strahan, 47-60.

STAPLEDON R.G. (1933) Climate and the improvement of hill land. In: Stapledon, R.G. (Eds). *Four Addresses on the Improvement of Grassland*. Aberystwyth, Welsh Plant Breeding Station, 27-36.

STAPLEDON R.G. (1928) Cocksfoot (*Dactylis glomerata* L.): ecotypes in relaton to the biotic factor. *Journal of Ecology*, 16, 71-104.

STAPLEDON R.G. and JENKIN T.J. (1916) Pasture problems: indigenous plants in relation to habitat and sown species. *Journal of Agricultural Science*, 8, 26-64.

TOOGOOD W. (1897) *Pastures and Pasture Plants*. London, Macmillan.

WELLS T.C.E. (1981a) Seeding for colour. *Gardener's Chronicle and Horticultural Trade Journal*, 189 (26) 28-9.

WELLS T.C.E. (1981b) Maintained in style. *Gardener's Chronicle and Horticultural Trade Journal*, 190 (2), 27 and 29.

WELLS T.C.E. (1981c) Creating attractive grasslands from seed in amenity areas. In Duffey, E. (Ed.) *Habitat Restoration and Reconstruction*. pp. 9-16. Huntingdon: Recreation Ecology Research Group.

WELLS T.C.E., BELL S and FROST A. (1981) *Creating Attractive Grasslands using Native Plant Species*. Shrewsbury, Nature Conservancy Council.

WELLS T.C.E., SHEAIL J., BALL D.F. and WARD L.K. (1976) Ecological studies on the Porton ranges: relationships between vegetation, soils and land-use history. *Journal of Ecology*, 64, 589-626.

WILLIAMS M.H. (1993) Rothamsted and the correspondence of Sir John Lawes and Sir Henry Gilbert. *Local Historian*, 23 (2), 85-91.

YOUNG A. (1795) Hampshire husbandry. *Annals of Agriculture*, 23, 355-71.

Grassland Management and Biodiversity

J. A. MILNE

Macaulay Land Use Research Institute, Craigiebuckler, Aberdeen AB15 8QH

ABSTRACT

The impact of the major tools of management, namely stocking density and grazing control, fertiliser application and cutting on the diversity of higher plants, invertebrates, birds and mammals in the UK is reviewed. Alpha-diversity of higher plant species can be described by a bell-shaped relationship with plant biomass. However for many grassland communities maximum diversity will be obtained by a combination of grazing management, fertiliser application and cutting regime. Invertebrate and mammal species diversity is likely to be maximised at low grazing pressures and levels of fertiliser application. Diversity of bird species is also likely to be higher at low grazing pressures but the habitat requirements of different species of birds vary widely, making it difficult to generalise. In general, diversity of higher plant, invertebrate, bird and mammal species, which is, however, only one component of diversity, is likely to be greater at lower grazing pressures than those found currently in the UK at present. However, it is through the combination of the various tools of management that maximum species diversity is likely to be achieved.

INTRODUCTION

Biodiversity in its broader sense is concerned with the diversity of living organisms. This can be interpreted in terms of the number and natural abundance of species and in terms of genetic diversity. There has been much effort, therefore, in describing the diversity and species numbers within grassland communities (alpha-diversity) and also, particularly in less managed grassland ecosystems, the variety of communities (beta-diversity). Recently there has developed a further focus on biodiversity in terms of diversity of ecosystem function. It is argued that it is important to maintain the diversity of the biological processes which drive ecosystem functioning (Solbrig, 1996). This has led to the consideration as to whether all species are needed within an ecosystem, *i.e.* the concept of functional redundancy, and to the concept of keystone species, *i.e.* species which are essential for the functioning of ecosystems. Our lack of knowledge of the functional significance of many of the taxa found in grasslands, for example those providing a decomposer function, makes it difficult to identify many of the species which may be essential for the functioning of different grasslands. In the context of temporate grasslands, large herbivores can be considered to be keystone species and, through their management by man, to have a major influence on biodiversity.

Most grasslands are not stable, climax communities. They have arisen and are maintained by grazing, fire, nutrient inputs, for example through rainfall, and management by man. The successional pathway a grassland will follow depends on edaphic and climatic as well as biotic factors and the number of end points that can be reached are large. Diversity in grasslands depends *inter alia* upon where the grassland is along a successional pathway and in consequence the consideration of biodiversity has to take into account the dynamic nature of grasslands.

Large herbivores, and indeed man, through activities such as removal of biomass in the making of silage and hay, have a major influence on sward structure which in turn have a major influence on biodiversity. This paper considers the major tools of management, particularly those associated with grazing, on the diversity of mammals, birds and invertebrates, as examples of animal taxa, and of the higher plants.

PLANT DIVERSITY

Of the 134 grassland communities described by Rodwell (1992) for Britain, ninety-two are dependent upon management by man for the maintenance of their plant species composition. The rest of the communities are maintained by extreme climatic and edaphic factors and are found mainly in montane, upland and coastal environments (Smith, 1994). The species composition of the ninety-two communities is influenced by the spatial and temporal pattern of grazing, cutting, and other management practices such as fertiliser application, draining, sub-soiling and application of herbicides (Crofts and Jefferson, 1994).

Impact of grazing

In general terms there is the widely accepted bell-shaped relationship between plant species diversity and biomass or grazing pressure (Figure 1). Very high or low grazing pressures lead to a few species whilst intermediate grazing intensities lead to maximum species diversity.

Figure 1   Relationship between grazing pressure by sheep and diversity of plant species (after Grime, 1979)

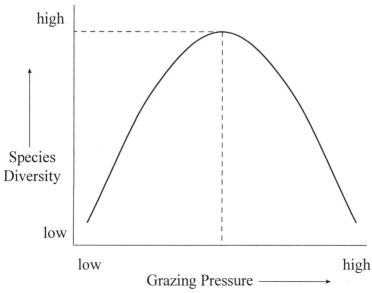

26

The precise nature of the relationship will depend upon the grassland community and the species of grazer. The species of grazer will influence the manner in which the biomass is removed through differences in the size of bites taken by these species and their degree of selectivity. The nature of excretal return and the extent of trampling damage will also influence the relationship. The plant species within a community also influence the shape of the curve by their resistance to the impacts of grazers described above. The position of the apical meristem is of significance with grasses being more resistant to grazing than forbs because of the relative positions of their apical meristems. Tussock grasses are less resistant to defoliation than tillering grasses and annual forbs are less resistant than perennials. A combination of low resistance to the impacts of grazers and a high preference by grazers creates a worst scenario for a plant species in their ability to compete with other plant species in a community.

Simple above-ground biomass measures are not likely to be adequate for predicting the impacts of sward structure on species diversity although sward height can be a useful surrogate in that it takes into account the influence of the number of flowering individuals. Using sward height as a measure, Marriott *et al.,* (1997) explored the extent to which shifts in plant species diversity occurred in typical upland grasslands which had received management for high agricultural output, *i.e.* low sward height together with N-fertiliser inputs for a number of years. Inputs of fertiliser were stopped and swards grazed at average sward heights of 4 or 8 cm for 6 years. The grazing intensity was reduced by proportionately 0.4 and 0.7 respectively at these heights compared with that of the previous management regime. Species diversity changed little. When grazing was stopped completely species composition changed markedly but species diversity did not alter. The results show that changes in plant diversity are unlikely to occur by a simple change in management to increase biomass, *i.e.* by reducing stocking density of the principal grazer by approximately a half, when plant species composition is initially low. Since stopping of grazing also did not increase biodiversity, decreases in stocking density by sheep greater than 0.5 are suggested or it may be that changes in diversity of plant species at decreases in stocking density of 0.5 will occur over a longer time period. Which of these options is correct may depend upon the rate at which heterogeneity of structure within the plant community develops. An alternative approach would be to use a combination of grazers to create heterogeneity of structure.

Impact of fertilizer and cutting

The effect of fertilizer on plant diversity would be predicted by Grime's (1979) 'hump-back' model to reduce species richness with either high fertilizer inputs or no fertiliser. There is evidence for this from Dutch research (Ver Meer and Berendse, 1983) and from experiments where fertilizer has been applied to calcifugous and upland grasslands (Jones, 1967), and calcareous (Davy and Bishop, 1984) and mesotrophic grasslands (Montford *et al.,* 1993). The effects of different plant nutrients and forms of fertiliser are reviewed by Smith (1994).

Management by cutting can lead to greater plant species diversity by removing the biomass of the potentially dominant species (Bakker, 1987). Timing of the cutting is important, for example in the maintenance of hay meadows (Smith and Jones, 1991), ensuring the production of adequate seed.

Interaction between grazing, fertiliser application and cutting.

It can be argued that to obtain and maintain high plant diversity requires a combination of grazing, fertiliser application and cutting. Pastures which are managed solely for grazing or cutting and are grazed by one species of grazer in a consistent manner, *e.g.* maintaining a sward height throughout a season, are unlikely to have a high species diversity. A good example of a management which combines elements of grazing, fertiliser application and cutting is that which is used to maintain hay meadows in the North Pennines area of England. These grasslands have a high biodiversity through specific grazing pressure by sheep and cattle in the spring and autumn, and specific fertiliser and cutting dates. Smith *et al.,* (1996) have shown that the further management moved away from these specific prescriptions, the greater was the reduction in plant species diversity.

Much of the discussion on plant diversity has focused on alpha-diversity because the management unit of the field tends to be associated with an area which is often a single plant community. By applying different managements to different fields within a farm, it would be possible to increase beta-diversity. This is a subject which has not yet received much attention in relation to grasslands (Baudry *et al.*, 1994).

INVERTEBRATE DIVERSITY

Invertebrates belong to many different guilds (Table 1), each of which depends on different aspects of the habitats that they occupy. Generally invertebrate herbivores depend on the presence of particular vegetation species and their abundance is a function of plant biomass. Predators depend more on the structure of the vegetation. Some invertebrate guilds depend upon the presence of large herbivores. For example dung and carrion are important for Diptera, beetles, earthworms and Tipulids. Similarly parasitic invertebrates may require large herbivore hosts.

Impact of grazing

In general a low grazing pressure from large herbivores is favourable to maximising biodiversity of invertebrates (Van Wieren, 1991). This is because structural diversity of the vegetation is greater and the frequency of defoliation and trampling are relatively low during any one season of the year and yet there is a supply of dung and carrion. However in some instances heavy grazing may increase diversity of invertebrates through creating niches for particular species. These conclusions can be illustrated by reference to calcareous and upland grassland.

In the absence of grazing for periods of less than three years, calcareous grassland exhibits an increase in species diversity associated with greater structural complexity of the vegetation and the absence of trampling (although in the longer term diversity can decline) (Morris, 1990a; Brown *et al.*, 1990; Gibson *et al.*, 1992). On the other hand, some invertebrate species are only found in heavily grazed calcareous grassland, for example thermophilic butterfly species and butterfly species with specific habitat needs, such as the adonis blue (*Lysandra bellargus*), which additionally require the presence of low-height vetches.

In two studies of upland pastures (Dennis *et al.*, 1995; Dennis *et al.*, 1997) the main conclusions were that (1) the number of spider species was more sensitive to reduction at higher stocking rates than beetle species and the largest invertebrate assemblages were found in ryegrass/white clover swards with heterogeneous mosaics of different structure (Dennis *et al.*, 1997) and (2) number of spiders, beetles and butterfly species were greater with grazing regimes on a *Nardus* grassland which created greater structural complexity of the vegetation (Dennis *et al.*, 1995).

Table 1. Major invertebrate guilds in grassland communities grazed by large herbivores (P. Dennis, personal communication)

Category	Food	Identify (examples)
Phytophages (plant eaters)	chew leaves	caterpillars (Lepidoptera and Symphyta), beetles (Coleoptera)
	suck plant sap	plant hoppers (Homoptera), nematodes (Nematoda)
	mine leaves and stems	micro-moths, flies (Diptera)
	gall leaves and stems	flies, gall wasps (Cynipidae)
	Consume roots	leatherjackets (Tipulidae), nematodes
Decomposers	plant litter	worms, beetles, millipedes (Diplopoda), snails
	saprophage fungi	springtails(Collembola), mites (Acarina), beetles, flies
	dung	flies, dung beetles (Scarabaeidae and Staphylinidae) earthworms
Scavengers	flesh, fibre	burying beetles (Silphidae), flies, moths
Predators	other invertebrates	beetles, spiders (Araneae), flies, wasps, dragon flies (near water)
Parasitoids	larvae in invertebrate hosts	parasitic wasps (Ichneumonoidea), tachinid flies
Parasites	vertebrate and invertebrate hosts	nematodes, fleas (Siphonaptera), ticks (Acarina), lice

Effects of fertiliser and cutting

Because of the greater biomass produced by fertiliser application there may be an increase in the number of phytophagous invertebrate species but the overall effect is to reduce species diversity (Morris, 1990b). Cutting tends to reduce invertebrate diversity (Morris, 1990a; Kirby, 1992) because of the extreme nature of the event and its timing when flowers and seeds of uncut herbage would be available to invertebrates.

BIRD AND MAMMAL DIVERSITY

Grazing by large herbivores can affect the diversity of bird species by (a) changing habitat composition and structure and hence altering food resources and indirectly predator pressure, (b) increasing invertebrate numbers through dunging, (c) destroying nesting sites through trampling and (d) increasing the amount of carrion available (Harding et al., 1994). The habitat and feed requirements of different species of birds vary widely, however, and are often in conflict with one another. Ground-nesting invertebrate feeders are likely to benefit from low grazing pressures as a result of increased food supply from invertebrates associated with greater structural diversity of the vegetation. Heavy grazing pressure will increase losses of nests due to trampling and greater risk of losses for predators because of lack of cover. In contrast, species like the chough, which are specialist feeders on dung invertebrates, are favoured by high grazing pressures (McCracken and Foster, 1993). Tussock-nesting birds require low to moderate grazing pressure to provide nesting sites but other species require short swards for feeding, for example geese in winter and waders in summer, which necessitates high grazing pressures of large herbivores. Carrion-feeders are also favoured by high grazing pressures whilst raptors which feed on live prey are likely to be favoured by low grazing pressures because greater structural diversity increases their sources of prey.

Whilst there is concern that population numbers have declined in many grassland-dominated areas over the last 20 years, the evidence that this is associated with changes in management of grassland is limited and difficult to separate out from other changes in land use and the impacts of man. The habitat requirements of many bird species are met not only by grassland but by other components of the landscape which may have changed also.

Mammals and other vertebrate fauna

Grassland management can affect the diversity of mammals and other vertebrates through large grazing herbivores a) altering competition for food and breeding sites, b) changing the structure of the vegetation and plant species present, c) influencing the transmission of disease and d) through the impacts of a), b) and c) on prey abundance for other species higher up the food chain.

Because most domestic ruminants are large, the smaller rabbits, hares and deer are at a competitive advantage and can compete well, particularly at lower levels of herbage biomass. There is evidence that greater structural heterogeneity of vegetation, associated with low grazing pressure, can increase the population of small mammals such as voles, shrews and field mice (Corbet and Southern, 1991). The mechanisms are likely to be associated with a greater food supply of invertebrates, improved nesting habitats and increased protection for predators. Increased heterogeneity of vegetation is also likely to favour grass snake, adder and lizard populations. A reduction in large herbivore numbers could reduce the transmission of disease to other mammals, for example Liver Fluke caused by *Faciola hepatica*. Increases in small mammals, associated with changes in the structure of vegetation as a result of grazing management, will also result in an increase in their predators such as stoats, weasel and foxes (Corbet and Southern, 1991).

CONCLUSIONS

This survey of the literature has attempted to identify the major components of management, *i.e.* grazing pressure, fertiliser application and cutting, that influence the species diversity of the higher plants, invertebrates, birds and mammals. It has concentrated on alpha-diversity rather than beta-diversity of species because of the dearth of information on the latter rather than its lack of importance. Species diversity within higher plants, invertebrates, birds and mammals is likely to be at a maximum under grazing pressures which are lower than those currently found on grassland in the UK which is reflected to some extent in the present ESA prescriptions. However as more knowledge becomes available it will be possible to be more specific in the prescriptions to achieve this objective. If diversity of ecosystem functioning becomes an important objective, a greater understanding of grassland ecosystems will be required before ESA prescriptions to meet such an objective can be set.

REFERENCES

BAKKER J.P. (1989) *Nature Management by Grazing and Cutting*. Dordrecht: Kluver Academic Press.

BAUDRY J., THENAIL, C., LE COEUR, D. BUREL, F. and ALARD, D. (1994) Landscape Ecology and Grassland Conservation. In: Haggar R.J. and Peel S. *Grassland Management and Nature Conservation. Occasional Symposium of the British Grassland Society*, No. 28, pp. 157-166.

BROWN V.K., GIBSON C.W.D. and STERLING P.H. (1990) The mechanism controlling insect diversity in calcarious grasslands. In: Hiller, S.H., Walton, D.W.H. and Wells, D.A. (eds.) *Calcareous grasslands - ecology and management*. Bluntisham, Bluntisham Books, pp. 79-87.

CORBET G.B. and HARRIS S. (1991) *The Handbook of British Mammals,* Oxford, Blackwell Scientific Publications.

CROFTS A. and JEFFERSON R.G. (1994) *The Lowland Grassland Management Handbook*. English Nature/The Wildlife Trusts.

DAVY A.J. and BISHOP G.F. (1984) The response of Hieraceum pilosella in Breckland grass heath to inorganic nutrients. *Journal of Ecology*, 72, 319-330.

DENNIS P., BENTLEY C. and JONES J.R. (1997) Impact of grazing systems on insects and spiders. *Proceedings of the 3rd International Livestock Systems Symposium*, Wageningen, Wageningen Press. In press.

DENNIS P., GORDON I.J. and ASPINALL R.J. (1995) Spatial response of arthropods to patchiness of upland, semi-natural grassland generated by different grazing regimes. In: Griffiths G.H. (ed.) *Landscape Ecology: Theory and Application*. Reading, University of Reading, pp. 190-192.

GIBSON C.W.D., BROWN V.K., LISITO L. and GAVIN G.C. (1992) The response of invertebrate assemblages to grazing. *Ecography*, 15, 166-176.

GRIME J.P. (1979) *Plant strategies and vegetation processes*. John Wiley and Sons, Chichester.

HARDING N.J., GREEN R.E. and SUMMERS R.W. (1994) *The effect of future changes in land use on upland birds in Britain*. Edinburgh, Royal Society for the Protection of Birds.

JONES L.I. (1967) Studies on Hill Land in Wales. *Technical Bulletin of the Welsh Plant Breeding Station* No. 2.

KIRBY P. (1992) *Habitat Management for Invertebrates: A Practical Handbook* Royal Society for the Protection of Birds, Joint Nature Conservation Committee and Natural Power

MARRIOTT C.A., BOLTON G.R., COMMON T.G., SMALL J.L. and BARTHRAM G.T. (1997) Effect of extensification of sheep grazing systems on animal production and species composition of the sward. *Proceedings of the 16th General Meeting of the European Grassland Federation, Grado, Italy*. In press.

MORRIS M.G. (1990a) The effects of management on the invertebrate community of calcareous grassland. In: Hillier S.H., Walton D.W.H. and Wells D.A. (eds.) *Calcarious grasslands - ecology and management*. Bluntisham, Bluntisham Books, pp. 128-133.

MORRIS M.G. (1990b) The Hemiptera of two sown calcareous grasslands. III Comparisons with the Auchenorhyncha faunas of other grasslands. *Journal of Applied Ecology*, 27, 394-409.

MOUNTFORD J.O., LAKHANI K.H. AND KIRKHAM F.W. (1993) Experimental assessment of the effects of nitrogen addition under hay cutting and aftermath grazing on the vegetation of meadows on a Somerset peat moor. *Journal of Applied Ecology*, 30, 321-332.

MCCRACKEN D.I. and FOSTER G.N. (1993) Surface-active invertebrate communities and the availability of potential feed for the Chough, Pyrrcorax pyrrhocorax L, on pastures in north-west Islay. *Pedobiologia*, 37, 141-158.

RODWELL J.S. (1992) *British Plant Communities Volume 3. Grasslands and Montane Communities*. Cambridge, Cambridge University Press.

SMITH R.S. (1994) Effects of fertilisers on plant species composition and conservation interest of UK grassland. In: Haggar R.J. and Pell S. *Grassland Management and Nature Conservation. Occasional Symposium of the British Grassland Society*, No. 28, pp.64-73.

SMITH R.S. and JONES L. (1991) The phenology of mesotrophic grassland in the Pennine Dales, Northern England: historic hay cutting dates, vegetation variation and plant species phenologies. *Journal of Applied Ecology*, 28, 42-59.

SOLBRIG O.T. (1996) The rangeland services of biodiversity. In: West N.E. *Rangelands in a Sustainable Biosphere*. Denver, Society of Range Management, pp. 113-116.

VER MEER J.G. and BERENSE F. (1983) The relationship between nutrient availability, shoot biomass and species richness in grassland and wetland communities. *Vegetatio*, 53, 121-136.

VAN WIEREN S.E. (1991) The management of populations of large mammals. In: Spellerberg F.B., Goldsmith C.B. and Morris M.G. (eds.) *The scientific management of temperate communities for conservation*. Oxford, Blackwells, pp. 103-128.

SESSION 3a

SCIENCE INTO PRACTICE

Chairman: Steve Peel
Agricultural Development and Advisory Service

Environmentally Sensitive Areas in the UK and their Grassland Resource

A. SWASH

Ecological Policy Adviser, Farming and Rural Conservation Agency, Nobel House, 17 Smith Square, London SW1P 3JR

ABSTRACT

There are 43 Environmentally Sensitive Areas (ESAs) in the United Kingdom: 22 in England, 6 in Wales, 10 in Scotland and 5 in Northern Ireland. Farmers within these designated areas are able to enter into voluntary, 10-year management agreements for which they receive annual payments for farming in a way which seeks to maintain and enhance the landscape, wildlife and historic or archaeological interest of the area. The combined area of the ESAs in the UK is 3,356,000 ha, covering around 15% of the agricultural land area. ESAs encompass the range of habitats which are influenced by agricultural operations, although grassland has been particularly targeted, there being 1,058,733 ha in total within the ESAs, 353,999 ha (33%) of which was under agreement at the end of 1996. A range of grassland types occurs in ESAs, including a significant proportion of the hay meadow, chalk downland and wet grassland communities which are important for their nature conservation interest. This paper provides an overview of the ESA Scheme, with particular reference to the grassland resource, and summarises the associated monitoring and research and development programmes which have been established in support of the scheme.

THE ENVIRONMENTALLY SENSITIVE AREA SCHEME

Background

The Environmentally Sensitive Area (ESA) Scheme was introduced in the UK in 1987 following the passage of the enabling legislation (Section 18 of the Agriculture Act 1986). The Broads Grazing Marshes Conservation Scheme had previously been run as a pilot in 1985-6 (MAFF, 1989) and similar voluntary management agreements were operated by the Exmoor National Park in the early 1980s. The aim of the ESA Scheme is to maintain the landscape, wildlife and historic value of defined areas by encouraging beneficial agricultural practices. The scheme is voluntary and farmers and other land managers with responsibility for agricultural land within the designated areas are able to enter into 10-year management agreements and to receive annual payments in return for adhering to specified management prescriptions.

Since 1987 the ESA Scheme has been expanded and there are now 43 in the UK covering some 15% of the agricultural land area. Of these, 22 are in England, 6 are in Wales, 10 in Scotland and 5 in Northern Ireland. A list of the ESAs in the UK is given in Table 1, with details for each of the date of designation, the area which is eligible to be entered into the scheme, the approximate area of grassland (all types) and the area of

Table 1. Environmentally Sensitive Areas in the UK (position as at end 1996)

ESA	Date of designation	Eligible area (ha)	Permanent grassland (ha)	Grassland under agreement (ha)
England				
Avon Valley	1992	3,800	3,300	968
Blackdown Hills	1993	32,014	29,389	3,900
Breckland	1988	51,600	3,500	2,639
Broads	1987	24,000	17,334	15,352
Clun	1988	18,900	15,000	4,201
Cotswold Hills	1993	66,100	28,000	14,087
Dartmoor	1993	84,514	34,600	10,171
Essex Coast	1993	23,000	12,700	2,486
Exmoor	1992	68,362	35,440	24,008
Lake District	1992	219,300	162,800	87,865
North Kent Marshes	1992	11,600	7,300	3,400
North Peak	1988	50,500	3,900	2,876
Pennine Dales	1987	39,100	39,132	25,471
Shropshire Hills	1993	34,900	34,400	7,760
Somerset Levels & Moors	1987	25,900	23,722	15,032
South Downs	1987	51,700	14,865	5,584
South Wessex Downs	1992	38,737	10,771	4,784
South West Peak	1992	27,000	23,500	14,031
Suffolk River Valleys	1988	32,600	13,100	8,917
Test Valley	1988	3,300	2,400	1,178
Upper Thames Tributaries	1993	23,194	10,686	4,081
West Penwith	1987	6,914	3,752	3,392
	Total:	937,035	529,591	262,183
Wales				
Anglesey	1993	60,000	45,000	3,346
Cambrian Mountains	1987	119,600	83,720	24,078
Clwydian Range	1994	26,000	19,500	937
Lleyn Peninsula	1988	39,700	27,790	2,205
Preseli	1994	104,000	78,000	1,325
Radnor	1993	80,000	60,000	7,812
	Total:	429,300	314,010	39,703
Scotland				
Argyll Islands	1994	177,400	14,175	1,723
Breadalbane	1987	140,000	10,926	948
Cairngorms Straths	1993	148,700	15,686	297
Central Borders	1988	28,800	11,339	89
Central Southern Uplands	1993	220,300	36,732	0
Loch Lomond	1987	36,900	4,017	130
Machair of the Uists, etc.	1988	12,000	4,025	641
Shetland Islands	1994	144,900	15,477	910
Stewartry	1988	48,500	22,220	743
Western Southern Uplands	1993	131,000	29,422	34
	Total:	1,088,500	164,019	5,515
Northern Ireland				
Antrim Coast	1993	21,840	12,977	12,495
Fermanagh	1993	28,280	17,953	15,779
Mourn Mountains	1993	14,559	3,029	2,692
Slieve Gullion	1994	2,462	1,119	882
Sperrins	1994	46,928	16,035	14,750
	Total:	114,069	51,113	46,598

grassland that had come into agreement by the end of 1996.

The criteria for ESA designation used in the latest round of English designations are that the area must be of national environmental significance and represent a discrete and coherent unit of environmental interest. In addition, its conservation interest must be dependent upon the adoption, maintenance or extension of particular farming practices which have either changed or are likely to change, or which could, if modified, result in a significant improvement in that interest (Harrison, *in press*).

Environmental Aim and Objectives

The overall environmental aim of the ESA Scheme is to maintain the landscape, wildlife and historic value of the designated areas by encouraging beneficial agricultural practices. This is achieved through specific objectives which, although broadly similar, are tailored to each ESA and focus on the priorities of the area concerned. The ESA Scheme is designed and run so as to integrate the landscape, wildlife and historic interests of each area and the specific objectives have been drawn up with this in mind. Details of the objectives for each ESA are given in MAFF (1994) but they typically make reference to:

- maintaining and enhancing the wildlife conservation value of each of the habitats for which the area is particularly noted;
- maintaining and enhancing landscape quality; and
- maintaining and enhancing the archaeological and historic resource.

Performance Indicators

'Performance indicators' have been defined for each objective in each ESA and specify the targets which should be achieved during the five year period following the launch of the ESA (or re-launch after each quinquennial review). They provide a means of measuring the success of the scheme and a framework for its management and evaluation through an associated monitoring programme. Performance indicators cover uptake and environmental impact and include a combination of:

- overall uptake targets (usually in the form of a percentage of a type of eligible land that should be under agreement);
- targets that relate only to agreement land (*e.g.* the percentage of a certain type of feature which should be renovated); and
- environmental impact indicators which relate to the desired result of the imposition of ESA management agreements on various types of land (*e.g.* the maintenance or enhancement of botanical diversity or bird populations).

Full details of the performance indicators for each ESA are presented in MAFF (1994). These, and the associated objectives, are being reassessed as part of the current round of quinquennial reviews.

Management Tiers and Prescriptions

Under the current rules of the ESA Scheme, farmers and land managers with land in the designated areas are able to enter into ten-year management agreements (although there is an option for termination after 5 years) for which they receive an annual payment.

Each ESA has one or more tiers of entry in which the agricultural practices, or prescriptions, which have to be followed are specified. The nature of each tier depends upon the particular circumstances of each ESA, but may include, for example:

- the protection and management of existing habitats and features;
- the traditional management of hay meadows;
- the maintenance of high water levels in wetland habitats; and
- the reversion of arable land to grassland.

Although the precise details of the management prescriptions within each tier vary, they usually place a restriction on the use of certain cultivation techniques, stocking rates, the use of fertilisers, fungicides and insecticides and the introduction of new drainage infrastructure. They also usually include a requirement to maintain watercourses and boundary features. Some tiers impose more stringent management regimes than others and may, for example, require specified water levels to be maintained or place restrictions on the level and timing of grazing and/or the application of fertilisers. The payment rates which apply to each tier reflect the income foregone and, if appropriate, the need to provide an incentive.

THE GRASSLAND RESOURCE IN ESAs

The habitats specifically targeted by each of the ESAs in England and Wales are summarised in Table 2. Grassland is of particular importance in the context of the scheme and is the only habitat targeted by all ESAs. The total amount of grassland (all types) in each ESA is shown in Table 1; the overall extent of the resource in the ESAs in the UK being approximately 1,058,733ha, some 353,999ha of which (33%) has come into agreement.

A wide range of grassland types is represented in ESAs and many are particularly important for nature conservation. The significance of the lowland grassland resource in England has been assessed for each of English Nature's Natural Areas (Jefferson, 1996). This involved scoring each Natural Area on a five point scale from 'outstanding' to 'negligible', based on the estimated extent of lowland semi-natural grassland. Since the boundaries of most ESAs correspond quite closely with Natural Areas, a subjective assessment of the relative importance of the grassland resource in each ESA can be obtained. Table 3 shows the assessments for Natural Areas which include or coincide with ESAs. This indicates that the grasslands in seven ESAs are classed as 'outstanding', with the remainder being at least of 'some' significance. In England as a whole the grassland resource is classified as 'outstanding' in 12 ESAs.

There are a large number of neutral, calcareous and acid grassland and mire plant communities of high botanical interest represented in English and Welsh ESAs. The presence of significant National Vegetation Classification (NVC) communities (Rodwell, 1991 et seq.) is summarised in Tables 4 and 5. These include important concentrations of the English resource of wet grassland associated with grazing marshes and river floodplains; calcareous grassland, in particular chalk downland; and hay meadows. For example, there is an estimated 53,000ha of wet grassland in English ESAs (Glaves, in press). This represents around 27% of the total English resource, estimated as 200,000ha

(Dargie, 1993; DoE, 1995). The South Downs and South Wessex Downs ESAs include around 9,200ha of calcareous grassland on chalk (ADAS, 1996; MAFF, *in prep.* j) which represents around 29% of the English resource of 32,000ha (Jefferson & Robertson, 1996). In addition, important concentrations of calcareous grassland on limestone occur in the Cotswold Hills, Lake District and Pennine Dales ESAs.

Table 2. Habitats targeted in English and Welsh ESAs.

ESA	Grass-land	Wet grass-land	Wet-land	Arable (rever-sion)	Arable field m'gins	Low-land heath	Moor-land	Water-courses	Stone walls	Hedge-rows	Wood-land
England											
Avon Valley	✓	✓		✓							
Blackdown Hills	✓					✓				✓	
Breckland	✓			✓	✓	✓					
Broads	✓	✓		✓	✓			✓			
Clun	✓			✓	✓						✓
Cotswold Hills	✓			✓					✓	✓	
Dartmoor	✓					✓	✓		✓	✓	
Essex Coast	✓	✓		✓							
Exmoor	✓					✓	✓			✓	
Lake District	✓		✓				✓		✓		
North Kent Marshes	✓	✓		✓							
North Peak	✓						✓		✓		
Pennine Dales	✓								✓		✓
Shropshire Hills	✓						✓			✓	
Somerset Levels & Moors	✓	✓						✓			
South Downs	✓			✓	✓						
South Wessex Downs	✓			✓	✓						
South West Peak	✓						✓		✓		
Suffolk River Valleys	✓	✓		✓							
Test Valley	✓			✓							
Upper Thames Tributaries	✓	✓		✓						✓	
West Penwith	✓					✓			✓		
Wales											
Anglesey	✓		✓	✓	✓	(✓)			✓	✓	✓
Cambrian Mountains	✓		✓	✓			✓		✓	✓	✓
Clwydian Range	✓		✓	✓	✓		✓		✓	✓	✓
Lleyn Peninsula	✓		✓	✓	✓	(✓)			✓	✓	✓
Preseli	✓		✓	✓	✓	(✓)			✓	✓	✓
Radnor	✓		✓	✓	✓		✓		✓	✓	✓

(✓) includes mosaics of maritime heath, maritime grassland and dune communities

Table 3.   Lowland grassland significance assessments for English Nature Natural
Areas which include English ESAs

ESA	Principal Natural Area	Significance assessment[1]
Blackdown Hills	Blackdowns	Some
Breckland	Breckland	Outstanding
Broads	Broadland	Significant
Clun	Central Marches	Some
Cotswold Hills	Greater Cotswolds	Outstanding
Dartmoor	Dartmoor	Considerable
Essex Coast	Thames Marshes	Some
Exmoor	Exmoor and the Quantocks	Some
Lake District	Cumbrian Fells and Dales	Outstanding
North Kent Marshes	Thames Marshes	Some
North Peak	Dark Peak	Some
Pennine Dales	North Pennines/Yorkshire Dales	Outstanding
Shropshire Hills	Shropshire Hills	Notable
Somerset Levels & Moors	Somerset Levels and Moors	Outstanding
South Downs	South Downs	Considerable
South Wessex Downs	South Wessex Downs	Outstanding
South West Peak	South West Peak	Some
Suffolk River Valleys	Suffolk Coast and Heaths	Notable
Upper Thames Tributaries	Oxford Clay Vales	Considerable
West Penwith	Cornish Killas and Granite	Some

Note: The small Avon Valley and Test Valley ESAs form or cross the boundaries of a number of
Natural Areas and are thus not included in the table.
[1] after Jefferson (1996).

MONITORING AND EVALUATION

An extensive programme of environmental monitoring has been established in order to
assess the degree to which the performance indicators are being met and thus the
achievement of the objectives of the scheme. An evaluation of the monitoring results is
undertaken to inform the review of each ESA which takes place every five years. An
analysis of the results of the monitoring exercise for the initial tranche of five ESAs which
were launched in England in 1987 was completed in 1996 and is presented in MAFF
(1996a–e). Grassland monitoring has also taken place in second and third tranche ESAs
(MAFF, *in prep.* a–k). Critchley (*in press*) provides an overview of the botanical
monitoring methods which have been used in ESA monitoring.

Although it is only possible within the scope of this paper to provide a broad overview
of the results from the monitoring programme, the overall indication is that the wildlife
conservation interest of the areas concerned is being maintained. This compares
favourably with the situation prior to designation where the interest of many of the areas
was deteriorating. The wildlife conservation value of hay meadows in the Pennine Dales,
for example, appears to have benefitted from the ESA Scheme; the species diversity of
unimproved meadows having been maintained, whereas a general decline was noted
during the period from 1978 to 1990 (DoE, 1993). Another indication that the scheme is

bringing positive benefits comes from the Somerset Levels and Moors where there is evidence of an increase in bird numbers. Other examples are described in the detailed monitoring reports (MAFF, 1996a–e; 1997a–k).

Table 4. Neutral grassland and fen-meadow or rush-pasture National Vegetation Classification communities (excluding moorland) of high botanical interest in ESAs in England and Wales (community types are described in Appendix 1)

ESA	Neutral grasslands							Fen-meadows and rush-pastures					
Community:	MG 2	MG 3	MG 4	MG 5	MG 8	MG 11	MG 13	M 22	M 23	M 24	M 25	M 26	M 27
England													
Avon Valley				*			*		*	*	*		
Blackdown Hills			*					*	**	**	**		*
Breckland			**										**
Broads				*	*		*	**	**	**			*
Clun			*						*		*		*
Cotswold Hills			**										
Dartmoor			*						**	**	**		*
Essex Coast						*							
Exmoor			*			*			**	**	**		*
Lake District		**		**	*				*		*	*	
North Kent Marshes						*							
North Peak			*						*		*		
Pennine Dales	**	**		**	**				*		*	*	
Shropshire Hills			**										
Somerset Levels & Moors		?	*	**	**	**	**	**	**	**	**		**
South Downs			**		*								
South Wessex Downs			**	*									
South West Peak			*						*		*		
Suffolk River Valleys			*			*	*	**	**		**		
Test Valley				*				*	*	*	*		*
Upper Thames Tributaries		**	*				**	*					
West Penwith			*						*		*		
Wales													
Anglesey			*					*	*		*		
Cambrian Mountains		?	*						*				
Clwydian Range				*									
Lleyn Peninsula				*				*	*		*		
Preseli			*			*			*		*		
Radnor		?	*	*				*	*		*		

Notes: Where the resource is important in terms of quality and/or extent this is indicated as **

Other NVC mestorophic grassland communities of lower botanical interest, in particular MG1, MG6, MG7, MG9 and MG10 are also widespread in ESAs

? indicates that similar communities have been described, but these are not typical or have yet to be confirmed

The monitoring programme has also shown that the scheme has been successful in maintaining the landscape quality of the five first tranche ESAs. Indeed, there has been a significant enhancement of the landscape quality of two of these ESAs where the reversion of arable land to grassland has led to major changes in the landscape. The objective of maintaining the archaeological and historical resource within ESAs seems largely to have been met, principally through affording increased protection to such features by encouraging the reversion of arable land to grassland (Harrison, *in press*).

Table 5. Calcareous, acidic and miscellaneous National Vegetation Classification grassland communities (excluding moorland) of high botanical interest in ESAs in England and Wales (community types are described in Appendix 1)

ESA Community:	Calcareous grasslands										Acid grasslands				Misc.	
	CG 1	CG 2	CG 3	CG 4	CG 5	CG 6	CG 7	CG 9	CG 10	OV 37	U 1	U 2	U 3	U 4	SD[1]	MC[2]
England																
Blackdown Hills		*		*							*	*	*	*		
Breckland		**	**			**	**				**	**			**	
Broads											*					
Cotswold Hills		**	**	**	**											
Dartmoor												*	*	**		
Exmoor												*	*	**		**
Lake District		**						**	**				*			
North Peak													*			
Pennine Dales		**						**	*	**		*	*			
South Downs	**	**	**	**	**							*		*		**
South Wessex Downs		**	**	**	**	**	**									
South West Peak													*			
Suffolk River Valleys											**					
West Penwith				*									*	*		**
Wales																
Anglesey	*	**											*		**	**
Cambrian Mountains											*		*			
Clwydian Range	**	**				**		**					*			*
Lleyn Peninsula											*		*			*
Preseli											*		*			*
Radnor													*			

Notes: Where the resource is important in terms of quality and/or extent this is indicated as **
Other NVC acidic grassland communities of lower botanical interest, in particular U20 (and other bracken communities) are also widespread in ESAs
[1] various sand dune communities
[2] various maritime grassland communities

RESEARCH AND DEVELOPMENT

An extensive programme of research and development has been and continues to be carried out in connection with MAFF's agri-environment programme. A summary of the research projects relevant to ESAs which had been completed or were ongoing in 1995 is presented in MAFF (1995). Many other projects have been initiated since then and MAFF's current funding commitment amounts to around £800,000 year. A number of the research projects funded by MAFF are the subject of papers at this conference.

ACKNOWLEDGEMENTS

I should like to thank Howard de Bolla, Ann Cowan, Richard Evans, David Glaves, Michael Harrison, Alan Hooper, and Kathryn Joyce, Joseph Kerr, Steve Morgan and Paula Whitfield for their assistance in the preparation of this paper.

REFERENCES

ADAS (1996) *Landscape monitoring in the South Downs ESA 1987–1995.* Unpublished report to MAFF. Oxford: ADAS.

CRITCHLEY C.N.R. (*in press*) Monitoring methods. In Sheldrick R.D. (*ed.*) *Grassland Management in ESAs. Occ. Symp. 32, British Grassland Society: Reading.*

DARGIE T.C. (1993) *The distribution of lowland wet grassland in England.* English Nature, Peterborough.

DoE (1993) *Countryside Survey 1990: Main Report.* HMSO.

DoE (1995) *Biodiversity: the UK Steering Group Report.* HMSO.

GLAVES D.J. (in press) Environmental monitoring of lowland wet grassland management agreements in the Somerset Levels and Moors Environmentally Sensitive Area, England. In Wade, M. & Joyce, C.: *European Floodplain and Coastal Wet Grasslands: Biodiversity Management and Restoration.* Wiley.

HARRISON M.D.K. (in press) English Environmentally Sensitive Areas. In *Proceedings of the OECD Seminar on Environmental Benefits from Agriculture, Helsinki, September 1996.*

JEFFERSON R.G. (1996) *Lowland grassland in Natural Areas: National assessment of significance.* Peterborough: English Nature.

JEFFERSON R.G. and ROBERTSON, H.J. (1996) *Lowland grassland: wildlife value and conservation status.* Peterborough: English Nature.

MAFF (1989) *Environmentally Sensitive Areas.* First Report, London: HMSO.

MAFF (1994) *Environmentally Sensitive Area Scheme: Environmental objectives and performance indicators for ESAs in England.* London: MAFF.

MAFF (1995) *Summaries of MAFF-funded research & development projects relevant to the Environmentally Sensitive Area Scheme.* London: MAFF.

MAFF (1996a) *Environmental Monitoring in the Pennine Dales ESA 1987–1995.* London: MAFF.

MAFF (1996b) *Environmental Monitoring in the Broads ESA 1987–1995.* London: MAFF.

MAFF (1996c) *Environmental Monitoring in the South Downs ESA 1987–1995.* London: MAFF.

MAFF (1996d) *Environmental Monitoring in the West Penwith ESA 1987–1995.* London: MAFF.

MAFF (1996e) *Environmental Monitoring in the Somerset Levels and Moors ESA 1987–1995.* London: MAFF.

MAFF (*In prep.* a) *Environmental Monitoring in the Breckland ESA 1988–1996.*

MAFF (*In prep.* b) *Environmental Monitoring in the Clun ESA 1988–1996.*

MAFF (*In prep.* c) *Environmental Monitoring in the North Peak ESA 1988–1996.*

MAFF (*In prep.* d) *Environmental Monitoring in the Suffolk River Valleys ESA 1988–1996.*

MAFF (*In prep.* e) *Environmental Monitoring in the Test Valley ESA 1988–1996.*

MAFF (*In prep.* f) *Environmental monitoring in the Avon Valley ESA 1993–1996.*

MAFF (*In prep.* g) *Environmental monitoring in the Exmoor ESA 1993–1996.*

MAFF (*In prep.* h) *Environmental monitoring in the Lake District ESA 1993–1996.*
MAFF (*In prep.* i) *Environmental monitoring in the North Kent Marshes ESA 1993–1996.*
MAFF (*In prep.* j) *Environmental monitoring in the South Wessex Downs ESA 1993–1996.*
MAFF (*In prep.* k) *Environmental monitoring in the South West Peak ESA 1993–1996.*
RODWELL J. (*ed.*) (1991–1996) *British Plant Communities*, 5 vols. Cambridge: Cambridge University Press.

APPENDIX 1
National Vegetation Classification grassland communities of high botanical interest in ESAs in England and Wales.

MG2	Meadowsweet–false oat-grass 'northern tall-herb grassland'
MG3	Sweet vernal-grass–wood crane's-bill 'northern hay-meadow'
MG4	Meadow foxtail–great burnet 'flood meadow'
MG5	Crested dog's-tail–common knapweed 'lowland hay-meadow/pasture'
MG8	Crested dog's-tail–marsh-marigold 'flood pasture'
MG11	Red fescue–creeping bent–silverweed 'inundation grassland'
MG13	Creeping bent–marsh foxtail 'inundation grassland'
CG1	Sheep's fescue–carline thistle 'warm temperate limestone grassland'
CG2	Sheep's fescue–meadow oat-grass 'lowland species-rich calcareous grassland'
CG3	Upright brome 'lowland calcareous grassland'
CG4	Tor-grass 'lowland calcareous grassland'
CG5	Upright brome–tor-grass 'lowland calcareous grassland'
CG6	Downy oat-grass 'lowland limestone grassland'
CG7	Sheep's fescue–mouse-ear hawkweed–wild thyme 'lowland calcareous grassland'
CG9	Blue moor-grass–small scabious 'northern sub-montane/montane carboniferous limestone grassland'
CG10	Sheep's fescue–common bent–wild thyme 'northern sub-montane calcareous grassland'
OV37	Sheep's fescue–spring sandwort 'metalliferous (calaminarian) grassland'
U1	Sheep's fescue–common bent–sheep's sorrel 'lowland acid grassland'
U2	Wavy hair-grass 'acid grassland'
U3	Bristle bent 'south-western acid grassland'
U4	Sheep's fescue–common bent–heath bedstraw 'sub-montane acid grassland'
M22	Blunt-flowered rush–marsh thistle 'lowland fen-meadow'
M23	Soft/sharp-flowered rush–marsh bedstraw 'western lowland rush-pasture'
M24	Purple moor-grass–meadow thistle 'lowland fen-meadow'
M25	Purple moor-grass–tormentil 'western lowland mire'
M26	Purple moor-grass–marsh hawk's-beard 'northern sub-montane mire'
M27	Meadowsweet–wild angelica 'lowland mire'
SD	Various sand dune communities
MC	Various maritime grassland communities

Monitoring Methods

C. N. R. CRITCHLEY

ADAS Newcastle, Kenton Bar, Newcastle upon Tyne NE1 2YA

ABSTRACT

In the UK, grassland monitoring programmes have been instigated to assess the performance of ESAs against their objectives. Comparisons between vegetation changes on land under ESA agreement and non-agreement land are desirable, but rarely possible. Sampling strategies have been determined by specific monitoring objectives, with the aim of adequately sampling the target vegetation. In any monitoring programme, field methods are always based on fixed units. In UK ESAs, estimates of plant species cover in fixed quadrats are commonly used. Traditional recording methods like this are theoretically based on counts of species' presence in sub-units of the fixed unit, but differ in the scale at which species are recorded. A new monitoring method was adopted in later monitoring programmes in England and Wales which increases the ability to detect changes by recording species at a range of scales. In England and Wales, goal vegetation was defined as that containing species suited to specified management and environmental conditions. Suited-species were determined by applying rule sets to a species-trait matrix, and scores calculated for each fixed unit for each year of survey. In the first English ESAs, grassland botanical quality was generally maintained, and there was some limited evidence of enhancement.

INTRODUCTION

The designation of Environmentally Sensitive Areas (ESAs) in the UK was enabled by the 1986 Agriculture Act. With this Act also came the requirement that Agricultural Ministers should keep the effects of designation under review and "from time to time publish such information ...... about these effects". To this end, following the designation of ESAs, monitoring programmes have been initiated in all four UK countries (WOAD, 1989; Hooper, 1992; McAdam *et al.*, in prep.; Cummins *et al.*, 1997). Grazed habitats form a major component of ESAs, and grassland monitoring programmes have been set up in most ESAs in England and Wales. Monitoring has addressed the quality of grasslands in terms of not only plant species and communities, but also land cover, landscape and, in a smaller number of cases, their use by breeding and wintering birds and invertebrates.

The purpose of these monitoring programmes is to assess the performance of ESAs, by determining whether the scheme objectives have been met. For English ESAs, there is a common overall aim which is *"to maintain and enhance the landscape, wildlife and historic value of the area by encouraging beneficial agricultural practices"*. Each ESA has its own objectives, but generally these include a requirement to maintain and enhance the wildlife conservation value of grasslands. Each monitoring programme must, therefore, determine whether grassland vegetation of existing high value is being maintained, and whether that which has degenerated through inappropriate management or previously been agriculturally improved, has been enhanced.

The aims of this paper are to highlight some issues which need to be considered in executing these monitoring programmes, to review the approaches used for the botanical monitoring of grasslands in ESAs and to discuss some results obtained.

SAMPLING STRATEGIES

To test the effect of ESA management prescriptions on grasslands, it would be necessary to obtain comparable samples from land under ESA management agreements (agreement land) and land which is not (non-agreement land). In practice, this is seldom possible for a number of reasons. Firstly, the uptake of a particular type of land into agreement may be so high that non-agreement land becomes a scarce commodity. Secondly, there is often a fundamental difference between agreement land and non-agreement land in an ESA. For example, in the Pennine Dales most non-agreement land was intensively managed grassland situated at lower altitudes in the ESA, whilst the unimproved hay meadows located further up the valleys, which were of greater wildlife conservation value, were more likely to be entered into ESA agreement (ADAS, 1996b). Thus, a direct assessment of the effects of ESA management could not be made, although trends occurring in the ESA could be measured. As ESA boundaries normally encompass all land of a certain type which exists in the area, comparable non-agreement land outside the ESA is seldom available for sampling. A further problem common to all ESAs is that any non-agreement land sampled may soon after become agreement land, especially where the ESA is popular! Occasionally, the converse may also happen. Therefore, monitoring programmes in ESAs can in most cases only detect what is happening to particular types of grassland, and cannot directly prove cause and effect. An exception to this is the heath grasslands in Breckland ESA, where stock were re-introduced to heaths as a result of the land being entered into ESA agreement. This enabled comparisons to be made between fenced plots (simulating the effects of the lack of stock in the absence of ESA management) and unfenced plots (agreement land) (ADAS, 1997b). In Scottish ESAs, the problem is being addressed by comparing trends between agreement land, land in the whole ESA, and national trends (Cummins et al., 1997).

With large-scale schemes such as ESAs, there will be a wide range of variation in grassland types in the designated area. In many, a substantial proportion of the area will be agriculturally improved grassland. The less improved grasslands, which are of greater wildlife conservation value, and inherently more variable, may be relatively scarce. To ensure that the grasslands of interest are adequately sampled, it is necessary firstly to define the entity to be targeted (usually a particular vegetation type), and secondly to have access to an inventory showing the extent and distribution of the target vegetation within the ESA. Once so defined, the statistical population to be sampled can be identified (usually in terms of fields). Stratified sampling can then be employed to ensure that an equal sample size of each grassland type is obtained.

The method of stratification, if done at all, is dependent on the specific objectives of monitoring in the ESA. In England, performance indicators have been specified for each ESA, which must be addressed by the monitoring programme. Where these refer to a particular type of vegetation, then that must be adequately sampled. For example, in the Somerset Levels and Moors ESA, there was a requirement to sample less agriculturally improved grasslands. However, species-rich semi-natural grassland only comprised 6% of the total area of the ESA (ADAS, 1996c; Glaves, in press). Therefore, to achieve an adequate sample of unimproved grassland, the sample was stratified by the level of agricultural improvement (Table 1). In practice, adequate inventories of the amount and location of different grassland types are seldom available, and repeated sampling has to be carried out in the field, until a sufficient representation of each grassland type has been obtained.

In the Broads ESA, it was necessary to obtain samples from grasslands under different tiers of ESA management, so that changes under the different regimes could be compared (ADAS 1996a). Where the main aim of monitoring is to detect changes in a defined grassland type throughout the entire ESA, irrespective of whether the land is under ESA agreement or not, then a completely random sample may be taken from the statistical population of that grassland in the designated area, as was done, for example, in the South Wessex Downs ESA (ADAS, 1997a).

Irrespective of the sampling strategy used, it is necessary to take account of the range of variation in the sample prior to carrying out analyses of change. If the variation is large, then a re-grouping of the sample may be necessary, to ensure that each sub-sample consists of broadly similar vegetation. Different plant community types can show different responses, even when located in the same management units (Critchley et al., 1996). Reducing the variation within each sub-sample before analysis increases the likelihood of detecting changes. In English ESAs, quadrats (see below) were re-grouped by applying TWINSPAN (Hill, 1979) to data from the first year of survey, and each endgroup was described within the framework of the National Vegetation Classification (NVC) (Rodwell, 1991 et seq.). In the case of stands (see below), NVC descriptions of each were used to group similar stands together.

Resources will often dictate sample size limits, although for Scottish ESAs sample sizes (and hence resources) necessary to detect specified levels of change have been calculated (Cummins et al., 1997).

Table 1. Summary of grassland types monitored and methods used in English ESAs. Year = year of designation of the ESA. Sample strat. = sample stratification: l = geographical location (as defined by landscape type, management unit, etc.); m = management tier or agreement status; s = soil type; v = vegetation type; - = none. Sample sizes may vary with losses and additions - numbers are those existing at most recent survey; q = quadrats (method adapted from Smith *et al.* (1985)); s = stands (ESA monitoring method (Critchley and Poulton, in prep.)). [1] sites with raised water levels; [2] includes 1835 quadrats with abundance estimates on DAFOR scale; [3] quadrats grouped in plots.

Year	ESA	Grassland or habitat types	Sample strat.	Sample size
1987	Broads	grazing marsh & river valley grassland	m, l, v, s	362q
	Pennine Dales	upland hay meadow & pasture	v, m, l	2152q[2]
	Somerset Levels & Moors	grazing marsh	m, v, s	500q
		grazing marsh[1]	l	25s
	South Downs	chalk downland	v, m	209q
		river valley grassland	-	40q
	West Penwith	'rough' land grassland	v	16s
1988	Breckland	heath grassland	v	120q[3]
	Clun	mesotrophic & calcifugous pasture & hay meadow	v	29s
		improved grassland	m	30s
	North Peak	upland pasture & hay meadow	m, v	35s
	Suffolk River Valleys	dry grassland	-	45q
		abandoned wet pasture	l	50q
	Test Valley	river valley grassland	v, m	138q
1993	Avon Valley	river valley grassland	m	44s
	Exmoor	grass moorland	l	24s
		enclosed semi-natural grassland	-	25s
	Lake District	upland rough grazing	l	110s
	North Kent Marshes	grazing marsh	-	40s
	South Wessex Downs	chalk downland	-	41s
	South West Peak	mesotrophic pasture & hay meadow	m, v	39s
		upland rough grazing	m, v	28s
1994	Blackdown Hills	mesotrophic & calcifugous grassland	-	26s
	Cotswolds	calcareous & mesotrophic pasture & hay meadow	m, v	44s
	Dartmoor	hay meadow	-	20s
	Essex Coast	-	-	-
	Shropshire Hills	calcifugous & mesotrophic pasture & hay meadow	m, v	32s
	Upper Thames Tributaries	river valley grassland	m	40s

FIELD METHODS

Monitoring differs from survey in that the former is dependent on repeated observations. Therefore, monitoring must always be based on *fixed units*. The fixed unit is defined here as the lowest level in the hierarchy of fixed locations within which repeated observations are made. It may be as small as a fixed quadrat or as large as a landscape type in an ESA. Within the fixed unit, observations may consist of a complete search of the area (a census), as is normally done within a fixed quadrat. Where the fixed unit is too large to carry out a census (e.g. a field) a sample of sub-units (e.g. a sample of non-fixed quadrats within the field) may be searched during each visit.

The requirement of monitoring is usually to detect changes in the presence, abundance or distribution of individual plant species, irrespective of whether data are ultimately expressed as individual species or as plant community variables. Although direct, non-destructive measures of plant species abundance may be done using counts of individual plants or plant parts, in practice the densely-packed shoots usually encountered in grassland swards make these direct measures prohibitively time-consuming in large-scale monitoring programmes. More usually, estimates of the abundance of individual species are made, using estimates of cover (by eye or using point frames), local frequency (*sensu* Greig-Smith, 1983) or presence in individual quadrats. The most widespread method adopted for grassland monitoring in ESAs in the UK has been to estimate by eye the cover of species in fixed quadrats. In ESAs in Northern Ireland (McAdam *et al.*, in prep.) and in monitoring projects commenced before 1993 in England and Wales (Critchley and Poulton, 1994), the method is based on that recommended by Smith *et al.* (1985), whereby cover estimates have been made on the Domin scale (Mueller-Dombois and Ellenberg, 1974) in 1 m × 1 m fixed quadrats. Each 1 m × 1 m quadrat is located centrally in a 2 m × 2 m quadrat, where the presence of additional species are also recorded. In these monitoring programmes, quadrats are objectively located on a transect across each enclosed field (usually 5 quadrats per field) or across a sampling area in unenclosed land. For ESAs in Scotland, cover is being estimated to the nearest 5% in 2 m × 2 m fixed quadrats, which are themselves randomly located within each sampling area (Cummins *et al.*, 1997). In all cases described thus far, the fixed quadrat constitutes the fixed unit.

A disadvantage of estimating cover by eye is that the method is susceptible to high variation between different observers (Poulton and Critchley, in prep.). By working in pairs, this variation can be reduced (Nilsson, 1992). Although this solution has been widely adopted, it can increase the overall resources required to carry out fieldwork.

Another important issue is that different species, or the same species under different environmental conditions, show a wide variation in their patterns of distribution and abundance, and in how these may change over time. For example, the above-ground parts of a rhizomatous grass such as *Poa pratensis* may be sparsely distributed within a quadrat, and may spread in an approximately linear fashion. This contrasts with the pattern of expansion of a tussock-forming species such as *Deschampsia caespitosa*, or the spread of individuals of *Veronica arvensis* by seed. These patterns also occur at a range of scales. For example, individual ramets of a mature patch of *Cirsium arvense* may be sparsely distributed over a large area, while *Cerastium fontanum* seedlings may be more densely packed, but in smaller patches. It follows that in order to maximise the likelihood of detecting changes in the abundance of a wide range of species, records should ideally be made at a range of scales, and in as large a fixed unit as available resources will allow.

It is useful to recognise that conventional recording methods measure species abundance within a fixed unit in essentially the same way. They are all based on counts of species presence in sub-units of the fixed unit. The key difference between them is the size of the sub-unit, i.e. variation in scale. For example, cover (whether estimated by eye or using a point frame) estimates species presence in (theoretically) infinitely small sub-units, frequency uses sub-units of a more tangible size, and presence/absence is where the fixed unit and sub-unit are the same size giving a maximum count of one. It has already been established that within a fixed unit, plant species occur at a range of scales and patterns. Methods which record at a single scale (i.e. sub-unit size) are thus capable of detecting fewer changes than those which use a range of sub-unit sizes. The size of the fixed unit itself will affect whether data for individual species are likely to be collected.

A simple solution to the requirement for recording at a range of scales, is to record the presence of species in a series of quadrats of increasing size, which are nested within each other (Hodgson *et al.*, 1994). Addressing also the need to maximise the fixed unit size, a field method utilising a nested system was developed specifically for vegetation monitoring in large areas such as ESAs (Critchley and Poulton, in prep.). The method has been used in new monitoring programmes since 1993 in ESAs in England (Table 1) and Wales. In summary, it comprises a fixed unit (called a 'stand') which is a rectangular area of 32 square sub-units (nests) in an 8 × 4 grid (Figure 1). Each holds a series of cells of increasing size (adapted from the nested quadrats of Hodgson *et al.*, (1994)). In each nest, a species is recorded in the smallest cell in which it occurs. Within a monitoring programme, a number of stands of constant size are used. The size is chosen to reflect the overall scale of the vegetation and is usually a compromise between being large enough to encompass the majority of species present, and small enough to be managed within available resources. The most commonly used size in grasslands is 8 m × 4 m. Stands have been positioned in randomly selected locations in unenclosed land. In enclosed fields, a single stand has been located randomly on a field diagonal.

Ideally, the interval between field surveys, and length of the total monitoring period, would be decided by considering the likely speed and magnitude of vegetation change. This will depend partly on how grassland management has changed with introduction of the ESA, and also on the capacity for the different plant communities to undergo rapid changes. In reality, resurvey intervals tend to be dictated by policy requirements, and the availability of resources. In England, ESAs are reviewed every five years (Coates, 1997), so resurveys are timed to enable the results of monitoring to be used at each review. In general, this has meant that grasslands in these ESAs have been resurveyed every three to five years.

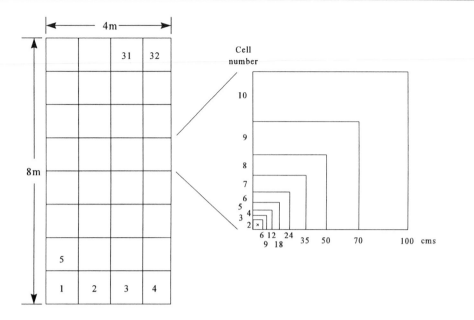

Figure 1. Layout of a 8m x 4m stand for monitoring vegetation (after Critchley and Poulton, in prep.). The enlargement shows the size and layout of the ten cells in each of the 32 nests in the stand. Cell number 1 (denoted by a cross) is a pin located centrally in cell number 2.

HYPOTHESIS TESTING

In a general surveillance programme, it may be sufficient to carry out exploratory analyses to find out the nature of any changes in vegetation over a period of time, without having preconceptions as to the likely outcome (Hellawell, 1991). However, in monitoring the performance of ESAs, it is necessary to determine acceptable standards of vegetation quality against which the vegetation of interest can be compared, so that a judgement can be made as to whether the ESA objectives have been met. For example, a particular NVC grassland plant community (Rodwell, 1992) may be a suitable goal towards which other plant communities would be expected to change. Alternatively, a plant community already present in the sample may be defined as the standard towards which others were expected to transform. For plant communities of existing high value, the requirement might be that they did not deteriorate.

Generally, grasslands of high wildlife conservation value are those which are the product of low intensity farming, which itself is partly controlled by ESA management prescriptions, and partly by the prevailing environmental conditions. Thus, the goal vegetation for an ESA can be defined as that which contains species suited to particular management and environmental conditions. In England and Wales, the success of ESAs is being assessed by the extent to which these groups of species (*suited-species*) are present in the sampled vegetation (Critchley *et al.*, 1996). For example, the criteria for unimproved grazing marsh are that the vegetation contains species suited to moderate grazing intensity, high prevailing soil moisture and low nutrient availability. Suited species have been defined by identifying a number of traits of plants which show a widespread and recurrent association with particular environmental conditions, for example the association of annual species with frequently disturbed ground. These traits were compiled as sets of rules which were then applied to a species-trait matrix to select suited-species for each criterion (Critchley, 1996b; Critchley *et al.*, 1996). This approach ensured that the status' of each species were determined in an objective manner, based on published information and applied nationally, rather than on a site-by-site basis. A score (*suited-species score*) was calculated for each fixed unit, for each year of observation. In the case of quadrat datasets, the score was calculated on the basis of the proportional contribution of suited-species to total cover. For data collected from stands, the score was calculated based on the proportion of suited-species present at the optimum scale for detecting change in each species. The scores were then used as a response variable to measure changes in the vegetation, and to compare with vegetation of known quality. From the wide range of grassland types which have been monitored in English and Welsh ESAs, it is now possible to ascertain the expected values for suited-species scores for broad grassland types. For example, unimproved calcareous grasslands tend to have relatively low Nu scores (a high proportion of species suited to low nutrient availability) high G scores (a high proportion of species suited to high grazing intensity), and high C scores (a high proportion of calcicoles) in comparison with agriculturally improved grasslands (Critchley *et al.*, 1996). Thus, the reversion of agriculturally improved grasslands to unimproved calcareous grasslands can be measured by reference to a number of suited-species scores. In the same way, any deterioration of grassland types of high value can be measured.

RESULTS OF MONITORING

Monitoring datasets become increasingly valuable as the total time period, and the number of repeated observations, increases. This allows short-term fluctuations, such as those caused by climatic differences between years, to be differentiated from the longer-term trends which are of main interest. Also, the reversion of agriculturally improved grasslands towards those of higher wildlife conservation value is a gradual process, and effects of past improvement can still be apparent for many years (Olff and Bakker, 1991). For the first ESAs designated in England, the monitoring has now spanned a period of up to eight years, with the first surveys conducted in 1987 in some ESAs, and the most recent in 1995. At present, this is the longest ESA monitoring dataset in the UK. In Northern Ireland the monitoring programme was initiated in 1992 (Cameron *et al.*, 1997), in Scotland the original monitoring programme was replaced with a revised programme in 1994 (Gauld *et al.*, 1997), whilst in Wales the quadrat-based method used in early grassland monitoring work was replaced by the new stand method from 1993.

Results from the first English ESAs showed that, in general, the objective of maintaining the existing wildlife conservation value of grasslands has been achieved. Clearly, it cannot be proven beyond doubt that detrimental changes have not occurred, but

51

considering the relative sensitivity of the methods used, one can be confident that there has been no major deterioration in the quality of grasslands sampled. This contrasts with the underlying trend of a general deterioration in the wider countryside (Barr *et al.*, 1993). Evidence of enhancement of grasslands within the ESA scheme is more limited, however, and where this has occurred, the changes are relatively small. These enhancements are often confined to grasslands which have been subjected to limited amounts of agricultural improvement in the past. Examples of this were seen in the South Downs ESA, where semi-improved calcareous grassland was the only community on chalk downland in which enhancement was detected (ADAS 1996d; Diack, 1997), and in the Pennine Dales ESA where slight enhancement occurred in some more improved communities (ADAS, 1996b).

These monitoring results have enabled not only the overall performance of the ESA scheme to be assessed, but have also highlighted the circumstances under which changes are most likely to occur (Critchley *et al.*, 1996). An important function of monitoring is to provide information which can be used to improve the performance of the ESA scheme, for example by amending management prescriptions when the scheme is reviewed (Critchley, 1996a). For example, in the recent review of the first English ESAs, monitoring results highlighted the risk of prolonged inundation to species-rich grassland communities in the Somerset Levels and Moors ESA (D.J. Glaves, personal communication). This enabled modifications to the management prescriptions to be made, to increase protection for these communities where raised water levels were applied.

CONCLUSIONS

The monitoring programmes for grassland vegetation in the ESAs described here have generally been successful in indicating the changes which have occurred in the plant communities sampled. Whether results can be extrapolated to each ESA in question, varies depending on the original objectives for monitoring, and the sampling strategy adopted. Monitoring based on traditional field methods has produced satisfactory results, but the new monitoring method implemented more recently in England and Wales increases our ability to detect change. Through definition of the goal vegetation for each sample, and measuring vegetation change in the context of predetermined ecological criteria, it is possible to evaluate the success of each ESA based on botanical field data. Although evidence of enhancement of the quality of grasslands in ESAs has thus far been limited, the monitoring datasets collected from each UK country are an invaluable resource not only for future, longer term assessment of ESA performance, but also for addressing the wider issues of environmental change and land use.

ACKNOWLEDGEMENTS

The ESA monitoring in England and Wales is funded by the Ministry of Agriculture, Fisheries and Food, and the Welsh Office Agriculture Department. It is carried out by numerous colleagues, many of whom have contributed to the information presented here. Information for Scotland was provided by Mr R.G. Cummins and for Northern Ireland by Dr J.H. McAdam and Dr C. Millsopp. Comments on a draft version were received from Mr M.D.K. Harrison, Mr S.M.C. Poulton and Dr M.J.W. Burke.

REFERENCES

ADAS (1996a) *Botanical Monitoring of Grassland in the Broads ESA, 1987 - 1994*. ADAS Report to MAFF.

ADAS (1996b) *Botanical Monitoring of Grassland in the Pennine Dales ESA, 1987 - 1995*. ADAS Report to MAFF.

ADAS (1996c) *Botanical Monitoring of Grassland in the Somerset Levels and Moors ESA, 1988 - 1995*. ADAS Report to MAFF.

ADAS (1996d) *Botanical Monitoring of Grassland in the South Downs ESA, 1987 - 1995*. ADAS Report to MAFF.

ADAS (1997a) *Environmental Monitoring in the South Wessex Downs ESA, 1993 - 1996*. ADAS Report to MAFF.

ADAS (1997b) *Lowland Heathland Monitoring in the Breckland ESA, 1987 - 1995*. ADAS Report to MAFF.

BARR C.J., BUNCE R.G.H., CLARKE R.T., FULLER R.M., FURSE M.T., GILLESPIE M.K., BROOM G.B., HALLAM C.J., HORNUNG M., HOWARD D.C. and NESS M.J. (1993) *Countryside Survey 1990. Main Report*. London: Department of the Environment.

CAMERON A., MILLSOPP C.A., MULLHOLLAND F. and McADAM J.H. (1997) Biological monitoring of grasslands in the West Fermanagh and Erne Lakeland Environmentally Sensitive Area in Northern Ireland. *This volume*.

COATES D. (1997) UK policy for ESAs. *This volume*.

CRITCHLEY C.N.R. (1996a) Monitoring as a feedback mechanism for the conservation management of arable plant communities. *Aspects of Applied Biology* 44, 239-244.

CRITCHLEY C.N.R. (1996b) *Vegetation of Arable Field Margins in Breckland*. PhD thesis, University of East Anglia.

CRITCHLEY C.N.R. and POULTON S.M.C. (1994) Biological monitoring of grasslands in Environmentally Sensitive Areas in England and Wales. In: Haggar, R.J. and Peel, S. (Eds). *Grassland Management and Nature Conservation, Occasional Symposium of the British Grassland Society*, No. 28, pp. 254-255.

CRITCHLEY C.N.R. and POULTON S.M.C. (in prep.) A method to optimise precision and scale in vegetation monitoring and survey.

CRITCHLEY C.N.R., SMART S.M., POULTON S.M.C. and MYERS G.M. (1996) Monitoring the consequences of vegetation management in Environmentally Sensitive Areas. *Aspects of Applied Biology*, 44, 193-201.

CUMMINS R.P., GAULD J.G., ELSTON D.A., BARR C.J. and BUNCE R.G.H. (1997) Monitoring vegetation in the Scottish ESAs - phase 2. *This volume*.

DIACK I.A. (1997) Grassland monitoring in the South Downs ESA. *This volume*.

GAULD J.H., CUMMINS R.P. and ELSTON D.A. (1997) ESA monitoring in Scotland - grasslands. *This volume*.

GLAVES D.J. (in press) Environmental monitoring of lowland wet grassland management agreements in the Somerset Levels and Moors Environmentally Sensitive Area, England. In: Wade, M. and Joyce, C. (Eds) *European Floodplain and Coastal Wet Grasslands: Biodiversity Management and Restoration*. Chichester: Wiley.

GREIG-SMITH P. (1983) *Quantitative Plant Ecology, third edition*. Oxford: Blackwell.

HELLAWELL J.M. (1991) Development of a rationale for monitoring. In: Goldsmith, F.B. (ed) *Monitoring for Conservation and Ecology*, pp. 1-14, London: Chapman and Hall.

HILL M. O. (1979) *TWINSPAN - a FORTRAN program for arranging multivariate data in an ordered two-way table by classification of individuals and attributes*. New York: Cornell University.

HODGSON J.G., COLASANTI R., PHILLIPSON P., LEACH S., MONTGOMERY S. and HUNT R. (1994) A simple method for monitoring grassland vegetation. In: Haggar, R.J. and Peel, S. (Eds). *Grassland Management and Nature Conservation, Occasional Symposium of the British Grassland Society,* No. 28, pp. 286-288.

HOOPER A.J. (1992) Field monitoring of environmental change in the Environmentally Sensitive Areas. In: Whitby, M.C. (ed) *Land Use Change: the Causes and Consequences, ITE Symposium,* No 27, pp. 53-59.

McADAM J.H., MILLSOPP C.A. and CAMERON A. (in prep.) *Re-monitoring of the West Fermanagh and Erne Lakeland ESA, The Mournes and Slieve Croob and the Antrim Coast, Glens and Rathlin - Biological Evaluation of the scheme between 1993 and 1996. Biological Monitoring of ESAs Year 4 - 1996.* DANI Report, Belfast.

MUELLER-DOMBOIS D.R. and ELLENBERG H. (1974) *Aims and Methods of Vegetation Ecology*. New York: Wiley.

NILSSON C. (1992). Increasing the reliability of vegetation analyses by using a team of two investigators. *Journal of Vegetation Science,* 3, 565.

OLFF H. and BAKKER J.P. (1991) Long-term dynamics of standing crop, vegetation composition and species richness after the cessation of fertiliser application to hay-fields. *Journal of Applied Ecology,* 28, 1040-1052.

POULTON S.M.C. and CRITCHLEY C.N.R. (in prep.) Observer consistency in estimating the plant species composition of grassland I. Variation due to recording method and vegetation characteristics.

RODWELL J.S. (ed.) (1991 *et seq.*) *British Plant Communities*. Cambridge: Cambridge University Press.

RODWELL J.S. (ed.) (1992) *British Plant Communities, Volume 3. Grasslands and Montane Communities*. Cambridge: Cambridge University Press.

SMITH I.R., WELLS D.A. and WELSH P. (1985) *Botanical survey and monitoring methods for grasslands, Focus on Nature Conservation, No. 10.* Peterborough: Nature Conservancy Council.

WOAD (1989) *Environmentally Sensitive Areas. Wales. First report on monitoring the effects of the designation of Environmentally Sensitive Areas*. Cardiff: Welsh Office Agriculture Department.

Biological Monitoring of Grasslands in the West Fermanagh and Erne Lakeland Environmentally Sensitive Area

A. CAMERON, C.A. MILLSOPP AND J.H. McADAM

Department of Applied Plant Science, The Queens University, Newforge Lane, Belfast,BT9 5PX, Northern Ireland

INTRODUCTION

The Environmentally Sensitive Areas (ESA) Scheme was introduced by the Department of Agriculture for Northern Ireland (DANI) in 1988 and currently covers 20% of the land area of Northern Ireland in five designated ESAs.

Monitoring of the ESAs requires an integrated multi-disciplinary approach, involving biological, landscape, historical and socio-economic monitoring. A baseline biological monitoring programme in the West Fermanagh and Erne Lakeland ESA was completed by DANI in 1993 (McAdam *et al.*, 1994). This survey provided baseline data on the plant species and invertebrates in a range of sites from target habitats within the ESA boundary.

Monitoring plant species is the most widely used method of assessing ecological changes in the environment, for example the relationship between plant composition and agricultural management (Hopkins & Wainwright 1989; Leader-Williams *et al.*, 1987). Ground beetles are habitat specific, easily trapped in pitfall traps and are reported to be a good indicator of biological change (Kirby, 1992). Invertebrate monitoring in association with the plant species provides a comprehensive indicator of the biodiversity of a habitat. Rare and threatened species have been found within the ESAs and their status and distribution documented (McAdam *et al.* 1994, 1995). These species will act as performance indicator species in assessing the effectiveness of the ESA scheme.

The West Fermanagh and Erne Lakeland ESA was remonitored in 1996, to allow an initial appraisal of the scheme's effectiveness in maintaining wildlife diversity. The habitats monitored in this ESA were hay meadows, wet grasslands, limestone, unimproved and improved grasslands, heather moorland and woodland.

METHODS

Re-monitoring field sampling programme

The number of habitat fields re-monitored were stratified initially on the distribution of the major habitat vegetation types (derived from baseline biological monitoring), to ensure a range of habitat qualities were remonitored. Sites were further stratified on the basis of participant and non-participants farms at the time of re-monitoring. As a result 30-60% of the baseline monitoring sites were resurveyed.

Biological monitoring

Plant monitoring: Habitats were monitored at the same season of the year as the baseline monitoring. In grasslands, five permanent equidistant $2m^2$ quadrats were relocated along a diagonal quadrat. Plant species were recorded and their percentage cover was estimated within a nested $1m^2$ quadrat. Any additional species were recorded in the outer quadrat. Permanent quadrats ($2m^2$ nested) in heathland and limestone grassland were relocated at 4 equidistant quadrats along a 60m transect. In woodlands permanent nested quadrats ($14m^2$, $7m^2$ and $2m^2$) were-monitored. Plant species and their percentage cover were recorded in the $2m^2$ quadrat. Additional species were noted in the outer quadrats.

Invertebrate monitoring: Carabid beetles were sampled at each site during three, four week periods between April and October 1993. Five pitfall traps (polythene containers 9 cm wide and 20 cm deep) part filled with ethylene glycol to prevent the escape and deterioration of specimens before collection were used at each site. Traps were placed 20 m apart in a line through the centre of each site. At the end of each sampling period traps were emptied and removed. At the beginning of the next sampling period traps were replaced and refilled with a fresh ethylene glycol solution. All adult carabid beetles taken in the traps were identified to species using Lindroth (1974).

Data analysis

Habitat diversity was measured by a combination of species richness, plant species groups, vegetation types, the relative proportions of species in each of the plant strategy theory CSR groups (Grime *et al.,* 1988), and the frequency and distribution of rare and threatened invertebrate species. Species richness, the total number of species found on a habitat is the most widely adopted diversity index (Magurran, 1983). In the plant strategy theory, species are defined in terms of whether they are chiefly ruderals (R), competitors (C), stress-tolerators (S), or intermediates. Each type occurs under different environmental conditions and therefore changes in their frequency may be indicative of changes in their environment. Multivariate analyses packages TWINSPAN and DCA were used to describe the data in terms of their vegetation types and species groups.

RESULTS

Plant species diversity

The changes in the plant species diversity for ESA participant and non-participant fields between 1993 and 1996 are discussed for each habitat.

Hay meadows: Hay meadows on participant farms had significantly more plant species per 2x2m quadrat in 1996 than in 1993 (Table 1).

Hay meadows on ESA participant farms had higher proportions of stress-tolerators than those not participating in the scheme. The proportion of stress-tolerators and the stress-tolerator intermediate groups (CS and SR) fell between years for non-participant farms.

Table 1. The mean number of plant species per 2m² quadrat for habitats which were under an ESA agreement and those which were not under an ESA agreement in 1993 and 1996.

Habitat	ESA scheme	n	Mean number of plant species per 2m² quadrat (standard error)		P - t-value n.s. not sig. *P <0.05 **P <0.01
			1993	1996	
Hay meadow	Participant	7	39 (2.5)	42 (2.8)	* t-value=-3 df=6
	Non-participant	9	30 (2.3)	29 (3.3)	n.s.
Wet grassland	Participant	9	42 (2.3)	43 (3.1)	n.s.
	Non-participant	6	36 (2.7)	34 (2.1)	n.s.
Limestone grassland	Participant	3	38 (4.5)	35 (1.7)	n.s.
	Non-participant	4	53 (11.9)	39 (7.8)	n.s.
Heather	Participant	7	24 (2.5)	19 (3.3)	n.s.
	Non-participant	4	31 (2.6)	26 (2.7)	** t-value=7.1 df=3
Improved grassland	Participant	2	20 (3.5)	19 (1.5)	n.s.
	Non-participant	6	25 (2.7)	20 (2.2)	**t-value=4.1 df=5
Unimproved grassland	Participant	6	44 (2.6)	43 (3.6)	n.s.
	Non-participant	4	43 (4.9)	38 (3.7)	n.s.
Woodland	Participant	3	19 (4.2)	16 (2.9)	n.s.
	Non-participant	6	25 (2.3)	18 (2.3)	n.s

There was a significant increase in the total number of species recorded from species-rich hay meadows, typified by a high frequency of sedges and stress-tolerator species, on ESA participant farms between 1993 and 1996 and a significant reduction in the number of species from hay meadows on non-participant farms.

Wet grasslands: Mean species numbers from wet grasslands had not significantly changed over the three years, therefore maintaining their species diversity. In 1993 the majority of the wet grasslands were classified as species-rich, typified by the presence of sedges, water mint (*Mentha aquatica*) and creeping jenny (*Lysimachia nummularia*). This diversity was enhanced in 1996, by the re-classification of one ESA participant wet grassland from species-poor (dominated by *Lolium perenne*, and *Poa trivialis*) to species-rich.

Limestone grasslands. There were no significant differences in the mean number of plant species between years for ESA participant or non-participant limestone grasslands. Species such as *Plantago lanceolata* have increased on non-participant sites since 1993. ESA participant limestone sites in 1996 exhibited the highest proportion of stress-tolerators (35%), rising slightly from 32% in 1993. The numbers of stress-tolerators on non-agreement farms fell from 34% in 1993 to 29% in 1996, with an increase in ruderal species.

Unimproved grasslands: There were no significant differences in the mean number of plant species between years for participant or non-participant grasslands. Species with a notable decrease between 1993 and 1996 were *Cardamine pratensis* which in 1996 was recorded from half the non-participant sites previously identified in 1993. ESA participant unimproved grasslands had slightly higher levels of stress-tolerators than non-participant farms.

Improved grassland: There were no significant differences in the mean number of plant species between years for participant grasslands and species diversity decreased on non-participant grasslands (Table 1). Improved grasslands harboured the lowest proportion of stress-tolerators of all monitored habitats. The proportion of stress-tolerators significantly decreased between 1993 and 1996 on non-participant farms, (8% and 3% respectively).

Heather moorland: The plant species diversity of sites which were not participating in the ESA scheme had significantly decreased over the three year period (Table 1). There was no significant difference in the number of plant species between years for ESA agreement sites. The frequency of *Juncus effusus, Trichophorum cespitosum, Poa trivialis* had doubled on non-participant sites since 1993. ESA participant farms had a significantly higher proportion of stress-tolerators than non-participant farms in 1996 (58% and 39% respectively).

Woodland: There were no significant differences in the mean number of plant species between years for participant or non-participant farms. *Ajuga reptans, Ranunculus acris* and *Ranunculus ficaria* all increased in frequency between 1993 and 1996 in woods under an ESA agreement.

Invertebrate species diversity

Mean numbers of carabid beetle species on heather moorland increased significantly on participant farms. There were no other significant changes in mean species number on other habitats over the monitoring period (Table 2).

Indicator carabid beetle species identified in the baseline monitoring programme (1993) were remonitored in 1996.

Carabus clatratus was found to be local but widespread in old hay meadows and lakeshore pasture. Re-monitoring indicated the continued presence of this species on hay meadow, wet grassland and unimproved grassland sites. *Carabus clatratus* was not found to be present on any improved sites.

Carabus nitens is locally distributed on wet upland heaths and blanket bog and has a close association with heather throughout its European range. This species indicates the continued presence and quality of heather sites in Fermanagh ESA. *C. nitens* has been lost from Holland and Germany due to the widespread destruction of its heathland habitat and efforts to re-introduce it have failed. Heather is the most diverse habitat in terms of carabid beetle numbers and the numbers of carabid species on this habitat have significantly increased on ESA participant farms from 1993 and 1996.

Blethisa multipunctata is widespread but extremely local in the swampy margins of lowland lakes and rivers subject to flooding. This species is not favoured by agricultural drainage and is probably in decline (R. Anderson personal communication). One

Table 2. The mean number of carabid beetle species per site in 1993 and 1996 for ESA participants and non-participants.

Habitat	ESA scheme	n	Mean nos.of beetle species per site (standard error) 1993	1996	P-t-value n.s. not sig *P <0.05
Hay meadow	Participant	1	10 ()	12 ()	n.s.
	Non-participant	7	12 (1.2)	11 (1.1)	n.s.
Wet grassland	Participant	6	14 (0.6)	12 (1.1)	n.s.
	Non-participant	1	14 ()	14 ()	n.s.
Limestone grassland	Participant	2	13 (0.5)	11 (3.0)	n.s.
	Non-participant	3	12 (0.3)	13 (2.5)	n.s.
Heather moorland	Participant	6	9 (2.1)	12 (2.2)	* t-value=3.95df=5
	Non-participant	2	14 (2.0)	16 (0.0)	n.s.
Improved grassland	Participant	1	7 ()	12 ()	n.s.
	Non-participant	3	12 (0.7)	12 (1.1)	n.s.
Unimproved grassland	Participant	5	12 (1.6)	14 (1.9)	n.s.
	Non-participant	3	11 (0.7)	14 (1.8)	n.s.
Woodland	Participant	2	13 (2.0)	18 (1.0)	n.s.
	Non-participant	2	9 (1.5)	16 (1.5)	n.s.

individual of this species was captured on a small improved grassland site close to the shore of Lough Scolban. Surrounding habitats were all unimproved grassland, wet grassland and woodland scrub on the shores of the Lough.

Chlaenius nigricornis was described as widespread and common in Ireland at the turn of the century.This species prefers base rich soils and it is thought that soil acidification due to fertiliser application may be partly responsible for its decline. It is now not found in the east of Ireland and is thought only to be present around Lough Erne on areas where there are base rich rocks. *C. nigricornis* has been found on six ESA monitoring sites, three unimproved grasslands two wet grasslands and one improved grassland.

DISCUSSION

The time scale between the baseline and the re-monitoring programme was only three years, a very short time to evaluate the impact of the ESA scheme in maintaining and enhancing the wildlife diversity of habitats. However, the re-monitoring programme has shown that the species diversity of all habitats on ESA participant farms have been maintained and in some habitats the diversity has been significantly enhanced. The plant species diversity of hay meadows from ESA participant farms had increased. The management prescriptions of low fertiliser inputs, low density grazing regime and late hay cutting dates, promote favourable habitat conditions for the maintenance and increase in the frequency and abundance of plant stress-tolerator species and sensitive carabid beetle indicators. The plant and invertebrate species diversity of heather moorland sites from ESA participant farms increased significantly, the plant species diversity of improved grasslands also increased (not significantly) since designation in 1993.

The habitat diversity of hay meadows, wet grasslands, limestone grasslands, unimproved grasslands and woodlands on non-participant farms, at the time of re-monitoring in 1996 was also maintained between 1993 and 1996. However some indications of reductions in species targeted for conservation, such as some of the stress-tolerator species from habitats on non-participant farms and an increase in more competitive, ruderal grass and weed species, suggest that the diversity of these habitats may be falling, although changes were not yet statistically significant. The species diversity of heather moorland and improved grasslands from habitats on non-participant farms was significantly reduced between years.

The re-monitoring programme in the West Fermanagh and Erne Lakeland ESA provides evidence for the success of the scheme in the maintenance and enhancement of the plant and invertebrate species diversity of habitats. Hence it appears that the overall wildlife value of habitats in the ESA have been maintained.

Further studies relating farming practices to all habitat species information should ensure differences be attributable to participation in the ESA scheme. This should highlight any differences between management practices on re-monitored farms' and those advocated by the ESA scheme. These results combined with continued re-monitoring exercises, taking into account new participants in the scheme and the time of their entry into an ESA agreement, should provide regular updates on the success of the scheme and provide quality controls for the evaluation of ESA management prescriptions.

REFERENCES

GRIME J.P., HODGSON J.G. and HUNT R. (1988) *Comparative Plant Ecology: a functional approach to common British species* London: Unwin Hyman.

HOPKINS A. and WAINWRIGHT J. (1989) Changes in botanical composition and agricultural management of enclosed grassland in upland areas of England and Wales, 1970-86, and some conservation implications. *Biological Conservation* 47, 219-235.

KIRBY P. (1992) *Habitat management for Invertebrates: a practical handbook*. Royal Society for the Protection of Birds. Bedfordshire.

LEADER-WILLIAMS N., SMITH R.I.L. and ROTHERY, P. (1987) Influence of introduced reindeer on the vegetation of South Georgia: results from a long-term exclusion experiment. *Journal of Applied Ecology* 24, 801-822.

LINDROTH C.H. (1974) *Handbook for the identification of British Insects*, vol IV Coleoptera, Part 2 *Carabidae*, Royal Entomological Society, London.

MAGURRAN A.E. (1988) *Ecological diversity and its measurement*. London: Croom Helm.

McADAM J.H., HEGARTY C.A., McFERRAN D., CAMERON A. and MULHOLLAND F. (1994) Environmentally Sensitive Areas in Northern Ireland. Biological Monitoring Report Year One - 1993.

McADAM J.H., HEGARTY C.A., MCFERRAN D., CAMERON A. and MULHOLLAND F. (1995) Environmentally Sensitive Areas in Northern Ireland. Biological Monitoring Report Year Two - 1994.

Monitoring Vegetation in the Scottish ESAs.

R.P.CUMMINS[1], D.A.ELSTON[2], J.H.GAULD[3,] C.J.BARR[4], R.G.H.BUNCE[4]

[1] Institute of Terrestrial Ecology, Hill of Brathens, Banchory AB31 4BY
[2] Biomathematics and Statistics Scotland, Craigiebuckler, Aberdeen AB15 8QH
[3] Macaulay Land Use Research Institute, Craigiebuckler, Aberdeen AB15 8QH
[4] Institute of Terrestrial Ecology, Merlewood, Grange-over-Sands LA11 6JU

INTRODUCTION

The Scottish ESAs Scheme was introduced in 1987 'to help conserve specially designated areas of the countryside where the landscape, wildlife or historic interest is of particular importance and where these environmental features can be affected by farming operations' (Scottish Office, 1993). The Scheme is voluntary and landholders who enter it can receive payments at two levels for undertaking specified environmentally friendly management practices. Standard (Tier 1) payments cover the whole of each landholding and aim to protect and maintain vegetation, and other features, by avoiding damage arising from, for example, mechanical disturbance, inappropriate use of agrochemicals, and overgrazing. A higher rate is paid for Tier 2 measures which are aimed at enhancing the conservation interest of selected parts of the holding by increasing the extent or 'quality' of prescribed features. Management requirements are specified for ESAs individually, as are the payments for different features and the maximum total payment available to each landholder.

The initial 5-year Scheme comprised five ESAs which were monitored, principally for changes in species composition and structure of selected vegetation types, by the Macaulay Land Use Research Institute (MLURI). A new 10-year Scheme was introduced in 1992-3 when five more areas were designated and most of the original ESAs were increased in size. ESAs now cover 14 913 km^2 (Scottish Office. 1994), equivalent to nearly 19% of Scotland. There are three ESAs focused on island complexes (the Shetlands, the Argyll Islands, and the machairs of the southern islands of the Outer Hebrides), three inland sites in northern Scotland (Cairngorm Straths, Breadalbane, and Loch Lomond) and four linked ESAs running across the southern uplands from Stewartry in the west to Ettrick and Lauderdale in the east.

MONITORING RATIONALE

With the introduction of the second phase of the Scheme, the Scottish Office commissioned the design and implementation of a new monitoring programme which was to take a broader approach than before. The objective was to assess changes not only in the composition of vegetation communities but also in their extent, together with elements of monitoring landscape and archaeological features. The contract was awarded to a consortium of the organisations named in the title together with Archaeological Operations and Conservation Scotland (AOC).

The principal remit of the monitoring programme was that it should assess the *effectiveness* of the ESA prescriptions: the Scheme could not be considered cost-effective if identical changes were observed both on land that was entered into the Scheme and on land elsewhere. The monitoring programme was not designed to provide quantitative information on the *reasons* for change as the Scottish Office has other programmes for such research.

This paper focuses on the procedures undertaken to determine a viable monitoring programme for the wide range of vegetation types in the Scottish ESAs, with special emphasis on grasslands. Further details about the vegetation monitoring procedures are given in Gauld *et al.* (1997).

SAMPLING STRATEGY

Assessing the effectiveness of the ESA prescriptions by comparison of control/treatment areas was rejected as a strategy because (a) it would have been difficult to find truly comparable areas, and (b) both control and treatment areas could be lost because landholders can opt into the scheme at any time and they also have the option to leave the Scheme after five years. Indeed, to guarantee the retention of valid control areas, a considerable number of farmers who join the Scheme would then have to undertake *not* to implement the ESA management practices for which they were receiving payment. This would have been an unacceptable use of resources. Therefore, it was decided that the underlying strategy of the monitoring would be to use repeated visits to the same sites to quantify changes in cover on land that has been entered into the scheme, to compare those changes with their equivalents in the ESAs as a whole and also with national changes identified in other programmes, particularly the ITE/Department of Environment's Countryside Surveys (Barr *et al.,* 1994) and MLURI's Land Cover of Scotland database (MLURI, 1993).

Within this broad strategy, it was necessary to monitor changes in the quantity (extent) and quality (composition) of vegetation as well as assessing the relative cost-effectiveness of the Tier 1 and Tier 2 payments. This resulted in a two-pronged approach and it was important to optimise the sampling programme for each approach.

1. Background monitoring: This involves the detailed mapping of a stratified random sample of 1 km squares throughout each ESA, regardless of uptake of the scheme, to provide information on changes in the extent and broad species composition of all the vegetation types present in the sample. Supplementary information on the species composition of certain key vegetation types is obtained from permanently marked quadrats ($4m^2$ for graminaceous vegetation, $200m^2$ for heathlands) in which all species are recorded together with percentage cover in 5% classes.

Most semi-natural vegetation is protected under Tier 1 and so one of the main challenges was to determine the optimum sample size (number of 1 km squares) for assessing future changes over a wide range of vegetation types. The target was that the sample size should give a statistical power of 0.75, for detecting changes, at the 5%

significance level, of 20% in the mapped extent of key vegetation types, commonly heather moorland, herb-rich grassland, wetlands and woodlands. [Note: the power of a statistical test, for a given change in cover, is the probability of deciding that a change *has* occured at a specified level of significance. Hence the power is a measure of the reliability of the sampling scheme to detect real changes. This contrasts with the significance level of a test which is the probability of stating that there has been a change when, in fact, there has been *no* real change].

Table 1. Statistical powers of different sample sizes for detecting changes of 20%, at a significance level of 5%, of the original cover in a selection of semi-natural vegetation types in three ESAs and for all the Scottish ESAs combined.

Vegetation type	No. of 1 km squares							
	25	35	55	105	25	35	55	105
	Cairngorm Straths				Argyll Islands			
DH	0.99	0.99	0.99	0.99	0.43	0.59	0.79	0.97
BW	0.99	0.99	0.99	0.99	0.78	0.91	0.99	0.99
MG	0.99	0.99	0.99	0.99	0.68	0.82	0.95	0.99
PMG	0.84	0.96	0.99	0.99	0.39	0.52	0.72	0.95
UG	0.19	0.24	0.30	0.54	0.06	0.07	0.10	0.15
UpG	0.99	0.99	0.99	0.99	0.15	0.20	0.30	0.54

	No. of 1km squares							
	25	35	55	250	100	200	300	400
	Loch Lomond				All ESAs			
DH	0.74	0.86	0.98	0.99	0.99	0.99	0.99	0.99
BW	0.60	0.76	0.92	0.99	0.99	0.99	0.99	0.99
MG	0.93	0.99	0.99	0.99	0.99	0.99	0.99	0.99
PMG	0.20	0.28	0.43	0.76	0.95	0.99	0.99	0.99
UG	0.04	0.05	0.05	0.07	0.18	0.24	0.33	0.42
UpG	0.30	0.40	0.58	0.90	0.94	0.99	0.99	0.99

DH - dense heath with >75% cover *Calluna/Erica spp.*, BW - broadleaf woodland, MG - moorland grass (usually dominated by spp. such as *Nardus stricta, Deschampsia flexuosa* and *Juncus squarrosus)*, PMG -purple moor grassland with >50% *Molinia caerulea*, UG - unimproved lowland grassland, UpG - upland grassland (unimproved, usually acidic with predominantly *Agrostis and Festuca spp)*. For fuller descriptions, see Barr *et al.* (1993).

The only suitable source of data for making these calculations was ITE/DoE's Countryside Survey records of vegetation change from 1984-1990, although it had to be assumed for this exercise that future rates of change would not be grossly different from past rates. These data were allocated, via aggregations of the ITE Land Classes, to the strata in each ESA. Sample sizes were determined for twelve major vegetation associations, both in ESAs individually and for all the ESAs combined. Selected examples are given (Table 1).

Different vegetation types vary widely in their rates of spatial change, both within and between ESAs. In Table 1, this is reflected in the wide range of sample sizes required to achieve any specific power value. Particularly large samples would be required to detect changes in the mapped areas of, for example, unimproved grasslands, which contain a high proportion of the herb-rich grassland key vegetation type. An unrealistic budget would be required to obtain absolute figures for such vegetation types and in these cases it is expected that only trends of change in extent will be identifiable (although changes in the composition of herb-rich grasslands are probably more pertinent to the ESA targets). In contrast, a sample of fewer than 25 squares would be adequate for key vegetation types such as broadleaf woodlands.

Whilst the sample size per ESA would obviously have to be a compromise of those required for individual vegetation types, a priority was that the total sample size would provide meaningful results for the ESAs nationally. From interpolation of the tables for all vegetation types in all ESAs, it was decided that the most cost-effective programme overall would be to sample 26 squares per ESA. Two very similar contiguous ESAs in the southern uplands were combined for sampling purposes in order to release resources for the more variable ESAs. As a result, a total of 236 squares were finally surveyed which, nationally, satisfies the criterion of 75% statistical power for most vegetation types. The increased sampling effort required to provide substantially improved powers for the highly variable vegetation types could not be justified in cost-benefit terms.

2. Prescription monitoring: The aim of this part of the programme is to assess changes on land for which the more expensive Tier 2 payments are made. Landholders have to map these areas on their applications for the Scheme so further mapping, as in background monitoring, is unnecessary. Consequently changes can be monitored by random sampling with quadrats in these designated areas.

Again, the sampling needed to be widespread because the statistical population is *all* the Tier 2 examples of a vegetation type in an ESA. The challenge here was to establish the most cost-efficient sampling strategy for fulfilling the same statistical criterion as above but this time for changes in species composition. The key question was 'For the specified statistical power, is it cheaper to record several quadrats on a few landholdings (sites) or a small number of quadrats on many holdings?'

Tables of statistical powers were calculated for different numbers of sites and quadrats per site, using MLURI's earlier data on the variability of change in specific vegetation types. An abbreviated example (Table 2a) is given, based on determining changes of 20%

in the occurrence of four indicator species in herb-rich grasslands in the Breadalbane ESA. The most notable feature of this table is the statistical strength of doing few quadrats at many sites: a sample comprising only one quadrat at 34 sites (total 34 quadrats) has the same power as 6 quadrats at 18 sites (total 108 quadrats). This pattern pertains for changes in other features as diverse as heather cover and the height of tree saplings, although the actual values vary.

However the *cost-effectiveness* of the various sampling options depends on the relative cost of moving to another site (i.e. landholding) compared with doing more quadrats in the original site. This is expressed as the Cost Ratio where, for example, a value of 2 indicates that moving between sites takes twice as many units as setting up and recording a quadrat; here the total cost to complete one quadrat is 3 units: 2 units for travel and 1 unit for recording the quadrat.

Cost ratios were calculated for the various combinations of 'numbers of sites x quadrats per site' determined in the power calculations. The equivalent data for Table 2a are given as an example (Table 2b). It should be noted that the generality of these tables allows the costs to be expressed in whatever units of money or time (e.g. hours, half-days) that the user chooses.

Table 2. (a) The number of quadrats and sites required to achieve statistical powers of 0.75, at 5% significance level, when determining 20% change in the occurrence of selected indicator species of herb-rich grasslands. (b) Equivalent costs (arbitrary units) for different ratios of {cost of changing sites:cost of recording one quadrat}.

(a)			*Number of quadrats per site*					
			1	2	3	4	5	6
No. of sites needed for power of 0.75			34	25	21	20	19	18
(b)			Unit costs for above values of 'quadrats x sites'					
Cost ratio:	1		68	75	84	100	114	126
	2		102	100	105	120	133	144
	3		136	125	126	140	152	162
	4		170	150	147	160	171	180

Where the cost ratio is 1 (*i.e.* it takes as long to record a quadrat as to move to a new landholding), there is a clear cost advantage in recording only one quadrat on a larger number of sites and this strategy has been adopted for graminaceous vegetation in the Scottish ESAs. An interaction, not quantified here, is that increasing the number of sites increases the site density within the ESA and, hence, reduces the travel times between sites. As the cost ratio increases, it becomes more efficient to do 2 or more quadrats per site but the extra costs can be marginal. In these circumstances it may be considered prudent to increase the resources slightly in order to get wider geographical distribution of the sampling units.

DISCUSSION

This monitoring programme was designed to assess whether or not the ESA prescriptions were achieving their aims and whether the trends of change identified were different from national trends. The assessments were also to be made over a broader scale than hitherto. Above all, it was important to use the best information available to guide us in the design of a cost-effective programme.

Any sampling scheme which has to use one set of samples to examine changes in the extent of a wide range of highly variable vegetation types (plus landscape features as diverse as walls, tracks and rubbish tips) will necessarily be a compromise. For some features, statistically robust figures for individual ESAs can be obtained by mapping a relatively small number of 1 km squares. Others, notably some grasslands, require large sample sizes that are financially impractical, even for national estimates using data from all the ESAs together. In these cases, indirect methods will be required, based on changes recorded in the quadrats.

Monitoring the effects of the Tier 2 prescriptions is more direct because the relevant areas of vegetation to be sampled have been pre-determined and mapped. Consequently, changes there can be determined by using quadrats situated at random within the sites. The analyses of power:cost ratios provided vital information for maximising the use of resources. Although using only one quadrat per site is markedly different from many monitoring programmes, the above results show that it can be appropriate when the population under study has been defined in 'whole-ESA' terms and where there is a need for geographically widespread samples.

REFERENCES

BARR C.J., BUNCE R.G.H., CLARKE R.T., FULLER R.M., FURSE M.T., GILLESPIE M.K., GROOM G.B., HALLAM C.J., HORNUNG M., HOWARD D.C. & NESS M.J. (1993) *Countryside Survey 1990: main report. Countryside 1990 vol.2*. London: Department of the Environment.

BARR C.J., BUNCE R.G.H. & HEAL O.W. (1994) Countryside Survey 1990: a measure of change. *Journal of the Royal Agricultural Society of England*, 155, 48-58.

GAULD J.H., CUMMINS R.P. and ELSTON D.A. (1997) ESA monitoring in Scotland. In: Sheldrick, R.D. (Ed.) *Grassland Monitoring in ESAs*. Occ. Symp. 32, British Grassland Society: Reading.

MACAULAY LAND USE RESEARCH INSTITUTE (1993) *The Land Cover of Scotland 1988. Final Report*. Aberdeen: Macaulay Land Use Research Institute

SCOTTISH OFFICE (1993) *The Scottish Environment - statistics*, 4, 114. Scottish Office.

SCOTTISH OFFICE (1994) *Cairngorms Straths ESA Explanatory leaflet for Farmers*. Scottish Office.

Experimental and Monitoring Studies of the Use of Raised Water-levels for Grassland Rehabilitation in Lowland ESAs

J.O. MOUNTFORD[†], J.R.B. TALLOWIN[¶], T.H. SPARKS[†], D.J.G. GOWING[‡], S.J. MANCHESTER[†], S.C. ROSE[·], J.R. TREWEEK[†], J.C. GILBERT[‡] and A.C. ARMSTRONG[*]

† NERC Institute of Terrestrial Ecology, Monks Wood, Abbots Ripton, Huntingdon, PE17 2LS

¶ BBSRC Institute of Grassland and Environmental Research, North Wyke, Devon, EX20 2SB

‡ Silsoe College, University of Cranfield, Silsoe, Bedford, MK45 4DT

* ADAS Land Research Centre, Gleadthorpe, Meden Vale, Mansfield, NG20 9PF

RAISED WATER-LEVELS IN ENVIRONMENTALLY SENSITIVE AREAS

Successful conservation of wet grassland is dependent upon suitable management, and fundamentally on the reinstatement of appropriate hydrological conditions. The control of water-levels in ditches has been adopted as a means of maintaining the biodiversity of lowland wet grassland in seven English ESAs *i.e.* Avon Valley, Broads, North Kent Marshes, Somerset Levels and Moors, South Downs, Suffolk River Valleys and Upper Thames Tributaries. However, where enhancement of the wildlife interest, or rehabilitation of previously improved swards is an objective, more affirmative water-management actions have been prescribed, notably in the Somerset Levels and Moors and the Broads, but also within Tier 2A of the Suffolk River Valleys. Where owners enter land for ESA payments, they may do so at a number of Tiers, where increasing constraints on agricultural practice are offset by increasing payments.

In the Broads and Somerset, the main purpose of Tier 1 is to maintain the characteristic grassland landscape, whereas Tier 2 attempts to enhance the ecological interest of grassland and ditches, through keeping water-levels in the latter above a certain height (MAFF, 1992). Tier 3 was conceived of as a means whereby raising of water-levels might further enhance the interest of grassland and ditches, and provide wet conditions in winter and spring to encourage waterfowl and wading birds. In addition to such biodiversity objectives, the agricultural challenge is to integrate the use of wildlife-rich grasslands into ecologically and economically sustainable livestock systems.

SURVEY AND MONITORING OF RAISED WATER-LEVEL SCHEMES

Beginning in 1991, the Ministry of Agriculture (MAFF) commissioned a programme of research to investigate both an integrated approach to the restoration of wet grassland, and an assessment of the effects on biodiversity of managed water-levels. The assessment approach included annual systematic monitoring of selected sites on both organic and mineral soils in the Broads and Somerset where raised water-level schemes had been recently imposed, or were planned during the span of the research project. Among the sites studied were Southlake Moor (raised water-level introduced winter 1993/4) and Walton Moor (winter 1994/5) in Somerset, and Berney Marshes (implemented 1986 and 1993/4) and Heigham Holmes (1993) in the Broads ESA. Monitoring comprised both ornithological and botanical survey of Tier 1 and 3 swards, with all quadrats (microsites) subject to micro-topographical survey, allowing the water-regime at each microsite to be characterised using the hydrological model of Youngs et al. (1989). For deep peats in Somerset, botanical and hydrological data have been integrated in *SCHAFRIM*, a model which may be used to predict the outcome of altered water-regimes on individual species and plant communities (Gowing et al., 1994). Data gathered as part of the present MAFF programme were compared with results of monitoring vegetation change in raised water-level areas by English Nature on Southlake Moor, and the Royal Society for the Protection of Birds (RSPB) on West Sedgemoor.

TADHAM MOOR EXPERIMENT, SOMERSET LEVELS AND MOORS ESA

Tadham Moor had previously been used in an experimental investigation of the effects of fertilizer use on old peat meadows, Phase I examining the short-term impact, and Phase II both longer-term changes, and the course of reversion following the end of nitrogen application (Mountford et al., 1994). Phase III comprised a study of the effects of water-levels raised to Tier 3 on both ecological and agronomic variables. Water-levels were raised in December 1994 in the original experimental site, and subsequent sampling compared changes in the unfertilized 'wet' plots with adjacent (also unfertilized) 'dry' plots where Tier 1 levels were maintained. Vegetation was recorded both by means of quadrat transects, whose positions were levelled as outlined above, and through matched pairs of quadrats. The matched pairs were located in the 'wet' and 'dry' plots in positions selected to have very similar water-regimes prior to the imposition of raised water-levels, allowing very accurate assessment to be made of sward change.

VEGETATION CHANGE FOLLOWING RAISED WATER-LEVELS

Tadham Moor and the Somerset Levels and Moors ESA

Although significant effects were observed in individual species, the most marked impact was in terms of species-richness (Table 1). The immediate effect of raised water-level was extensive sward death, with a corresponding increase in bare ground, and reduction in the number of species in each permanent quadrat. Though there was some recovery in species-richness in 1996 within 'wet' plots, they remained significantly more species-poor than where water-levels were unchanged, and diversity (Simpson's index) was 0.71 in contrast to 0.87 in 'dry' plots ($P<0.01$). Corresponding reductions in species/m^2 were observed in bunded Tier 3 on West Sedgemoor, from 19.2 in 1988 to 16.0 in 1994 (Prosser and Wallace, 1995).

Table 1.   Tadham Moor: Results for matched quadrat pairs in 'dry' and 'wet' (water-level raised Dec.1994) plots. **T**: total individual species with significantly higher % cover in dry or wet plots; **M**: mean number of species per m^2; and **B**: bare ground (% cover). <u>Key</u>: ns = not significant; * = $P<0.05$; ** = $P<0.01$. Compared using paired t-tests for

	T	M	B
1994 Dry	4	21.3	1.9
1994 Wet	1	19.3	6.9
Significance		ns	ns
1995 Dry	15	21.5	2.7
1995 Wet	2	14.2	35.0
Significance		**	**
1996 Dry	9	24.7	5.8
1996 Wet	2	17.2	2.3
Significance		*	ns

Use of *SCHAFRIM* correctly predicted that two species would spread under the water-regime imposed in 'wet' plots at Tadham: *Agrostis stolonifera* and *Caltha palustris*. Other species anticipated to benefit as yet show no significant response in this experiment, though monitoring at Southlake Moor by English Nature (Leach, 1995) provided corroboration of the predicted response for *Carex nigra*, *C. riparia*, *Glyceria fluitans*, *Ranunculus flammula*, *R. repens* and *Senecio aquaticus*.

Following the imposition of Tier 3 at Tadham, aeration stress (potential anoxia) in the 'wet' member of each matched pair attained a level where certain grasses were predicted to decrease, and indeed significantly reduced covers were observed in *Cynosurus cristatus*, *Festuca rubra*, *Holcus lanatus* and *Luzula campestris*. Similarly predicted declines were recorded in certain forbs at Tadham: *Cirsium dissectum*, *Filipendula ulmaria* and *Plantago lanceolata*, and in addition at Southlake *Cerastium fontanum*, *Rumex acetosa*, *Taraxacum* and *Trifolium pratense* (Leach, 1995).

Observed trends at Tadham ran contrary to that predicted for three species which were expected to benefit from raised levels but in fact declined: *Cardamine pratensis*, *Festuca pratensis* and *Leontodon autumnalis*. Some results of monitoring Tier 1 and raised water-level Tier 3 at Walton Moor were also unexpected, for as well as abundant *A. stolonifera*, Tier 3 swards had significantly more of the finer pasture grasses (*Agrostis capillaris*, *F. rubra* and *H. lanatus*) two years after raising of water-levels. Tier 1 was dominated by *Lolium perenne* with *Alopecurus pratensis* and *Trifolium repens*.

Broads ESA

Monitoring of clay sites in Norfolk provided some results comparable with the predicted behaviour of species on Somerset peats *e.g.* Berney Marshes Tier 3 grassland had abundant *A. stolonifera* and *Alopecurus geniculatus*, whilst Tier 2 swards were dominated by *A. capillaris*, *C. cristatus*, *H. lanatus* and *L. perenne*. In contrast, although *A. stolonifera* and *L. perenne* showed a similar response at Heigham Holmes, *F. rubra* and *H. lanatus* were markedly commoner under raised water-levels. Such apparently contradictory behaviour in species between sites in both ESAs may be largely explained by reference to site history. At Tadham, Southlake and Berney Marshes, the grasslands had been long managed extensively for nature conservation, and until the introduction of raised water-levels, sward composition was broadly similar in areas allocated to the different tiers in 1993/4. At both Heigham Holmes and Walton Moor, land entered for Tier 1 had previously been intensively managed with *L. perenne* encouraged at the expense of most other pasture grasses and forbs. In these two sites, land selected for Tier 3 raised water-levels had been of lower productivity with a mixed sward composition, and despite altered water-regime, fine pasture grasses remained significantly commoner than on adjacent Tier 1 land. Such discrepancies underline the need for controlled experiments in addition to the monitoring of schemes on ordinary farmland.

AGRICULTURAL PRODUCTION

Combining productive agriculture and wet grassland rehabilitation

For both agricultural and environmental reasons, grassland management should provide conditions where high individual animal growth can be achieved *i.e.* efficient feed conversion. Semi-natural grasslands that impose severe limits on productive livestock performance will be marginalized by the farming community. Wildlife conservation objectives require that many semi-natural grasslands, including wet meadows, are cut for hay at a phenologically advanced stage of development for most of the plant species present. The quality of the resulting hay will therefore be low compared with forages cut at more vegetative stages of growth. Within the present research programme an assessment was made of whether Tier 3 conditions imposed additional constraints on livestock farming over and above those presented by the management of 'dry' semi-natural grasslands.

Tadham Moor

Interim results for the Phase III of the Tadham experiment are available *i.e.* averages of 2 out of the 3 years' data. In meadows with no history of inorganic fertilizer input, dry-matter yield under Tier 3 conditions was c. 4.5. tonnes/ha. If representative, this yield would be 15-20% lower than the average obtained under the drier soil regime of Phases I and II of the experiment (Kirkham and Wilkins, 1994; Tallowin and Smith, 1994). Pepsin cellulase digestibility and metabolizable energy values of the hay tended to be slightly higher, and consequently the metabolizable energy output as hay appeared to be similar under the Tier 3 conditions and within the 'dry' plots. Mineral contents and yields in the hay were similar in the Tier 3 and in the drier soil regime for nitrogen, phosphorus, potassium and magnesium, but both calcium and sodium availability appeared to be reduced by 45-50% under the raised water-level conditions. Both live-weight produced and the estimated utilized metabolizable energy (UME) output obtained from grazing the regrowth from the hay harvest appeared to exceed (by up to 40%) the outputs achieved under the previous drier soil regime. Individual animal performance was consistently high (1 kg live-weight gain per day) under Tier 3 conditions. Overall UME output (hay + grazing) tended to be 20-25% higher in raised water-level plots compared with that achieved during Phases I and II.

REFINING ESA PRESCRIPTIONS

Agronomic implications

On the Tadham site, the raised water-levels prescribed under Tier 3 of the Somerset Levels and Moors ESA appeared to provide no additional constraints on forage quality or UME output as hay, compared to extensively managed grassland where water-levels have not been raised. Tier 3 conditions seemed to offer some agronomic benefits in the form of enhanced livestock output and high individual animal performance from mid-late summer grazing. If consistent between years, such benefits make Tier 3 grassland a potentially valuable forage resource in the mid-summer to autumn period and would allow its use to be readily integrated into current productive livestock systems.

Botanical implications

Preliminary experimental results from Tadham, monitoring of raised water-level schemes in the Broads and Somerset, and the use of predictive modelling together led to the expression of concern as to the impact of Tier 3 water-levels on species-rich grassland (MAFF, 1996). A revised Tier 3 was suggested for Somerset whereby levels be slightly lowered in March-April to prevent anoxia and sward death (Gowing, 1996). Despite initial increases in breeding waders, the long term effect on bird numbers is not yet clear, and the Ministry has proposed that existing schemes in Somerset be reviewed in consultation with English Nature, to decide whether all the environmental benefits of such agreements might be better served by the suggested revision to Tier 3. The present research programme has confirmed the importance of micro-topographic variation and of ditch spacing and geometry in providing a range of water-regime conditions in wet grassland. Distinct plant communities can be observed by foot-drains or grips, demonstrating the benefits from the reinstatement of such features. The Ministry has acknowledged both the need for flexibility in the promotion of biodiversity objectives, and for having regard to the full range of biota that inhabit lowland wet grassland. Successful restoration of biodiversity demands that an accurate assessment be made of the present value (ecological and agricultural) of a site, and that attempts to enhance some particular aspect be planned in the widest context.

ACKNOWLEDGEMENTS
The research reported here was commissioned by the Ministry of Agriculture.

REFERENCES
GOWING D.J.G. (1996). *Examination of the potential impacts of alternative management regimes in the Somerset Levels and Moors ESA.* Report to the Ministry of Agriculture. Silsoe College.

GOWING D.J.G., YOUNGS E.G., CLARKE M.F., MOUNTFORD J.O., CHAPMAN J.M., LEEDS-HARRISON P.B. and SPOOR G. 1994. *SCHAFRIM (Silsoe College Hydrology and Flora Risk Identification Model).* Silsoe: Silsoe College

KIRKHAM F.W. and WILKINS R.J. (1994). The productivity and response to inorganic fertilizers of species-rich wetland hay meadows on the Somerset Moors: the effect of nitrogen under hay cutting and aftermath grazing. *Grass and Forage Science*, 49, 152-162.

LEACH S.J. (1995). Monitoring vegetation on Southlake Moor SSSI 1993-5. *Proceedings of a workshop on vegetation change in raised water-level areas, 1995.* Taunton: English Nature

MINISTRY OF AGRICULTURE, FISHERIES AND FOOD (1992). *Environmentally Sensitive Areas. 2. Broads. 6. Somerset Levels and Moors.* London: MAFF.

MINISTRY OF AGRICULTURE FISHERIES AND FOOD (1996). *Consultation documents on proposals for the future of Environmentally Sensitive Area Schemes: 1997-2002. 1. Broads. 2. Somerset Levels and Moors.* London: MAFF.

MOUNTFORD J.O., TALLOWIN J.R.B., KIRKHAM F.W. and LAKHANI K.H. (1994). Sensitivity, productivity and reversibility: a case study on the use of fertilisers on flower-rich hay-meadows on the Somerset Levels. In: Haggar, R.J. and Peel, S. (ed) *Grassland Management and Nature Conservation.* British Grassland Society Occasional Symposium No. 28, pp.74-85.

PROSSER M. and WALLACE H. (1995). Vegetation change at West Sedgemoor 1988-95. *Proceedings of a workshop on vegetation change in raised water-level areas, 1995.* Taunton: English Nature.

TALLOWIN J.R.B. and SMITH R.E.N. (1994). *The effect of inorganic fertilizers on botanical diversity and agricultural production on the Somerset Levels.* Eighth and final report to the Management Group of the Tadham Project for the Ministry of Agriculture, Fisheries and Food, the Department of the Environment and English Nature.

YOUNGS E.G., LEEDS-HARRISON P.B. and CHAPMAN J.M. (1989). Modelling water-table movement in flat low-lying lands. *Hydrological Processes*, 3, 301-315.

Hay meadow grassland types in the West Fermanagh & Erne Lakeland Environmentally Sensitive Area

G. M. HOPPÉ, F. MULHOLLAND and J.H. McADAM

Applied Plant Science Research Division, Department of Agriculture for N.I., Newforge Lane, Belfast, BT9 5PX, N. Ireland.

INTRODUCTION

Grasslands (natural and semi-natural) make up a large part of the landscape of Northern Ireland and are therefore an important habitat type. Farms are small, family based and almost completely reliant on grassland for cattle and sheep production. Changes in management practices over the last decade aimed at intensification of agricultural production has occurred on what could be termed "marginal" land. As a consequence there has been a loss and fragmentation of important grassland habitats, loss of species diversity and decreased wildlife value of grasslands (Oomes *et al.*, 1996). With changes in agricultural policy within the EU, emphasis is increasingly being placed on conservation and biodiversity (at both species and landscape levels) and the benefits of "environmentally friendly" farming practices. Northern Ireland has five Environmentally Sensitive Areas (ESAs) covering almost 20% of agricultural land. Their aims are to maintain (and enhance) the landscape, wildlife and historical features within the designated areas. The Department of Agriculture for N.Ireland has an ongoing and expanding research and monitoring (McAdam *et al.*, 1995; Cameron *et al.*, 1997) programme in grassland habitats. This paper details part of the research programme into the agricultural and conservation potential of hay meadow types in the West Fermanagh & Erne Lakeland ESA.

Traditional hay meadow management

Meadow grassland in County Fermanagh is utilised to provide a hay crop during the summer on which animals depend during the following autumn, and also provide grazing at other times of the year. The combination of spring grazing (weather dependant), followed by the closing up of the hay crop, usually ensures aftermath grazing in the autumn. The intermittent use of farmyard manure and the lack of mineral fertilisers has resulted in the creation of meadows which are highly valued for their floristic diversity and are a feature of the Fermanagh landscape. Only 39% of meadows are cut in June, 56% at the beginning of July and 89% by the middle of the month. Mid-July is the most frequent cutting date for hay (Eakin, 1994). Records also show hay cut in August and as late as September.

West Fermanagh & Erne Lakeland ESA management prescriptions

In order to encourage farmers to participate in the ESA scheme different levels of conservation management (tiers) were introduced and appropriate payments set. The management prescriptions for hay meadows limit nutrient input levels (maximum 25kg N/ha and 13kg P & K/ha) and stipulate dates before which meadows should not be cut for hay or silage (1st and 16th July). The mid July cutting date is aimed at causing minimum disturbance to ground nesting birds and to allow plants to shed ripe seed. Aftermath grazing by cattle is recommended

METHODS
Site and sampling methodology
The sixteen sites selected were a sub-sample of those used in the monitoring programme (McAdam *et al.*, 1994) and were representative of a range of species-rich and species-poor hay meadow types.

At each site herbage samples were harvested from early-June to late-July 1994 & 1995 by cutting to ground level five randomly located samples, each two trips 1m x 10cm in length. All the clipped herbage was bulked and a representative sub-sample used for biomass (dry matter) determination and herbage quality (no data presented). The remaining cut herbage sample was hand separated to species level for the determination of species composition (by weight). Sward height measurements are based on a measure of the longest leaf length at each of 30 random locations per site.

A minimum of four hay meadow sites per species were selected and used for a species phenology study. Phenologies were constructed using the method of Smith and Jones (1991) for *Plantago lanceolata* (Plantain), *Trifolium pratense* (Red clover), *Luzula campestris* (Wood rush), *Cerastium arvense* (Mouse-ear chickweed), *Lychnis flos-cuculi* (Ragged robin), and *Filipendula ulmaria* (Meadowsweet). For the selected plant species a minimum of 25 plants were recorded for the number of morphologically distinct development stages.

Soil samples were collected (to a depth of 10cm) in April 1995 to determine soil nutrient status; pH, K, Mg, S, Ca, N, OM (data not presented) and P.

Data analysis
Each variable (dry matter determination, soil nutrients, herbage quality) was subject to analysis of variance (ANOVA) each year. Sward species composition data were transformed using angular transformation prior to ANOVA. The relative proportions of each species in each of the plant strategy theory CSR groups (Grime *et al.*, 1988) was calculated for each hay meadow type in both years.

RESULTS
Production
The results for sites classified into species-rich and species-poor groups for dry matter (DM) herbage yields during the harvesting periods (Figure 1) show no significant difference for any of the harvest dates with the exception of the final sample date in late July 1994. The trend in sward yield in 1994 was such that species-poor sites had slightly higher (not significant) DM accumulation values than species-rich meadows.

Figure 1.   Agricultural production (t DM/ha) for species-rich and species-poor hay meadows in the West Fermanagh & Erne Lakeland ESA in 1994 and 1995.

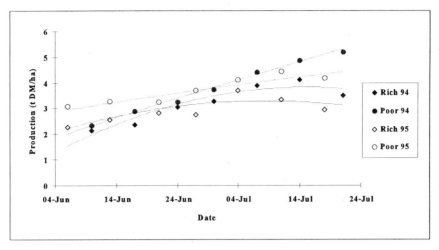

During the drier year of 1995 biomass was reduced compared with 1994, although the species-poor sites remained higher (not significant) relative to the species-rich swards (Figure 1). The effect of reduced DM production in 1995 was an increase in species-rich meadow types (data not presented). Mean sward height was similar for all harvest dates with the exception of the last harvest date where the species-rich swards were significantly taller than the species-poor swards. Mean sward height was a good predictor of sward DM yield during the measuring period in 1994 ($r = 0.875$, significant $P < 0.05$).

The mineral composition of herbage in 1994 and 1995 for species-rich and species-poor swards is presented (Table 1). Generally there were no significant differences in the herbage quality variables analysed of either meadow type in 1994 and 1995. The exceptions were the significantly higher ($P < 0.001$) levels of P in both years (Table 1) for the species-poor meadows. Mean P values (both years) are 0.283% and 0.212% for species-poor and species-rich hay meadows respectively.

Conservation value

Species composition and diversity The species-rich meadows are characterised by *Carex nigra*, *Juncus acutiflorus*, *Rannunculus acris* and *Carex panacea*. This group had the highest diversity with a mean number of species per clipped quadrat of 22 and a total of 178 species identified (combined 1994 & 1995). The soil properties of the species-rich meadows were not significantly different from the species-poor for pH and Mg. However, this group did have lower values of soil phosphorus (Table 1) and potassium perhaps indicating these meadows received smaller inputs of fertiliser than the species-poor meadows.

Table 1. Herbage quality variables and soil P for species-rich and species-poor hay meadows in the West Fermanagh & Erne Lakeland ESA in 1994 and 1995.

	Herbage Quality Variables					Soil P
	% N	% P	% K	Fibre (mg/l)	% DMD	mg/l
1994						
Species-rich	1.597	0.218	1.474	300.9	68.35	-
Species-poor	1.698	0.296	1.591	296.8	68.86	-
SE(x1)	0.075	0.015	0.133	7.30	0.913	-
n1,n2	7, 9	7, 9	7, 9	7, 9	7, 9	-
F value	ns	***	ns	ns	ns	-
1995						
Species-rich	1.600	0.206	1.378	305.0	67.83	10.0
Species-poor	1.798	0.270	1.763	296.2	68.93	23.7
SE(x1)	0.092	0.013	0.131	6.37	0.786	5.6
n1,n2	7, 9	7, 9	7, 9	7, 9	7, 9	7, 9
F value	ns	***	ns	ns	ns	*

Note: Figures in the same column : ns are not significantly different; *** figures are significantly different at $P > 0.005$.; x1 refers to the species-rich treatment.

The species-poor hay meadow vegetation is characterised by *Lolium perenne* and *Holcus lanatus* as the major species contributing to the sward. Other common species were *Alopercurus pratensis*, *Agrostis capillaris* and *Trifolium repens*. In this group a total of 156 plant species were found (combined 1994 & 1995) and a mean of 16 species per clipped quadrat. The maximum number of species recorded per clipped quadrat in the species rich and poor meadows were 35 and 29, respectively. In 1995, the species-rich meadows had a higher proportion of stress-tolerators (45 species) compared with the species-poor meadows (25 species). The proportion of stress-tolerators and stress-tolerator intermediate groups (CS & SR) were higher for the more diverse meadows in both years.

Phenology study During the sampling period (1994 & 1995), the relative abundance of the developmental stages for each species measured was vastly different and ripe seed was not present at the same time each year for all recorded species. Differences in phenological development between species was found in the timing of phenological stages and the duration of each developmental stage. For example, *Lychnis flos-cuculi* displayed both an early and relatively short phenological cycle which was completed by the end of June 1994. This contrasted with *Filipendula ulmaria* which remained in the bud stage until mid-July 1994 (the end of the recording period), after which development was rapid (field observation). All other species, namely *Plantago lanceolata*, *Cerastium arvense*, *Trifolium pratense* and *Luzula campestris*, spread their phenological development over the whole growing season in both 1994 and 1995. Of the species in the study, only *Luzula campestris* displayed any appreciable amount of ripe seed by late July (tier 2 of the ESA prescription), irrespective of year.

DISCUSSION

The productivity (Figure 1) of diverse species-rich hay meadows in the West Fermanagh & Erne Lakeland ESA does not differ significantly from the grass dominant species-poor hay meadows. Wilkins and Harvey (1994) outlined the conflicting management goals for grasslands when used for agricultural and wildlife conservation objectives. It is widely recognised that a high level of nutrient input to species-rich grasslands leads to higher agricultural production per hectare at the expense of reduced conservation value of the sward because of the loss of floristic diversity. This was not the case for the two groups of hay meadow sampled. The application of this to management prescriptions and policy guidelines is that additional fertiliser restrictions could be considered for introduction into the scheme targeted at species-poor hay meadows. The marginal gains from the species-poor meadows in grass production per hectare are at the expense of reduced conservation value. Evidence to date indicates these restrictions would not result in any reduction in the aount or quality of the hay crop yet should increase the potential for enhancing species biodiversity. The results clearly show that in a drier year (1995) the reduction in hay crop resulted in a greater species richness primarily due to the less competitive nature of the graminoid species, allowing a greater proportion of herbs and sedges in the sward.

It is well documented there is a compromise between bulk (yield) and herbage quality. Examination of herbage nutrients and quality from the two hay meadow types show no differences in digestibility, fibre and minerals (Table 1). The exceptions were the higher levels of P (%) content of the herbage for the species-poor swards compared with the species-rich meadows. This is in part related to a greater nutrient availability in the soil substrate under species-poor meadows and the higher nutrient applications (data from 1994 farm survey study) compared to the species-rich meadows. These results conflict with Smith and Jones (1991) who found quality to be reduced with late cutting (species-rich sites) but confirms studies by Kirkham and Tallowin (1995). Smith, *et al.*, (1996) state that increased levels of P reduces biodiversity hence nutrient inputs to hay meadows should be minimized.

The faster phenological development of species recorded in 1995 compared with 1994 can be explained by differences in rainfall (May - July) and air temperatures; a 31% deficit in rainfall combined with 19% higher heatsum values. The current cutting dates for hay meadows allowing first cut dates after the 1st July and the 16th July provide for varying amounts of seed rain (as found by Smith and Jones, 1991) and is highly dependant upon species and the weather conditions over the growing season and at harvest time. Inter-season variability in species composition may ensure that sufficient ripe seeds are set at least once every five years. The current ESA prescription for cutting dates provides the option of cutting late in the season, (September) one year in five. This would appear from other studies (Smith and Jones, 1991; Smith *et al.*, 1996) to provide sufficient seed set to maintain species in the seed bank and sward. Further research on hay meadows in the West Fermanagh & Erne Lakeland ESA will be required to confirm this to be the case.

Further analysis of the data has revealed that the species-rich and species-poor hay meadows can be divided into those sites with a large amount of within site species distribution. It is felt that these variable sites offer the greatest potential for enhancing biodiversity.

REFERENCES

EAKIN M.R. and COPPER A. (1994). Species-rich Hay Meadows and their Relationship to the Socio-economic Status of Farmers. In: Haggar, R.J. & Peel, S. *(eds) Grassland Management and Nature Conservation. British Grassland Society Occasional Symposium No. 28,* 190-194.

CAMERON A., MILLSOPP C.A. and McADAM J.H. (1997) Biological monitoring of grasslands in the West Fermanagh and Erne Lakeland Environmentally Sensitive Area. In: Sheldrick, R.D. (ed) *Grassland Management in the ESAs. British Grassland Society Occ. Symposium, No. 32.*

GRIME J.P., HODGSON J.G. AND HUNT R. (1988) *Comparative Plant Ecology: A Functional* Approach *to Common British Species.* London: Unwin-Hyman.

KIRKHAM F.W. and TALLOWIN J.R.B. (1995) The influence of cutting date and previous fertiliser treatment on the productivity and botanical composition of species-rich hay meadows on the Somerset Levels. *Grass and Forage Science,* 50, 365-377.

McADAM J.H., HEGARTY C.A., MCFERRAN D., CAMERON,A. and MULHOLLAND F. (1995) Environmentally Sensitive Areas in Northern Ireland. Biological Monitoring Report Year Two - 1994. Queens University of Belfast, Belfast.

OOMES M.J.M., OLFF H. and ALTENA H.J. (1996). Effects of vegetation management and raising the water table on nutrient dynamics and vegetation change in wet grassland. *Journal of Applied Ecology,* 33, 1-13.

SMITH R.S. and JONES L. (1991) The phenology of mesotrophic grassland in the Pennine Dales, northern England: historic hay cutting dates, vegetation variation and plant species phenologies. *Journal of Applied Ecology,* 28, 42-59.

SMITH R.S., BUCKINGHAM H., BULLARD M.J., SHIEL R.S. and YOUNGER A. (1996) The conservation management of mesotrophic (meadow) grassland in Northern England. (I) Effects of grazing, hay cut date and fertiliser on the vegetation of a traditionally managed sward, *Grass and Forage Science,* 51,278-291.

WILKINS R.J. and HARVEY H.J. (1994) Management options to achieve agricultural and conservation objectives. In: Haggar, R.J. & Peel, S. *(eds) Grassland Management and Nature Conservation. British Grassland Society Occasional Symposium No. 28,* 86-94.

SCIENCE INTO PRACTICE - APPLICATION

Chairman: Richard Jefferson
English Nature

Upland Meadow Grasslands in the Pennine Dales Environmentally Sensitive Area (ESA)

R.S.SMITH

Department of Agricultural and Environmental Science, The University of Newcastle upon Tyne, Newcastle upon Tyne, NE1 7RU

ABSTRACT

The management of individual 'northern' meadows (Anthoxanthum odoratum-Geranium sylvaticum meadows) *to maintain their plant species composition requires the continued application of 'traditional' regimes, particularly autumn grazing with cattle, no mineral fertilizer and a mid-July hay cutting date. Change in any one of these components can cause significant change in the vegetation. Six years of data from a split-split-split-plot trial in the Yorkshire Dales shows that the recreation of 'northern' meadows after a 'modern' management regime also requires the long-term reinstatement of all components of traditional management, plus the sown seed of desired species.*

Forty-five years of data from 14 meadows in southern Cumbria suggests that meadows on a farm tend to be cut in the same sequence from year to year, with variability in hay cutting date, greatest in the later cut meadows, as a normal feature of the traditional management of whole farms. It is suggested that this variability might be important for the long-term maintenance of the plant species composition

INTRODUCTION

Traditional meadow management is usually considered to involve the application of farmyard manure (FYM), spread during the spring (April-May), without the use of mineral fertilizer. Grazing livestock are removed before mid-May to allow the grass sward to grow and this growth is cut for hay, not silage, sometime during late-June to late-August. It is common practice for cattle to be grazed in the meadow for 3-4 days immediately after the baled hay crop has been removed, when they eat the uncut vegetation from steep banks and field edges. The sward is then allowed to regrow during the late summer and is grazed by cattle during August to October and sheep from November to mid-May. These various components of the traditional regime influence the plant species composition of meadow vegetation and interactions with soil and climate produce distinct communities (Smith, 1985; Rodwell, 1992). In the Pennine Dales ESA the most distinctive is the *Anthoxanthum odoratum-Geranium sylvaticum* grassland, *Briza media* sub-community, otherwise known as the 'northern' meadow. This has an exceptionally high species number, an average of 35 species per m² (Rodwell, 1992), with many attractive flowering forbs, some of which are also found in woodlands, *e.g.* wood crane's-bill (*Geranium sylvaticum*), pignut (*Conopodium majus*) and wood anemone (*Anemone nemorosa*), indicative of a woodland origin for this plant community (Pigott, 1956).

Many 'northern' meadows have been altered through the use of mineral fertilizer and earlier cutting for silage, often being converted to rye-grass (*Lolium perenne*) dominated communities. Protection of all the remaining northern meadows is a high priority in the Pennine Dales Environmentally Sensitive Area (ESA) and parallels the protection given by English Nature in Sites of Special Scientific Interest (SSSI) in the Yorkshire Dales and North Pennines. Restoration management of rye-grass swards to reinstate northern meadow vegetation requires the restoration of all the components of traditional meadow management together with the addition of seed. A long-term perspective is needed, with the continued application of the traditional regime, possibly for more than 20 years. This view is illustrated with data from a six year old split-split-split plot trial on a rye-grass sward at Colt Park Meadows on the Ingleborough National Nature Reserve, North Yorkshire (R.S. Smith, R.S. Shiel, D. Millward, P. Corkhill and T. Barden, unpublished).

Whilst stability in the application of traditional management regimes is important for the long term restoration of northern meadows, it is possible that, paradoxically, variability in hay cutting date is also important. This view is illustrated with data from 14 meadows at Bowberhead and Piper Holes SSSI, Ravenstonedale, Cumbria.

THE ROLE OF STABLE TRADITIONAL MANAGEMENT REGIMES

The Colt Park Meadows experiment included three grazing treatments, replicated three times and randomly allocated to three blocks of 12 x 36m plots (0.043 ha), with livestock allowed free access to the plots. The treatments were: (1) autumn and spring grazing, with beef cattle (10.9 cattle per ha) for four short periods, mid-July to late-August, 0.9 cattle per ha throughout October, 7.5 lambs per ha throughout August, 2 hoggets (sheep less than 1 year old) per ha from October to mid-March, 6.9 ewes per ha lambed in the meadows and adjacent pastures from mid-April to mid-May; (2) spring grazing, as above from 1 January to 15 May with no grazing the rest of the year; (3) autumn grazing, as above from early September to 1 January, with no grazing the rest of the year. Each plot was sub-divided into three 12 x 12m sub-plots and three hay cutting date treatments (14 June, 21 July, 1 September) randomly allocated to them. Each of these sub-plots was divided into two 6 x 12m sub-sub-plots and two fertilizer treatments (no fertilizer or 25 kg/ha nitrogen plus 12.5 kg/ha phosphorus and potassium) randomly allocated to them. Each of these plots was further subdivided into two 6 x 6m sub-sub-sub-plots, to give a total of 108 sub-sub-sub-plots, and a seed addition treatment randomly allocated to one of them. This treatment used commercial sources of seed for 19 species, plus seed from adjacent woodland, roadside verges and uncut field edges, sown as an impure mixture. Three one year old plants of wood crane's-bill were planted into the seed treatment sub-sub-sub-plots in mid-May 1995. Further details of the treatments are given in Smith *et al.* (1996b).

Each of the 108 sub-sub-sub-plots was sampled with two randomly positioned 4-m^2 quadrats within which all vascular plant species were identified and their contribution to the total vegetation cover estimated by eye. Treatment effects on species number were assessed with analysis of variance. The overall effect on species was assessed with a species-treatment biplot produced by redundancy analysis (ter Braak, 1988; 1990).

In the first four years of the trial vegetation change was relatively slow. Traditional

Table 1. Meadow management trial, Colt Park, Ingleborough, 1990-96: treatment effects on species number per 4m^2.

	Mean	SE
Fertilizer effect: _P<0.001_		
No fertilizer	17.9	0.3
Fertilizer	16.4	0.3
Cutting date effect: _P<0.001_		
14 June	17.8	0.4
21 July	18.2	0.4
1 September	15.5	0.3
Grazing effect: _P<0.05_		
Autumn and spring	19.6	0.4
Spring	14.8	0.3
Autumn	17.1	0.4
Seed addition effect: _P<0.001_		
No seed	16.4	0.3
Seed	18.0	0.4

Table 2. Meadow management trial, Colt park, Ingleborough, 1990-96: a significant interaction ($P<0.01$) between the effect of seed, cutting date and grazing treatments on species number per 4m^2.

SEED TREATMENT: No seed added	Grazing treatment		
	Autumn & spring	Spring	Autumn
Cutting date treatment			
14 June	18.8	14.4	16.8
21 July	18.0	15.6	18.2
1 September	17.6	13.1	14.8
SEED TREATMENT: seed added	Grazing treatment		
	Autumn & spring	Spring	Autumn
Cutting date treatment			
14 June	21.2	15.9	19.6
21 July	23.3	15.0	19.2
1 September	18.5	14.8	14.3

yields of hay were quickly achieved but the small, significant increases in species number were limited to the no fertilizer and the 14 June and 21 July cutting date treatments (Smith _et al._, 1996b), with an average of only one extra species in the four years of the trial. This increase was similar to that reported elsewhere (Bakker, 1989; Olff and Bakker, 1991; Berendse *et al.*, 1992). However, after six years there were many more changes, with each of the individual treatments producing significant results. More species were present under each of the traditional variants of fertilizer, cutting date and grazing regime (Table 1); the greatest difference being between grazing treatments, when the absence of autumn grazing resulted in a 25% decline in species number. After six years the seed addition treatment had produced a significant increase in species number. The combination treatment involving seed addition to traditional regimes produced the highest species number, with a 44% reduction in species number when the absence of autumn grazing was combined with 1 September cutting date and no seed addition (Table 2).

The response of individual species was illustrated in a species-treatment biplot (Figure 1). Most of the species were associated with the traditional combination of treatments, with individual deviations resulting in an increase in the abundance of a few species that tended to dominate the sward. Yorkshire fog (*Holcus lanatus*), red fescue (*Festuca rubra*), lesser celandine (*Ranunculus ficaria*) and cock's-foot (*Dactylis glomerata*) increased when the sward was cut on the 14 June, the latter species also increasing when autumn grazing ceased and fertilizer was applied. Common bent (*Agrostis capillaris*), creeping buttercup (*Ranunculus repens*), rough-stalked meadow grass (*Poa trivialis*), meadow foxtail (*Alopecurus pratensis*) and common sorrel (*Rumex acetosa*) increased when the sward was cut on the 1 September, the last three of these also responded positively to the application of fertilizer. Common bent and meadow foxtail also increased in the absence of autumn grazing.

High plant species number requires the continued application of an appropriate combination of management treatments. This would be maintenance management for existing 'northern' meadows, with the continuation of traditional treatments that had been in place for decades, if not centuries. The creation of 'northern' meadows from other 'improved' communities involves similar treatments with the addition of seed and/or plants of the desired species. This process is likely to take some time. The changes at Colt Park meadows were not linear over the first six years of the experiment. Relatively little change occurred in the first four years, followed by major increases in plant species number by the sixth year, when recognisable MG3b grasslands were found where there was autumn grazing and a 21 July hay cutting date. The prediction of future rates of change is uncertain. If we assume that these will be linear and continuous, which is unlikely given the pattern of change seen in years 1-6, it will take about 20 years for species number to increase to levels seen in northern meadows elsewhere. When species are not artificially introduced into 'improved' swards, new species can only arrive through natural dispersal from outside, possibly dispersed by wind, as seed on imported hay or on sheep fleece (Fischer *et al.*, 1996). The Colt Park trial suggests that reliance on this process could considerably extend the time taken to recreate 'northern' meadows.

Figure 1.   Species-treatment biplot[#] , meadow management trial, Colt Park, 1990-96.Δ, cutting date treatment (1, 14 June; 2, 21 July; 3, 1 September); O, fertilizer treatment (F, fertilizer applied; NF, no fertilizer applied); □ , grazing treatment (AS, autumn and spring grazing; A, autumn grazing; S, spring grazing).

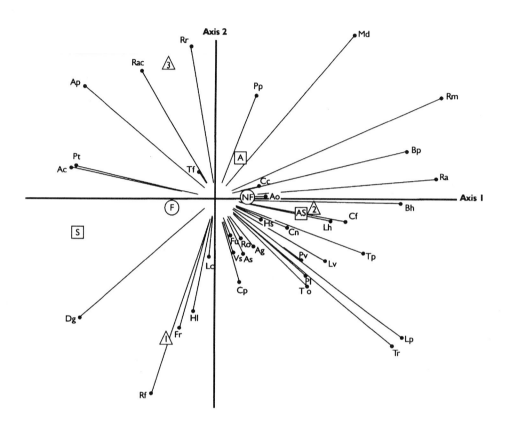

Ac, *Agrostis capillaris*; Ag, *Alchemilla glabra*; Ap, *Alopecurus pratensis*; Ao, *Anthoxanthum odoratum*; As, *Anthriscus sylvestris*; Bp, *Bellis perennis*; Bh, *Bromus hordeaceus*; Cf, *Cerastium fontanum*; Cc, *Cynosurus cristatus*; Cn, *Centaurea nigra*; Cp, *Cardamine pratensis*; Dg, *Dactylis glomerata*; Fr, *Festuca rubra*; Fu, *Filipendula ulmaria*; Hl, *Holcus lanatus*; Hs, *Heracleum sphondylium*; Lc, *Luzula campestris*;   Lh, *Leontodon hispidus*; Lp, *Lolium perenne*; Lv, *Leucanthemum vulgare*; Md, *Myosotis discolor*; Pp, *Phleum pratense*; Pl, *Plantago lanceolata*; Pt, *Poa trivialis*; Pv, *Prunella vulgaris*; Ra, *Ranunculus acris*; Rf, *Ranunculus ficaria*; Rr, *Ranunculus repens*; Rm, *Rhinanthus minor*; Rac, *Rumex acetosa*; Ro, *Rumex obtusifolius*; To, *Taraxacum officinalis*; Tp, *Trifolium pratense*; Tr, *Trifolium repens*; Tf, *Trisetum flavescens*; Vs, *Veronica serpyllifolia*.

[#] species were omitted if they occurred in less than 5 plots or had very short arrows in the biplot.

PLANT SPECIES PHENOLOGY AND VARIATION IN HAY CUTTING DATE

The need for stability in the application of traditional management regimes is probably partly a consequence of the reproductive biology of the individual plant species, operating in a moderately fertile environment, where the upland climate reduces the growing season to the mid-May to early-September period. The maximum agricultural use of traditional meadows is achieved by removing grazing livestock, for growth of the hay crop, as soon as temperatures begin to rise in mid-May. This allows the hay crop to be cut and dried during July-August, the warmest part of the year, and still leaves time for aftermath growth of the sward, for use as a grazing resource.

This association between management and a changing annual climate creates a vernal niche for species like wood anemone, pignut and goldilocks buttercup (*Ranunculus auricomus*) and prevents late growing species such as timothy (*Phleum pratense*) from dominating the sward (Figure 2). Species number is greatest in May and June (14.3 and 13.9 species per 0.0625 m^2), declining significantly in late-July (12.2 species per 0.625 m^2) and late-August (10.5 species per 0.0625 m^2). There are distinctive flowering and seed production phenologies (Smith and Jones, 1991). The few annuals such as hay rattle (*Rhinanthus minor*) and soft brome (*Bromus hordeaceus*) flower early and set ripe seed before mid-July. If the sward is cut early these species will disappear. Grass species such as cock's-foot, meadow fescue (*Festuca pratensis*) and red fescue set seed very late and hay cut on 1 September will contain very large amounts of seed of these and other grass species (Smith *et al.*, 1996c). However, cock's-foot, Yorkshire fog and red fescue are more associated with early regular hay cutting on 14 June; with the earlier flowering rough-stalked meadow grass and the late flowering common bent associated with regular late hay cutting on 1 September (Figure 1).

Meadows provide conserved fodder for over-wintering livestock and the meadows on a farm are managed as a group for this purpose. They are often cut in the same sequence year after year, although there is some variability in each meadow's position in this sequence. The first meadows to be cut are often those closest to the farmstead. Grazing livestock may have been removed early from these and they may have been given large amounts of farmyard manure. Starting dates for cutting have varied around 1 July over the 1950-90 period in the Yorkshire Dales (Smith and Jones, 1991), the starting date in any given year depending upon the amount of grass growth during May and June and the likelihood of a suitable hot period during which the cut swathe can be dried and baled (Figure 3). In a hot, dry summer, such as in 1976, all the hay meadows on a farm could be cut in a short period (14 days). In cool, wet summers, such as 1981 and 1985, the late cut meadows could be cut very late, although the early cut meadows may have been cut at about the normal date. In the 14 meadows at Bowberhead and Piper Holes SSSI, over the 1955-1991 period, the first six meadows in the cutting sequence were rarely cut after 15 July, with standard deviations of cutting date ranging between 7.2 and 9.8 days (Table 3). The five meadows usually cut last in the sequence were cut after the 15 July every 2-3 years, with standard deviations between 9.4 and 16.5 days. These latter include the MG3b communities (Figure 4), whereas the former, despite otherwise identical management practices, including the absence of mineral fertilizer, are similar to *Alopecurus pratensis* -

Sanguisorba officinalis grassland (MG4), or, when field burnet (*Sanguisorba officinalis*) is absent, improved variants of northern meadows (MG3a) or *Lolium perenne* leys (MG7d).

Figure 2. The phenology of relative abundance of plant species in a 'northern' meadow. The phenology was derived by weighted averages regression (ter Braak and van Dam 1989; Fritz *et al.*, 1991) of species percent cover in 54 plots from a meadow management trial in Upper Teesdale (Smith *et al.*, 1996a), from 4 sampling periods in 1990 (14-25 May, 5-15 June, 11-27 July, 20-31 August). The species optima (.), the centre of distribution along the time gradient, and tolerance (----), the standard deviation along the gradient and a measure of niche width (ter Braak 1988), are rank ordered against date. Species in italics showed significant differences in relative cover between sample periods; tested, after arcsine square root transformation, by one-way analysis of variance.

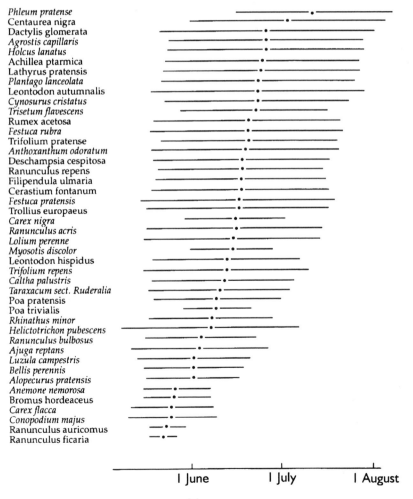

Table 3.   Hay cutting dates 1955-1990 at Bowberhead and Piper Holes meadows.

Meadow name	Type[#]	Cutting date Mean date	SD (days)	Earliest date	Latest date
High Stintings	MG7d	28 June	9.0	12 June	20 July
Low Stintings	MG4	29 June	9.1	12 June	20 July
Near Scar	MG4	30 June	7.8	14 June	16 July
Top Scar	MG4	2 July	7.5	19 June	19 July
Low Scar	MG4	2 July	7.2	19 June	19 July
Undergate Top	MG4	4 July	9.8	20 June	1 August
Low Burnhills	-	5 July	8.6	17 June	2 August
Upper Burnhills	MG4	7 July	8.9	20 June	2 August
Undergate Bottom	MG3a	8 July	9.3	22 June	2 August
1st Quarry Field	MG3b	11 July	9.4	22 June	29 July
Great Bottom	MG3a	12 July	16.1	21 June	19 September
Little Bottom	MG6	16 July	13.8	30 June	6 September
2nd-3rd Quarry Field	MG3b	17 July	12.9	28 June	6 September
Piper Hole	MG3a	19 July	16.5	1 July	27 September

[#] The vegetation types were derived using TABLEFIT (Hill, 1996) and use the plant community nomenclature and codes from Rodwell (1992). MG3a, *Anthoxanthum odoratum-Geranium sylvaticum* grassland, *Bromus hordeaceus hordeaceus* sub-community; MG3b, *Anthoxanthum odoratum-Geranium sylvaticum* grassland, *Briza media* sub-community; MG4, *Alopecurus pratensis-Sanguisorba officinalis* grassland; MG6, *Lolium perenne-Cynosurus cristatus grassland*; MG7d, *Lolium perenne-Alopecurus pratensis* grassland.

Variability in hay cutting date is, therefore, a normal part of the traditional management regime of most meadows; the variability being greatest for those meadows cut late in the sequence. The consequences for individual species depends upon their developmental stage at the time they are cut, including their flowering phenologies and their ability to reproduce vegetatively. A regular early cutting date at the Colt Park trial favoured Yorkshire fog, red fescue and cock's-foot. These late flowering species could not have increased their cover through population increase by seed regeneration. Whilst red fescue could have increased its cover by vegetative spread, Grime *et al.* (1988) note that the other two regenerate primarily by seed. Their increased cover must be achieved by other means, maybe through the growth of established plants. An occasional late cutting date subsequent to regular early cutting would probably result in a large input of seed from these species (Smith *et al.*, 1996c), further reinforcing their populations to the detriment of the other species. Common sorrel and creeping buttercup increase their cover under regular late cutting, possibly because the later flowering female plants of the former are able to regularly produce large amounts of seed and, under late cutting, the latter

Figure 3.   Hay cutting dates for three meadows from Bowberhead and Piper Holes SSSI, Cumbria, 1955-90. High Stintings and Piper Hole meadows were normally the first and last to be cut (Table 3); Upper Burnhills was normally cut mid-sequence. Cutting dates are given as number of days from 1 June.

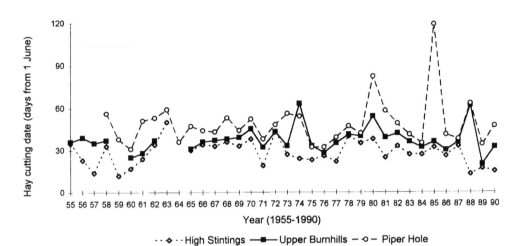

Figure 4.   The relative cover of three typical 'northern' meadow (MG3b) species in fields within the Bowberhead and Piper Holes SSSI.

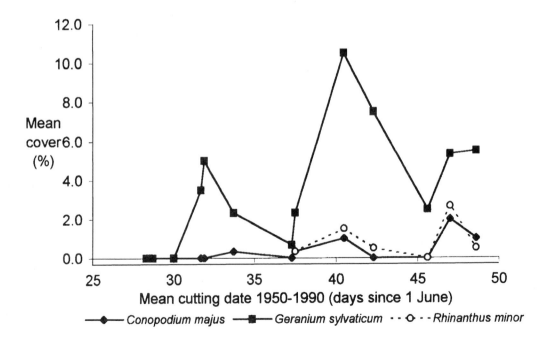

probably has time to vegetatively establish many daughter ramets.

Whatever the underlying reasons for these changes it is suggested that the conservation management of 'northern' meadows requires a traditional regime applied to both the whole farm and the individual fields. For individual fields there should be no application of mineral fertilizer, the sward growth after the hay cut should be grazed with cattle in late-summer and autumn; and hay should be cut no earlier than 15 July. At the whole farm level variability in management from field to field needs to be recognised, particularly variability in cutting date. Whilst a regular cutting date of 21 July has increased species number at Colt Park meadows, data from Bowberhead and Piper Holes SSSI suggests that relatively frequent cutting one or two weeks later may be important for the long-term maintenance of 'northern' meadows.

ACKNOWLEDGEMENTS

The data from the Colt Park trial is a summary of an unpublished, multi-authored research report funded by the Ministry of Agriculture, Fisheries and Food and I am pleased to acknowledge my co-authors on this report, R. Shiel, University of Newcastle upon Tyne, D. Millward and P. Corkhill (English Nature). Helen Buckingham, Peak Park Planning Board, collected the vegetation data used to construct Figure 2. J. Frankland provided the data for Figure 3. R.G.H. Bunce and others from the Institute of Terrestrial Ecology (Merlewood Research Station), helped with data collection for Figure 4.

REFERENCES

BAKKER J.P. (1989) *Nature Management by Grazing and Cutting*. Dordrecht: Kluwer Academic Publishers.

BERENDSE F., OOMES M.J.M., ALTENA H.J. and ELBERSE W.Th. (1992) Experiments in the restoration of species-rich meadows in the Netherlands. *Biological Conservation*, 62, 59-65.

FISCHER S.F., POSCHLOD P. and BEINLICH B. (1996) Experimental studies on the dispersal of plants and animals on sheep in calcareous grasslands. *Journal of Applied Ecology*, 33, 1206-1222.

FRITZ S.C., JUGGINS S., BATTARBEE R.W. and ENGSTROM D.R. (1991) Reconstruction of past changes in salinity and climate using a diatom-based transfer function. *Nature*, 352, 706-708.

GRIME J.P., HODGSON J.G. and HUNT R. (1988) *Comparative Plant Ecology*. London: Unwin Hyman.

HILL M.O. (1996) *TABLEFIT version 1.0 For Identification of Vegetation Types*. Huntingdon: Institute of Terrestrial Ecology.

OLFF H. and BAKKER J.P. (1991) Long term dynamics of standing crop and species composition after cessation of fertilizer application to mown grassland. *Journal of Applied Ecology*, 28, 1040-1052.

PIGOTT C.D. (1956) The vegetation of Upper Teesdale in the North Pennines. *Journal of Ecology*, 44, 545-586.

RODWELL J.S. (1992) *British Plant Communities. Volume 3. Grasslands and Montane Communities*. Cambridge: Cambridge University Press.

SMITH R.S. (1985) *Conservation of northern upland meadows*. Bainbridge, Yorkshire Dales National Park.

SMITH R.S., BUCKINGHAM H., BULLARD, M.J., SHIEL, R.S. and YOUNGER A. (1996a) The conservation management of mesotrophic (meadow) grassland in northern England. 1. Effects of grazing, cutting date and fertilizer on the vegetation of a traditionally managed sward. *Grass and Forage Science*, 51, 278-291.

SMITH R.S., CORKHILL P., SHIEL R.S. and MILLWARD D. (1996b) The conservation management of mesotrophic (meadow) grassland in Northern England. 2. Effects of grazing, cutting date, fertilizer and seed application on the vegetation of an agriculturally improved sward. *Grass and Forage Science*, 51, 292-305.

SMITH R.S. and JONES L. (1991) The phenology of mesotrophic grassland in the Pennine Dales, Northern England: historic hay cutting dates, vegetation variation and plant species phenologies. *Journal of Applied Ecology*, 28, 42-59.

SMITH R.S., PULLAN S. and SHIEL R.S. (1996c) Seed shed in the making of hay from mesotrophic grassland in a field in northern England: effects of hay cut date, grazing and fertilizer in a split-split-plot experiment. *Journal of Applied Ecology*, 33, 833-841.

TER BRAAK C.J.F. (1988) *CANOCO - a FORTRAN Program for Canonical Community Ordination by [Partial] [Detrended] [Canonical] Correspondence Analysis, Principal Components Analysis and Redundancy Analysis*. Wageningen: Agricultural Mathematics Group.

TER BRAAK C.J.F. (1990) *Update notes: CANOCO version 3.10*. Wageningen: Agricultural Mathematics Group.

TER BRAAK C.J.F. and VAN DAM H. (1989) Inferring pH from diatoms: a comparison of old and new calibration methods. *Hydrobiologia*, 178, 209-223.

My Experiences of Hill Farming in the Pennine Dales ESA

N. J. HOWARD

Howard Farms, High Studdon, Allendale, Hexham, Northumberland. NE47 9DH

ABSTRACT

The farm is described briefly together with the farming policy which predated entry into the ESA Scheme - production orientated and supported by development grants. The requirements of the ESA Scheme are described as part of the decision process whether or not to join. The main changes resulting from joining stem from limitations on fertilizer and manurial inputs, the fact that grassland productivity can no longer be improved and restrictions on the way it can be managed and when meadows can be cut. Stocking levels have had to be adjusted to the amount of keep available, and more land has had to be rented. Recent changes to the scheme requirements should prove beneficial and conservation plans are a real help in preserving traditional features such as stone walls. The ESA payments help compensate for meeting the requirements in order to enhance an attractive environment. The farm remains a viable unit, thus helping to perpetuate traditional employment in the area.

THE PENNINE DALES ESA

The Pennine Dales Environmentally Sensitive Area (ESA) was designated in March 1987. It now covers 55300ha in the upper reaches of 27 dales (valleys) in the mid and north Pennines.

The area was designated because over a long period farming and nature have combined to produce an attractive landscape of stone walls, woodland and also, particularly in the Yorkshire Dales of some field barns. The area also contains examples of traditional hay meadows - one of Britain's rarest and most fragile habitats. These features had become endangered by modern farming practices based on intensive production and in some cases ranching.

This part of the Area is at the heart of what was once a busy lead mining district. The miners typically lived on smallholdings which supported them when mining was slack. As mining declined in the first half of the century this gave rise to a number of small grassland farms, generally dairying with Shorthorn cattle. By the 1960's some of these were starting to be abandoned or amalgamated into larger units supporting suckler herds. Population in the East and West Allen Dales has fallen dramatically, from 6500 when mining was at its peak in 1860 to just over 2000.

There has been a corresponding fall in the number of farms which has been most marked in the higher areas. At lower levels some small dairy farms have survived, keeping numbers up.

The ESA Scheme was launched locally at a meeting early in 1992. About two thirds of those now participating joined in the first year, with the highest uptake amongst livestock farmers in the upper Allen Dales.

My Farm

My farm is in fact a family partnership made of two farms, High Studdon (111.8ha) which we own and where my parents live and Parkgates (64.7ha) which I have rented from the Allendale Settled Estates since November 1991. The farms which are adjacent to one another are 3km south of Allendale in the East Allen Valley near the northern boundary of the ESA. The land rises from 250m at the lowest point to almost 400m with an average altitude of 330m. Despite being steep in places most land is accessible by tractor. The grassland is mainly on clay and is made up at follows.

Table 1.   Grassland Areas

Usage	Area (Ha)
Meadow (Tier 1)	47.5
Pasture	125.1

The remainder of the farm area is made up of woodland, buildings and steadings. There are grazing rights for 250 sheep on Allendale Common. I am also allowed to graze 40 sheep for set times of the year on a 29ha allotment which was in the previous Parkgates tenancy but which the Allendale Estates then retained to enter into a Countryside Stewardship Scheme for heather regeneration. The allotment had been heavily overgrazed for about ten years such that the heather which had once been profuse had almost disappeared. New growth is now well established and the scheme aim of 40 percent coverage after five years has probably been bettered.

The farms each have typical Northumbrian stone built farmhouses and traditional buildings together with ranges of modern buildings including cubicle housing and under-cover feeding for cattle. General purpose buildings are also used for lambing but there are no lambing sheds as such. I have added to the buildings at both farms.

An additional 37ha has been rented on a 364 day tenancy since 1982. This land is about 3km south of the main holding and is now subject to an ESA agreement held by the owner. The two meadows (7.1ha) are in Tier 2 and the remainder of the land is pasture with some woodland. There are also two seasonal rentings within the ESA both of which are adjacent to the land we own, 17.2ha of pasture and 9.8ha of Tier 1 meadow. Finally three meadows totalling 4.2ha outside the ESA are rented for their crop only, an arrangement which predates my entry into the Scheme. The total area farmed is 273.7ha plus grazing rights on the Common.

The land we own has been built up by the gradual purchase of what were previously four farms and a smallholding; the previous owner sold part of one of them as a golf course, but we have been able to keep the remainder in agriculture.

Farming Policy before the ESA

Emphasis was on production. The first farm we bought had only traditional buildings so we added modern housing and general purpose buildings, an open slurry pit and effluent tanks, all with benefit of grant aid. Indeed full advantage was taken of the Farm and Horticultural Development Scheme and its predecessors.

Improvement of the land we owned was an important factor. Extensive drainage was undertaken and lime and slag applied to improve quality. Meadows, which had previously been farmed with very low inputs were ploughed out and reseeded with a mixture of rape and grass or barley and grass to provide extra feed. Reseeding was on a 3-4 year rotation.

Fertilizer application on all meadows was 200kg/ha 20.10.10 in the spring followed by 50kg/hg nitrogen after cutting to assist growth of the fogg except when a second cut was to be taken when 100kg/ha 20.10.10 would be applied after the first cut. All farmyard manure was spread on the meadows in a number of applications. Typical yields were 30-40 round bales of silage per hectare. Pastures received at least 100kg/ha of 20.10.10 which significantly improved the productivity of a fundamentally good sward. The policy for rented land was to apply organic fertilizer in similar quantities to my own but not to plough, reseed or otherwise improve the land with the exception of weed control.

Immediately prior to obtaining the tenancy of Parkgates in 1991 and just before the ESA Scheme was launched locally I was farming 140ha and carrying 60 suckler cows and 300 sheep. I had no grazing rights on Allendale Common.

THE DECISION TO JOIN THE ESA SCHEME

Before I could decide whether to join I had to consider the requirements of the scheme, which constrain one's freedom in deciding how to farm, and the other alternatives available.

The main requirements of Tier 1 with which I would have to comply are

- Maintain grassland
  - cultivate meadows only with chain harrow or roller. To be done as early as possible after stock have been removed. No reseeding.
  - no harrowing or rolling of pastures.
- Meadows to be managed as such throughout the 10 year Agreement
  - stock to be excluded at least 7 weeks before first cut and by 1st June at the latest.
  - no cutting before 8 July. All meadows must have their first cut in August once every five years.
  - aftermaths must be grazed.
  - grass cut for silage must be wilted and turned before removal.
- Fertilizers, lime and slag
  - artificial fertilizer not to exceed 125kg/ha 20.10.10, applied in one application.
  - only farm yard manure produced on the farm to be applied; not to exceed 12.5 tonnes/ha and applied in a single dressing.
  - no slurry or poultry manure to be used.
  - no lime or slag etc. to be applied to reduce soil acidity.
- Fungicides and insecticides not be used.

- Herbicides to be applied only to control
  - nettles
  - spear, creeping or field thistle
  - curled or broad leafed dock
  - ragwort
  - When herbicides are applied only spot treatment or weedwiper to be used.
- Existing areas of rushes in pastures are not to be cut or sprayed.
- Land not to be grazed so as to cause poaching, under- or over-grazing.
- No new drainage to be installed, nor are existing drainage systems to be substantially modified.
- Stockproof walls and hedges to be maintained in a stockproof condition using traditional materials.
- Obtain written advice within two years of entering the scheme on the management of existing woodland or planting new.

For meeting these I would receive annual compensatory payment of

Meadow Land	£135 per ha
Other grassland	£95 per ha

Tier 2, which I did not consider joining is aimed at improving the nature conservation quality of hay meadows and imposes more severe restrictions on meadows; specifically

- stock to be excluded by 15 May
- no inorganic or artificial fertilizer to be used
- all meadows must be cut and the crop removed
- Hay, do not cut before 15 July
- Silage, do not cut before 1 August

The compensatory payment is £240 per ha.

The alternative was to continue high input farming. However Parkgates needed substantial land improvements including drainage and reseeding, particularly of its 28ha allotments. When I improved our own land, grants had been available for these purposes and for fertilizers, but none such would be available for Parkgates so I would have had to pay for all improvements myself which would have been expensive over a long period.

Also farming trends are towards lower levels of production with environmental grants replacing the types of grant previously available under the Farm and Horticultural Development Scheme.

There was merit in swimming with the tide, so I decided to join the Scheme in 1992.

An added bonus in joining the Scheme is the conservation plan, which is very relevant where stone walls have fallen into a poor state of repair. Conservation plans, which are not compulsory are designed to improve the landscape or wildlife habitats or to preserve historic remains on any of the land within the ESA boundary. In carrying out any capital works local practices and traditions should be used as well as materials in keeping with these. The maximum grant payable per annum is £2000 and total payments under conservation plans must not exceed £20000 over the ten year period of the scheme.

Current levels of grant relevant to my present conservation plan and to future proposals are shown in Table 2.

Table 2.   Conservation Grant Rates

Eligible Item	Standard payment Rate £	Percentage Grant
Protection of Historic Features		80
Rebuilding or provision of stone walls -£4/m supplement where significant quantities of stone need to be brought in	£14/m	80
Renovation of traditional farm buildings - field barns		80
Tree planting	£1.15 each	80

In some situations other forestry grants such as the Woodland Grant Scheme may be more appropriate for tree planting.

Stone Walls   Repair includes the rebuilding of collapsed, leaning or bulged walls. Grants do not cover the cost of maintenance of existing stockproof walls.

Traditional Buildings are valuable landscape and historic features but the high cost of renovation can cause them to fall into disrepair. Renovation must use traditional materials and methods and includes work necessary to ensure the building is sound and weatherproof. Major works such as complete re-roofing and rebuilding severely damaged walls are eligible.

My Farming under the ESA Scheme

I joined the ESA Scheme in April 1992. A condition of joining was that during the period between deciding to join and the Scheme becoming effective I must farm as if I were already in the Scheme. This meant that proposals for land improvement including the upgrading of the allotments at Parkgates in line with previous farming were shelved, which in turn had a bearing on my then projected stocking levels which were 95 Suckler cows and 1000 Breeding ewes and hoggs for the farm as a whole. As the previous tenant had not fertilized the allotments I was unable to do so.

It is fortunate that I had not yet completed the process of building up stock to these levels when I entered the ESA. I was therefore able to increase numbers to the level at which the farm's grassland would support them in the new situation. Current stocking levels are 83 Suckler cows and 930 Breeding ewes and hoggs which appear to be sustainable figures now that I rent the 27.0ha of pasture and meadows referred to above. The former assists in having adequate grazing whilst the latter is essential to self-sufficiency in hay and silage. It is to be noted however that prior to entering the ESA 90% of my lambs were sold fat; the percentage is now 30% with the remainder sold as stores. This probably arises because I am unable to fertilize the aftermaths.

The way in which ESA requirements affect my farming can best be described by following the headings set out in the previous section which describe the requirements of the scheme.

Maintaining Grassland The requirements do not present any major problems other than in dealing with molehills on pastures. Despite regular annual mole catching, moles seem to thrive on my land. In some cases special dispensation has had to be sought (and granted) to harrow them.

Meadows Cutting dates can present problems. Previously I started to cut meadows once they were ready, generally late in June and in exceptional years all my fields had been gathered by mid-July.

The altitude of meadows on the farm varies by 120m so the lower lying ones are generally ready first, particularly where they are south-facing. The 8 July cutting date can therefore delay harvesting some of these although it is a realistic date so far as the higher meadows are concerned.

Late cutting on a rotational basis can cause real difficulties. In a fine droughty summer and/or where meadows are on gravel it is likely that grass will burn off and a poor hay crop result. There are also often no aftermaths to graze. In these circumstances late cutting can be disastrous. It would be preferable to have variable late cutting dates better linked to the time different categories of meadow are likely to ripen.

Fertilizers, lime and slag The main point is that less fertilizer means less grass which in turn means either

-       less stock
-       buy/rent more land to maintain existing stock
-       buy in more feed

or a combination of these.

It will be noted that I have adopted the first two of these, partly by not building up stocking to previously planned levels and partly by renting land on a seasonal basis.

Whilst in the past farm yard manure (FYM) was applied in multiple applications to meadows only, the Tier 1 meadows now receive their full 12.5 tonnes/ha in one go. There is a balance left over which is used on the pastures, but this balance is insufficient for all the pastures. The 364-day tenancy land, including its Tier 2 meadows does not receive any farm yard manure as there is not enough to go round and it is in any case a long haul from where it is stored at High Studdon and Parkgates.

The fact the FYM has to be applied in one application rather than little and often puts pressure on storage. Large middens have had to be built at both High Studdon and Parkgates with enough capacity to hold several months output as the occasions during the winter when the land is hard enough to spread muck without damaging the fields are limited. This has been expensive and it is regrettable that capital grant-aid is not available for what appears to be a natural consequence of the scheme.

All fields receive their maximum permissible application of inorganic fertilizer.

Feeding cattle on silage can produce runny muck which is not far short of slurry. I therefore feed straw with the silage and also bed with more than before to stiffen up the muck. The midden at High Studdon was covered to prevent rain dilution of the muck when stored; not so at Parkgates where the budget for a rented farm is more limited.

In the first two years after entering the Scheme there did not appear to be any significant difference in meadow yields, but more recently these have reduced for Tier 1 from 30-34 round bales per hectare to 20-25. Part of this 30 percent loss may be attributable to seasonal variations but it is hoped that it has now 'bottomed out' but only time will tell. The Tier 2 meadows have become very poor yielders; it probably costs more to conserve one of them than the value of the crop it produces especially as I do not receive the ESA payment.

Fungicides The fact they cannot be used has not proved to be a problem.

Herbicides The farm does suffer from nettles, dock and thistles. Docks and thistles were particularly bad on Parkgates when I obtained the tenancy and permission was granted after consultation with the botanists for the worst fields to be blanket sprayed. Following this consultation an area of wetland in one field was excluded because it contained rare plants including orchids. Spot treatment by manpack sprayer is tedious but life has been made rather easier and treatment quicker by the use of an ATV-mounted sprayer with a handheld lance on a long lead. Weed control is an annual event but I am slowly winning, however it takes much longer than blanket spraying and therefore has adverse cost implications.

Rushes Some fields are heavily infested with rushes, notably the allotments at Parkgates, which would have been improved had I not entered the ESA. I can however live with rushes except in one instance where a gas pipeline crosses the High Studdon land. What used to be good pasture has become overgrown with rushes. As this is a special situation permission has been granted for these rushes to be sprayed.

Grazing I regard the conditions applied to grazing as entirely sensible, and an example of good husbandry.

Drainage I am perhaps fortunate in that my land does not have any severe drainage problems probably because much of it was drained by me under previous schemes. Normal maintenance is of course necessary and no doubt drains will require replacement if they fail badly. Collapsed stone drains are becoming commonplace in some parts of the farm.

Stockproof Walls Maintenance of stockproof stone walls is a continuing requirement of any reasonably run farm although not all farmers see it that way. I have always striven to keep my walls in good repair and the conservation plan, which will be referred to later has been of great assistance.

Woodlands The requirement to obtain written advice within two years of joining the Scheme on management and planting was met until recent land ownership changes took place. I am now starting afresh with the intention of improving and enlarging shelter belts on my land. The Allendale Estates have retained all the woodland at Parkgates.

Conservation Plan I have just completed my first conservation plan which was mainly concerned with the rebuilding of badly bulged and slipping stockproof walls. The fact that grants are available has meant that I could employ people to do the work thoroughly taking the walls down to their foundations rather than the patch and mend basis I would have had to adopt had I been relying on my own resources and the part-time farm labour I employ. The fact of being able to lighten the load so far as my labour resources are concerned means there is more time available for routine wall maintenance and other tasks.

A particular feature of this conservation plan was the renovation of an historic feature, an old stone bridge over a stream between two fields at Parkgates. The sidewalls had begun to slip away and it was satisfying to be able to have this useful feature properly rebuilt rather than having it shorn up with timbers.

My second conservation plan, concerned wholly with walling has just been approved. I intend my third to concentrate on the traditional buildings at High Studdon and Parkgates which need reroofing and other repairs.

The business implications of being in the scheme are that I am unable to stock the farm fully and I cannot sell as many fat lambs. Additional straw has to be purchased because cattle are housed earlier and muck needs stiffening up to meet scheme requirements. Feed has to be bought to flush ewes for which aftermaths would previously had sufficed. Meeting scheme requirements are labour intensive and more land has to be rented to maintain production at an acceptable level. The costs relating to these items are very considerable.

In my case the ESA payment appears to be a satisfactory compensation to cover the restriction on business size and the additional costs involved.

RESEARCH AND LIAISON
ADAS are conducting botanical monitoring of meadows and pastures in the Dales ESA. One of the Parkgates meadows is included in this exercise with the species found in several quadrats of the field being analysed every three years. The first survey took place in 1992 and the second in 1995.

A bird survey is also being carried out at Parkgates.

My farm has been the subject of an ESA orientated farm walk and also a visit by members of the British Grassland Society from Cumbria.

Close liaison is maintained with the ESA Project Officer and a fruitful relationship has developed which is helping to harmonise farming needs with those of the ESA.

RECENT CHANGES TO THE ESA SCHEME
The Ministry has very recently revised the ESA Scheme. The main changes are
- the restriction on harrowing and rolling pasture land only applies during the period 1 April to 15 July
- the late cutting date is brought forward to 22 July.
- farmyard manure can be bought-in provided MAFF has given prior written approval.
- lime application is permitted on meadows subject to certain conditions.
- a grazing management plan is to be agreed for allotments in new schemes.
- it is intended to remove the limit on the amount of conservation plan grant which can be sought.

The easing of the restriction on harrowing etc. is to be welcomed as it will make management easier. Bringing forward the late cutting date is also helpful in overcoming some of the problems I have mentioned previously. It will also now be easier to apply lime.

Whilst buying-in farmyard manure could make it possible to fertilize more land it is unlikely that I will take advantage of the provision because of difficulties in obtaining supplies and the fact that even if they were available a long haul would be involved.

The allotment provisions will not affect my agreement which still has five years to run; they would however impact on any future agreement.

The fact that there may be no financial ceiling on conservation plans is welcome, as is the proposed introduction of a five year programme for stone wall renovation. Taken together these will allow more countryside features to be restored than would otherwise have been the case.

CONCLUSION

I have found no great difficulty in farming under ESA Scheme requirements although there are some aspects I feel could be improved. I am sure this could be said of any scheme. Most important, farming has remained profitable since the scheme was introduced.

There is no doubt that the ESA objectives help to protect the environment and character in a unique part of the country and I am pleased to be part of the process.

ESA staff have proved helpful and understanding and it has been useful to be consulted about proposed changes to the scheme both directly and through the NFU. It is to be hoped this will continue and that the concerns of farmers will be understood and taken into account.

Finally I feel it a privilege that I have been able to create a viable farming unit from a number of otherwise uneconomic farming units which can help enhance the ESA in the future.

Lowland Wet Grasslands in ESAs

J.R.B. TALLOWIN[1] and J.O. MOUNTFORD[2]
[1]IGER, North Wyke, Okehampton, Devon. EX20 2SB
[2]ITE, Monks Wood, Abbots Ripton, Huntingdon.PE17 2LS

ABSTRACT

ESAs probably contain over 30% of the total wet grassland area of lowland England. Most of the wet grassland is either agriculturally improved or semi-improved. For those ESAs where information was available, unimproved wet grassland of high biodiversity represented less than 10% of the total wet grassland area. Monitoring information was lacking on wildlife-rich wet grasslands in some ESAs making it difficult to assess whether the maintenance of their wildlife value was being achieved. Some ESAs are failing to achieve management agreement targets for their surviving areas of unimproved wet grassland. The effectiveness of management agreements to ensure maintenance of existing unimproved species-rich wet grasslands may be limited by factors such as inadequate or inappropriate hydrological conditions and lack of information on management requirements for specific habitats. It is also contended that sustainable managements, with adapted livestock systems, to maintain long-term ecological stability of unimproved wet grasslands need to be developed and that this would require both a multidisciplinary approach and long-term commitment. Elevated soil fertility appears to be a wide scale problem impeding restoration of wet grasslands with high biodiversity on former improved or semi-improved fields. Further research and development requirements are discussed.

INTRODUCTION

For the purposes of this paper, wet grasslands will be categorized according to broad habitat types (HMSO, 1995) and the National Vegetation Classification (Rodwell, 1991; 1992). Lowland wet grassland may be defined as managed pastures or meadows that occur on land below 200m above sea level and which have a high water table and/or subjected to periodic inundation (Dargie, 1993; Jefferson and Grice, in press). Figure 1 illustrates a categorization of wet grassland types that occur in lowland UK.

The total area of wet grassland in England is estimated to be 215-220,000 ha most of which is agriculturally improved or semi-improved and of low nature conservation value (Dargie, 1993; Jefferson and Grice, in press).

Throughout the history of agricultural development in lowland Britain wet grasslands have suffered extensive destruction, damage or modification by various human activities (HMSO, 1995). The surviving area of unimproved semi-natural wet grassland probably amounts to less than 30,000 ha (Jefferson and Grice, in press), representing less than 5% of the resource that was present in the 1930s (Fuller, 1987). Relict unimproved wet grasslands now commonly exist as small, isolated and often fragmented sites. Many sites are at risk from activities such as borehole abstraction, drainage or eutrophication of water sources within catchment areas, inappropriate agricultural management or abandonment (HMSO, 1995). Wet grasslands are a major landscape element in eight of the present twenty two ESAs in England. Maintenance of the wildlife riches of this resource is a key objective of specific ESA management agreements as detailed, for example, in the monitoring reports for the Somerset Levels and Moors and the Broads ESAs (ADAS, 1996a; 1996b). The aims of this paper will be to quantify the extent of wet grasslands in the eight ESAs, to evaluate whether agri-environmental management agreements are likely to maintain the surviving areas of unimproved wet grasslands and the potential for restoration of wet grasslands of high biodiversity within ESAs.

Figure 1. Categorization of lowland wet grasslands

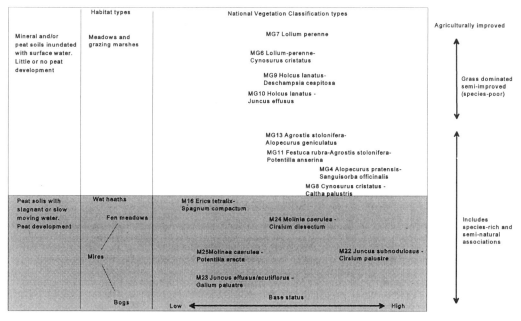

Sources: Hughes and Heathwaite (1995), Jefferson and Grice (in press) and Benstead et al (in press)

WET GRASSLAND RESOURCES WITHIN THE PRINCIPAL WETLAND ESAs

The total extent of wet grassland within the eight "wetland" ESAs in England is approximately 60-70,000 ha (Table 1), representing about 30% of the wet grassland area in lowland England.

Much of this wet grassland is agriculturally improved or semi-improved (ADAS, 1996a, b, c, d, 1997a, b, c, d.). Estimates of the area of unimproved wet grassland of high biodiversity (data were available for only four of the wetland ESAs, Table 1), represents less than 10% of the total area of wet grassland within these ESAs. If extrapolated to the national situation this percentage would accord with the estimate by Jefferson and Grice (in press) for the area of unimproved wet grassland remaining in lowland England.

Broads ESA In the Broads ESA only four grassland associations were recorded in the monitoring exercise (ADAS, 1996d). Two represented species-poor agriculturally improved or semi-improved communities namely, *Lolium perenne* leys (MG7), *Lolium perenne-Cynosurus cristatus* grassland (MG6) a third species-poor community was the semi-natural *Festuca rubra-Agrostis stolonifera-Potentilla anserina* grassland (MG11) (Rodwell, 1992). Only one unimproved semi-natural wet grassland community of high biodiversity was sampled, the *Juncus subnodulosus-Cirsium palustre* fen-meadow (M22) (Rodwell, 1991), with a total extent of about 110 ha (ADAS, 1996d). A small (*ca.* 34 ha) area of the nationally scarce and highly valued *Molinia caerulea-Cirsium dissectum* fen-meadow (M24) (Rodwell, 1991) is also present on the ESA (ADAS, 1996d). From the monitoring information available it is not possible to ascertain how much of the fen-meadow resource is protected by ESA or other agri-environmental management agreements. The presence of such high conservation value sites provides a rationale for targeting agreements and providing high biodiversity "core" areas within the ESA. Without monitoring information on such wildlife-rich core areas it is difficult to fully assess whether key ESA objectives of maintaining wildlife conservation value are being achieved.

Table 1. Total area and approximate areas of grassland, wet grassland and, where available, unimproved wet grassland (ha) of high conservation value within the "wetland" ESAs.

	Total	Grassland	Wet grassland	High conservation value wet grassland
Broads	36175	20148	*ca.* 17500 <14000$	*ca.* 150 ha of fen-meadow
Somerset Levels and Moors	27678	23840	*ca.* 23500	*ca.* 1750
Suffolk River Valleys	43000	13000	<7000$	
Essex Coast	28609	6232	4400	
North Kent Marshes	13715	7825	5255*	2299*
Test Valley	4777	2396	<2000$	*ca.* 877 (SSSI total area includes reedbed and fen carr)
Avon Valley	5171	3257	2630	
Upper Thames Tributaries	27000	10600	*ca.* 5244	

Sources: ADAS, 1996a; 1996b; 1996c; 1996d; 1997; MAFF and ESA project officers.
*Kent Wildlife Habitat Survey Partnership (1990-94), contact Kent County Council.
$ maximum "guestimates" based on county total per Dargie (1993).

About 47% of the eligible area of the Broads ESA was under a landscape maintenance agreement (tier 1) which allowed an input of up to 125 kg of nitrogen fertilizer per ha per year and a silage (or hay) crop to be taken (ADAS, 1996b). Evidence from botanical monitoring indicated that one ESA objective for semi-improved and improved fields was adversely affected by tier 1 management, namely "to maintain and enhance the wildlife conservation value of permanent grassland". Specifically wetland elements in the flora of semi-improved fields declined (ADAS, 1996d), probably due to the dominance of more productive species with a relatively high evapo-transpiration rate causing biological drying of the site (Rabotnov, 1977). Under the more restrictive management agreement of tier 2, where fertilizer nitrogen input was limited to 44 kg/ha per year and late hay-cutting was required, wet grassland elements in the flora were apparently maintained (ADAS, 1996d). Thus, for the 37% (6331 ha) of the ESA area under tier 2 agreement (ADAS, 1996b) any degradation of the wet grassland resource should be slow relative to that observed in tier 1. However, it seems unlikely that unaltered tier 1 and 2 prescriptions for fertilizer will lead eventually to an increase in wet grasslands of high conservation interest (Mountford, et al., 1994).

Somerset Levels and Moors ESA Ten grassland communities/sub-communities were identified during the botanical monitoring of this ESA (ADAS, 1996c). Some notably species-rich communities of national conservation importance were represented in the sample such as the *J. subnodulosus-Cirsium palustre* fen-meadow (M22), the *Cynosurus cristatus-Caltha palustris* grassland (MG8) and a transitional variant between these two (Prosser and Wallace, 1996; ADAS 1996c). Within the ESA there are approximately 1750 ha of unimproved species-rich wet grassland representing about 6% of the total area of the ESA (ADAS 1996c). About 69% of the area of species-rich grassland is either under ESA agreement or is managed by nature conservation organisations. Other rather less species-rich unimproved wet grasslands reported within the ESA include the *J. effusus/acutiflorus-Galium palustre* (M23) rush pasture, the *Agrostis stolonifera-Alopecurus geniculatus* (MG13) inundation pasture, the *Holcus lanatus-Juncus effusus* (MG10) rush pasture and the *H. lanatus-Deschampsia cespitosa* (MG9) grassland (Rodwell, 1991; ibid, 1992). Semi-improved and improved grasslands include the *L. perenne-C. cristatus* (MG6) and *L. perenne-Alopecurus pratensis-Festuca pratensis* (MG7c) damp meadows. About 11,000 ha, 46% of the eligible area of the ESA, were under tier 1 agreement, the objective of which is to maintain the grassland landscape (ADAS, 1996a). Where the ESA objective is the enhancement of ecological interest in the grassland (tier 2) only 2413 ha (about 10% of the eligible area) are so designated (ADAS, 1996a). A total of 992 ha of the grassland area was under tier 3 or a raised water level area (RWLA) supplementary agreement, representing only about 40% of the target eligible area for the ESA (ADAS, 1996a).

Within the Somerset Levels and Moors there appears to have been no reduction in the overall area of unimproved grassland since the inception of the ESA. Botanical monitoring indicated that on land under ESA agreement there was no reduction of species suited to high soil moisture content (ADAS, 1996c). However, there is evidence that prolonged spring flooding, particularly in raised water level areas, may lead to a reduction in the conservation value of existing species-rich grasslands e.g. *Cynosurus cristatus-Centaurea nigra* (MG5), *C. cristatus-Caltha palustris* (MG8) and variants (Prosser and Wallace, 1996). Monitoring also provided little indication of any reversion of previously improved or semi-improved swards under tier 2 management agreements to more species-rich communities (ADAS, 1996c). Species indicative of high nutrient availability (Grime *et al.*, 1988; Ellenberg, 1988), increased in many communities and if continued, this trend would seem to compromise the ESA objective of enhancing the ecological interest of grasslands under management agreement (ADAS, 1996a). It has been suggested (ADAS, 1996c) that this lack of progress in the reversion of the wet grasslands may in part be due to nutrient import with flood water. It may also be that within former improved or semi-improved fields the soil nutrient availability is too elevated for significant reversion to occur in the short-term.

Test Valley ESA Communities identified within the Test Valley ESA are detailed in ADAS (1997a), and included, the *Briza media-Trifolium repens* sub-community of *J. subnodulosus-Cirsium palustre* fen-meadow (M22b), a semi-improved transitional community with affinities to *Holcus lanatus-Deschampsia cespitosa* (MG9), *H. lanatus-Juncus effusus* (MG10), *C. cristatus-C. palustris* (MG8) grassland and *Festuca rubra-Agrostis stolonifera-Potentilla anserina* (MG11) grassland.

Evaluation of the ESA scheme by ADAS (1997a) indicated that maintenance of the grassland with highest wildlife conservation value was achieved on agreement land. However, on non-agreement land, significant deterioration was observed in the quality of high conservation value grassland. Within at least part of the ESA, hydrological conditions for the maintenance of wet grassland species may be sub-optimal (ADAS, 1997a). Monitoring of agreement land between the baseline year and 1995 showed little change both in species indicative of low nutrient availability in fen-meadows, and in the nutrient indicator scores of semi-improved and improved wet grassland. These results imply no significant decrease in site fertility. It is likely that reduced fertility will take a long time in former agriculturally improved permanent grassland in the Test Valley (ADAS, 1997a), and until this is achieved, rehabilitation of wet grassland of high conservation value will be impeded.

North Kent Marshes ESA In the North Kent Marshes ESA there are approximately 5-6000 ha of grazing marsh, much of which is unimproved or semi-improved with a residual saline influence (ADAS, 1997/in press). The grazing marsh communities have affinities with *L. perenne-C. cristatus* (MG6) grassland, *L. perenne* leys (MG7) and *Festuca rubra-Agrostis stolonifera-Potentilla anserina* (MG11) grassland. Although not particularly species-rich, the unimproved grasslands and associated banks, rills and ditches of the North Kent Marshes have considerable ecological value, supporting plant communities that are now restricted in distribution, a number of scarce or rare plant and invertebrate species and a large population of breeding waders (ADAS, 1997, in press). About 4100 ha of the grazing marsh are under some form of agri-environmental agreement: 3354 ha (45% of the eligible area) are under ESA agreement, designed to maintain the grassland landscape (tier 1) or enhance the ecological interest of wet grassland areas (tier 1A). The first monitoring review of this ESA covers the period since its launch in 1993 up to 1996.

It is thus not yet appropriate to evaluate the impact of management agreements on qualitative changes in the vegetation. However, since inception there has been little further apparent loss of unimproved grazing marsh within the ESA. Management agreements also appear to have maintained the populations of breeding and wintering birds (ADAS, 1997, in press).

Avon Valley ESA The Avon Valley ESA contains a wide range of damp/wet grassland communities and sub-communities (ADAS, 1997c). Much of the eligible area of the ESA comprises relatively species-poor agriculturally improved or semi-improved grassland namely, *L. perenne-C. cristatus* (MG6a), *L. perenne-Poa trivialis* (MG7b), *L. perenne-Alopecurus pratensis* (MG7d) and *Holcus lanatus-Juncus effusus* rush-pasture (MG10 - typical and *J. inflexus* sub-communities) and the species-poor semi-natural *Agrostis stolonifera-Alopecurus geniculatus* (MG13) inundation pasture. The presence of *Arrhenatherum elatius* grassland (including *Festuca rubra*, MG1a, and *Urtica dioica*, MG1b, sub-communities) and *Holcus lanatus-Deschampsia cespitosa* (MG9) meadow, is indicative of prolonged local under-grazing. Some areas of *Cynosurus cristatus-Caltha palustris* (MG8) grassland are also present, representing the most botanically rich sites. A total of 827 ha of grassland are under tier 1 management agreement, 79% of which is in the river floodplain covering about 40% of the historic water meadows. However, only about 10% of these water meadows are under the high water level agreement (tier 2, option 1), which could afford greater protection to their ecological interests (ADAS, 1997c). Unfortunately no information is available on change in either area or botanical composition of the more species-rich grassland, and the effectiveness of the ESA scheme to maintain this resource thus cannot be evaluated (ADAS, 1997c).

On the basis of figures for percentage uptake of management agreements on eligible land, both the North Kent Marshes and Avon Valley ESAs fall below their potential to protect and/or enhance the ecological interest of the wet grassland resource.

MANAGEMENT TO MAINTAIN WILDLIFE RICHNESS

A number of factors limit the potential of ESA management agreements to ensure maintenance of high biodiversity in existing areas of unimproved wet grassland. Among these are inadequate knowledge of the hydrological, edaphic and management requirements of specific habitats. As a result only generalized and possibly inappropriate management prescriptions have been applied. For example, the tier 3 hydrological prescriptions for the Somerset Levels have allowed standing water to be retained beyond mid-March. This now appears to be inappropriate for the conservation of some of the existing botanically rich meadows and more appropriate for the development of more species-poor inundation communities. Recent research has indicated that modification of RWLA management may reduce the risk of damage to highly valued and now scarce species-rich meadow communities of this ESA (Gowing, 1996). Clearly further research needs to be invested in determining specific habitat hydrological and/or hydro-chemical requirements and in ensuring that refinement of management agreements do in fact achieve the long-term maintenance of existing ecological richness.

Inadequacy of water supply and/or inappropriate quality of water are probably going to be major threats to the future of many biodiverse wet grasslands. The challenge will increasingly be to establish strategies for the use of limited water supplies to maintain core areas of unimproved wet grassland. This will require an ability to monitor the long-term stability of these communities. There is, therefore, a need to develop early warning indicators of degradation in the botanical composition of wet grasslands of high biodiversity. Change in the populations and/or phenology of key target plant (and/or animal) species of semi-natural communities, for which autecological data is available, could provide such indications of site degradation.

Management agreements that do not allow any nutrient input may in fact not maintain the ecological interest of some mesotrophic species-rich wet grasslands (Crofts and Jefferson, 1994). It has long been recognized that in addition to careful hydrological management, including maintenance of surface water courses and ditches, periodic nutrient input through flooding was important for the maintenance of floristic diversity in the renowned *Alopecurus pratensis - Sanguisorba officinalis* (Rodwell, 1992) flood meadows of the Thames valley (Baker, 1937). Anecdotes suggest that in addition to regular flooding, periodic applications of farmyard manure have in the past allowed the maintenance of species-rich wet mesotrophic grasslands on the Somerset Levels. Research on species-rich meadows at Tadham Moor on the Somerset Levels has shown that hay-cutting over a 5-10 year period with no nutrient input reduced the availability of potassium (Tallowin *et al.*, 1997). Research on a wide range of semi-natural grasslands, including data from species-rich meadows on the Somerset Levels, indicated that the maintenance of high botanical diversity is associated with a specific range in the quantity of major nutrients, particularly phosphorus and potassium, in the soil (Janssens *et al.*, in press). Decline in the availability of these soil nutrients below their optimum range for the maintenance of maximum botanical diversity is, therefore, likely to adversely affect community structure.

The efficacy of using periodic inputs of farmyard manure to maintain productivity and the wildlife interest of semi-natural meadows is widely accepted (Smith, 1994; Crofts and Jefferson, 1994; Simpson and Jefferson, 1996). There is, however, a lack of specific information on different semi-natural wet grassland communities on what would constitute a sustainable manuring management. Research is urgently needed to define the timing, frequency and amount of farmyard manure that can be applied to safeguard the long-term stability of existing mesotrophic species-rich communities.

The conservation management of semi-natural wet grasslands often has a complex set of goals with animal production being but a relatively minor one. It is recognized that what constitutes 'good' agricultural management does not necessarily also constitute 'good' conservation management (Crofts and Jefferson, 1994). Maintenance of high biodiversity requires the creation of spatial and temporal heterogeneity within the established community, *i.e.* niche regeneration *sensu* Grubb (1977). Such conditions generally run counter to agricultural management objective of achieving a high level of utilization of the available forage. To date experimental grazing managements on wet grasslands within ESAs have tended to be agronomically orientated, as in the case of the studies by Kirkham and Wilkins (1994) and Tallowin and Smith (1996), and not focussed on providing heterogeneity criteria, such as canopy structural parameters, for the maintenance of high biodiversity. A factor impeding the development of 'good' conservation management practices is the lack of information on specific habitat requirements for many key wet grassland species, particularly invertebrates. Thus, management criteria remain, at best, rather general. There is an urgent need for multidisciplinary research on wet grassland systems to include studies on controls of faunal diversity, such as interactions with management, and to examine the functional role of fauna, such as invertebrates, in wet grassland systems (Clymo et al., 1995).

Little research has been done on either improving the integration of environmentally sensitive management of unimproved/semi-natural wet grasslands into productive livestock farming systems, or on the development of adapted livestock systems, such as organic enterprises, that are based either in part or wholly on unimproved wet grasslands. Satisfactory integration will depend upon the management of unimproved wet grasslands providing, at the very least, maintenance requirements of the livestock. On wet grasslands where either the amount and/or the nutritional quality of the forage is marginal for productive animals considerable constraints are imposed on the type of livestock that can be used (Tallowin, 1997). Future research should examine whether more traditional or rare breeds of livestock have physiological or behavioural traits that could be exploited in the management of unimproved wet grasslands. Research on adapted livestock systems should also evaluate the wider socio-economic and landscape benefits emanating from the maintenance of wet grasslands of high biodiversity.

MANAGEMENT TO ENHANCE WILDLIFE RICHNESS

Wet grassland restoration programmes should be targeted on to areas where there is a realistic chance of long-term success in reconstituting species-rich plant-animal assemblages. Within the ESAs examined there was little or no evidence from the monitoring results of a general recovery of species indicative of low nutrient status on farmland under management agreement. Under the present management agreements it appears unlikely that ESAs will make a substantial contribution toward achieving the national target for the rehabilitation of wet grassland habitats of high biodiversity in lowland UK by the year 2000 (HMSO, 1995). Eutrophic conditions appear to be a key factor impeding the recovery of species-rich wet grasslands on semi-improved or improved sites. The achievement of low soil phosphorus availability appears to be a fundamental requirement for the restoration of high species-richness (Marrs, 1993; Janssens et al., in press). Where high inputs of phosphatic fertilizer had been applied for only four years on the Somerset Levels and Moors, recovery of a species-rich meadow flora was particularly slow and uncertain (Tallowin et al., in press). Recovery of wet grasslands with high floristic diversity on previously improved or semi-improved fields appears to depend, at least in part, upon achieving extractable soil phosphorus amounts of less than 5mg/100 g dry soil (Janssens et al., in press).

Raising water-levels and/or removal of the topsoil can result in a rapid reduction in soil nutrient availability, but the long-term effectiveness of such restorative management depends upon soil type, ground-water quality and fluctuation in water-table depth. On nutrient-enriched soils, raising the ground-water level may be insufficient in the long-term to allow species-rich wet grassland vegetation to develop (Oomes *et al.*, 1996). Agricultural improvement of wetland soils are likely to have caused fundamental and long-term changes to soil structure, organic matter breakdown/mineralization processes and, as a consequence, have major effects on fluxes in nutrient availability compared with undamaged wetlands. There is, therefore, a need to develop species-rich wet grassland restoration programmes on the basis of a sound understanding of the hydrology and microbiology of existing wetland communities, which, as Clymo *et al.* (1995) point out, is a priority area needing further multidisciplinary research.

Recovery of species-richness may also be impeded by a severely impoverished species pool in the surrounding landscape and the soil seed-bank (Bakker, 1989). Severe declines or loss of semi-natural grassland species from the soil seed bank can occur rapidly as shown by the studies of Smith *et al.* (in press). Within 5-10 years of imposing fertilizer treatments on plots on species-rich meadows on the Somerset Levels changes in the soil seed bank were recorded which were associated with increased abundance of competitive species and decline in the more prostrate slow-growing species in the established vegetation. Many semi-natural grassland species have short-lived or no persistent seed bank in the soil (Thompson *et al.*, 1996) and, once lost from a landscape, these species will need to be re-introduced. It is contended that reintroduction of lost species would not be worthwhile unless soil nutrient availability and hydrological conditions are comparable with existing unimproved wet grassland. It also appears that lack of knowledge on the specific regeneration requirements of many wet grassland species may, at present, limit the scope of restoration programmes. Research in the Upper Thames Tributaries ESA has been evaluating different techniques for reintroducing lost wetland species (Manchester, *in press*) and from these studies more cost-effective guidelines for restoration management agreement should be developed.

CONCLUSIONS

The effectiveness of ESA management agreements to maintain the high biodiversity of existing areas of unimproved wet grassland has been and continues to be limited by inadequate knowledge of hydrological, edaphic and management requirements for specific habitats. Elevated soil fertility appears to be a wide-scale problem impeding reversion to more ecologically valuable wet grassland on former improved or semi-improved fields. Current research funded by the Ministry of Agriculture, Fisheries and Food using controlled laboratory and field experimentation, together with detailed field survey linked to hydrological modelling, has the potential to achieve more accurate and robust predictions of the impact of altered water management on wet grassland communities (Mountford *et al.*, in press). Serious deficiencies in our knowledge on functional controls of wet grassland systems, including microbiological and invertebrate roles, could continue to limit our effectiveness in trying to restore lost biodiversity. Definition and development of ecologically sustainable management (with adapted livestock systems) are urgently needed for unimproved wet grasslands, requiring both an interdisciplinary research approach and long-term commitment.

ACKNOWLEDGEMENTS

Richard Jefferson of English Nature is warmly thanked for his helpful comments and suggestions on this paper. Michael Harrison of the Conservation Management Division of MAFF is thanked for kindly providing drafts of monitoring reports for a number of ESAs. Alan Bullivant, Alistair Helliwell, Geoff Newsome and George Gittins are all thanked for the valuable discussions and comments that they provided during the preparation of this paper.

REFERENCES

ADAS (Agricultural Development and Advisory Service) (1996a) Environmental monitoring in the Somerset Levels and Moors ESA, 1987-1995. Report: Ministry of Agriculture, Fisheries and Food. HMSO, London.

ADAS (Agricultural Development and Advisory Service) (1996b) Environmental monitoring in the Broads ESA, 1987-1995. Report: Ministry of Agriculture, Fisheries and Food. HMSO, London.

ADAS (Agricultural Development and Advisory Service) (1996c) Botanical monitoring of grassland in the Somerset Levels and Moors ESA, 1988-1995. Report: Ministry of Agriculture, Fisheries and Food. HMSO, London.

ADAS (Agricultural Development and Advisory Service) (1996d) Botanical monitoring of grassland in the Broads ESA, 1987-1994. Report: Ministry of Agriculture, Fisheries and Food. HMSO, London.

ADAS (Agricultural Development and Advisory Service) (1997a/in press) Botanical monitoring of grassland in the Test Valley ESA, 1988-1995. Report: Ministry of Agriculture, Fisheries and Food. HMSO, London.

ADAS (Agricultural Development and Advisory Service) (1997b/in press) Environmental monitoring in the North Kent Marshes ESA, 1993-1996. Report: Ministry of Agriculture, Fisheries and Food. HMSO, London.

ADAS (Agricultural Development and Advisory Service) (1997c/in press) Environmental monitoring in the Avon Valley ESA, 1993-1996. Report: Ministry of Agriculture, Fisheries and Food. HMSO, London.

ADAS (Agricultural Development and Advisory Service) (1997d/in press)Botanical monitoring of grassland in the Suffolk River Valleys ESA, 1988-1996. Report: Ministry of Agriculture, Fisheries and Food. HMSO, London.

BAKKER J. P. 1989. *Nature management by grazing and cutting*. Kluwer, Dordrecht. Pp 240-245.

BAKER H. (1937) Alluvial meadows: a comparative study of grazed and mown meadows. *Journal of Ecology*, 25, 408-420.

CLYMO R.S., DAWSON F.H., BERTRAM B.C.R., BURT T.P., GILMAN K., INGRAM H.A.P., JAMES R., KIRKBY M.J., LEE J.A., MALTBY E., WHEEELER B.D. and WILCOCK D. (1995) Directions for Research on Wetlands in Britain. In: Hughes, J.M.R. and Heathwaite, A.L. (eds). *Hydrology and Hydro-chemistry of British Wetlands*. Pp. 63-82. John Wiley and Sons Ltd, Chichester, UK.

CROFTS A. and JEFFERSON R.G. (eds) (1994) *The lowland grassland management handbook*. English Nature/The Wildlife Trusts. English Nature, Peterborough.

DARGIE T.C. (1993). The Distribution of Lowland Wet Grassland. English Nature Research Report No. 49. English Nature, Peterborough.

ELLENBERG H. (1988) *Vegetation Ecology of Central Europe*. Cambridge University Press, Cambridge, UK.

FULLER R.M. (1987) The changing extent and conservation interest of lowland grasslands in England and Wales: a review of grassland surveys 1930-1984. *Biological Conservation* 40, 281-300.

GOWING D.J.G. (1996) Examination of the potential impacts of alternative management regimes in the Somerset Levels and Moors ESA. Report to the Ministry of Agriculture. Silsoe College.

GRIME J.P., HODGSON J.G. and HUNT R. (1988) *Comparative Plant Ecology: A Functional Approach to Common British Species*. Unwin-Hyman, London.

GRUBB, P.J. (1977) The maintenance of species-richness in plant communities: the importance of the regeneration niche. *Biological Reviews* 52, 107-145.

HMSO (1995) *Biodiversity*: The UK Steering Group Report. Volume 2: Action Plans. HMSO, London.

JANSSENS F., PEETERS A., TALLOWIN J.R.B., SMITH R.E.N., BAKKER J.P. BEKKER R.M., VERWEIJ G.L., FILLAT F., CHOCARRO C. and OOMES M.J.M. (In press) Relationship between soil nutrients and plant diversity in grasslands: definition of limits for the maintenance and the reconstruction of species-rich communities. European Grassland Federation, Occasional Symposium, Warsaw May 1997.

JEFFERSON R.G. and GRICE P.V. (in press) The conservation of lowland wet grassland. In: Joyce, C.B.and Wade, P.M. (eds) *European wet grassland: biodiversity, management and restoration*. John Wiley, Chichester.

KIRKHAM F.W. and WILKINS R.J. (1994) The productivity and response to inorganic fertilizers of species-rich wetland hay meadows on the Somerset Moors: nitrogen response under hay cutting and aftermath grazing. *Grass and Forage Science* 49, 152-162.

KIRKHAM F.W., MOUNTFORD J.O. and WILKINS R.J. (1996). The effects of nitrogen, potassium and phosphorus addition on the vegetation of a Somerset peat moor under cutting management. *Journal of Applied Ecology,* 33, 1013-1029.

KIRKHAM F.W. and TALLOWIN J.R.B. (1995) The influence of cutting date and previous fertilizer treatment on the productivity and botanical composition of species-rich hay meadows on the Somerset Levels. *Grass and Forage Science,* 50, 365-377.

MANCHESTER S.J., TREWEEK J.R., MOUNTFORD J.O., PYWELL R.F. and SPARKS T.H. (In press) Restoration of a target wet grassland community on ex-arable land. In: Joyce, C.B.and Wade, P.M. (eds) *European wet grassland: biodiversity, management and restoration*. John Wiley, Chichester.

MARRS R.H. (1993) Soil fertility and nature conservation in Europe: Theoretical considerations and practical management solutions. *Advances in Ecological Research* 24, 241-300.

MOUNTFORD J.O., TALLOWIN J.R.B., KIRKHAM F.W. and LAKHANI K.H. (1994) Effects of inorganic fertilizers in flower-rich hay meadows on the Somerset Levels. In: Haggar, R.J. and Peel, S. (eds) *Grassland Management and Nature Conservation*. Occasional Symposium No. 28. British Grassland Society. Reading, UK. pp. 74-85.

MOUNTFORD J.O., TALLOWIN J.R.B., SPARKS T.H., GOWING D.J.G., MANCHESTER S.J., ROSE S.C., TREWEEK J.R., GILBERT J.C. and ARMSTRONG A.C. (in press). Experimental and monitoring studies of the use of raised water-levels for grassland rehabilitation in lowland ESAs. In: SHELDRICK, R.D. (ed) *Grassland management in the ESAs.*Occasional Symposium, British Grassland Society, Reading, UK.

OOMES M.J.M., OLFF H. and ALTENA H.J. (1996) Effects of vegetation management and raising the water table on nutrient dynamics and vegetation change in a wet grassland. *Journal of Applied Ecology*, 33, 576-588.

PROSSER M.V. and WALLACE H.L. (1996) National Vegetation Classification survey of West

Sedgemoor. Report to The Royal Society for the Protection of Birds. The RSPB, Sandy, Bedfordshire.

RABOTNOV T.A. (1977) The influence of fertilisers on the plant communities of mesophytic grassland. In: Kraus, W. (ed.) *Applications of Vegetation Science to Grassland Husbandry*. Junk; The Hague. pp. 461-497.

RODWELL J.S. (1991) *British Plant Communities. Volume 2. Mires and heaths.* Cambridge: Cambridge University Press.

RODWELL J.S. (1992) *British Plant Communities. Volume 3. Grasslands and montane communities.* Cambridge: Cambridge University Press.

SIMPSON, N.A. and JEFFERSON, R.G. (1996) Use of farmyard manure on semi-natural (meadow) grassland. English Nature Research Reports, No150. English Nature, Peterborough, UK. Pp. 1-97.

SMITH, R.S. (1994) Effects of fertilizers on plant species composition and conservation interest of UK grassland. In: Haggar, R.J. and Peel, S. (eds) *Grassland Management and Nature Conservation. British Grassland Society Occasional Symposium No. 28.* Reading, UK. pp. 64-73.

SMITH R.E.N., BEKKER R.M. and TALLOWIN J.R.B. (In press) Impact of inorganic fertilizer on the soil seed bank of species-rich meadows on the Somerset Levels and Moors ESA. In: Sheldrick, R.D. (ed) Grassland management in the ESAs. *British Grassland Society Occasional Symposium No. 32.* Reading,

TALLOWIN, J.R.B. and SMITH R.E.N. (1996) Management options to conserve a *Cirsio-Molinietum* and integrate its use into productive livestock systems. In: Vegetation Management in Forestry, Amenity and Conservation Areas: Management for Multiple Objectives. *Aspects of Applied Biology*, 44, 203-210.

TALLOWIN J.R.B. (1997) The agricultural productivity of lowland semi-natural grassland: a review. Contract No. F80-32-09. English Nature, Peterborough, UK.

TALLOWIN J.R.B., SMITH R.E.N. and KIRKHAM F.W. (1997) Potassium availability decrease in species-rich hay meadows at Tadham on the Somerset Levels and Moors - cause for concern? In: Sheldrick, R.D. (ed) Grassland management in the ESAs. *British Grassland Society Occasional Symposium No. 32.* Reading,

TALLOWIN J.R.B., KIRKHAM F.W., SMITH R. E. and MOUNTFORD J.O. (in press). Residual effects of phosphorus fertilization on the restoration of floristic diversity to wet hay meadows. In: *European Lowland Wet Grasslands: Their Ecology, Management and Restoration.* International Centre of Landscape Ecology, Loughborough, UK, December 1994.

THOMPSON K., BAKKER J.P. and BEKKER R.M. (1997) The soil seed banks of North West Europe: methodology, density and longevity. Cambridge: Cambridge University Press.

WHEELER B.D. and SHAW S.C. (1995) Plants as hydrologists? An assessment of the value of plants as indicators of water conditions in fens. In: Hughes J.M.R. and Heathwaite A.L. (Eds). *Hydrology and Hydro-chemistry of British Wetlands.* Pp. 63-82. John Wiley and Sons Ltd, Chichester, UK.

Farming in the Antrim Coast, Glens and Rathlin ESA

P. J. CASEMENT

Magherintemple, Ballycastle, Co.Antrim, BT54 6PN

ABSTRACT

This paper describes the author's farm within the Antrim Coast, Glens and Rathlin ESA, and outlines the ways in which involvement in the ESA scheme has influenced farming activities. These include improved maintenance of boundary features, planting of new hedges and trees, and the creation of wildlife corridors linking new and existing unfarmed areas.

The problem of conflict between different agricultural support schemes is raised and it is proposed that a unified, flexible and farmer-friendly environmental enhancement scheme should be set up, that can take account of regional and personal differences.

THE ESA

The north-east corner of Northern Ireland contains one of the most spectacular coastlines in Europe, with steep-sided glens sweeping down from the Antrim Plateau to the Irish Sea and the Atlantic Ocean. The ESA covers the enclosed land lying within two Areas of Outstanding Natural Beauty, the Antrim Coast and Glens (including Rathlin Island) and the Causeway Coast, virtually all of which is designated as Less Favoured Area. Farms are generally small, owner-occupied units, with sheep and suckler cows the predominant enterprises. Tillage is almost non-existent, due to the topography and the climate.

The landscape is dominated by a variety of field boundaries, including hedgerows, earth banks and stone walls, which are important both for their visual impact and as wildlife habitats. Small patches of woodland and scrub along the sides of watercourses and on very steep slopes are also characteristic of the glens, and include perhaps the most important sites for wildlife in the ESA. The overall effect is a pleasing mosaic of small fields, divided by numerous hedges and walls, which form links between scraps of woodland and wetland.

Designation as ESA was in two phases, with the southern and eastern portion of the glens covered in 1989, joined by the northern coast and Rathlin Island in 1993.

MAGHERINTEMPLE FARM

Magherintemple farm lies in the north-east corner of the ESA, on the slopes of Glenshesk, about 2km from the Atlantic Ocean, close to its junction with the Irish Sea. The farm covers 75 hectares, much of it on steeply sloping ground, and the soils are predominantly free-draining sandy loams, overlying the remains of a post-glacial delta. The annual rainfall averages c1200mm. and the coastal situation means constant exposure to strong winds, often salt-laden.

A forage area of 62 hectares is basically all grass, though in most years 3-4 hectares of undersown spring barley are grown and cut green as whole-crop silage. Stock consists of

55 Aberdeen Angus cross suckler cows, mated to Blonde d'Aquitaine and Limousin bulls, about 15 replacement heifers, and 175 ewes, a mixture of cross-breds, mules, Suffolk crosses and Texel crosses. All calves are taken through to beef at 16-22 months and all lambs are finished on the farm.

The remainder of the farm consists of woodland, wetland habitats, gardens and buildings. The woodland is a mixture of post-war coniferous plantations, older hardwood plantations and small awkward areas that have been planted with smaller trees and shrubs. A few fragments of semi-natural woodland survive along streamsides. Wetland habitats include ponds, areas of springs, and fragments of peat in waterlogged hollows.

PRE-ESA MANAGEMENT

When I took over a long-neglected farm 20 years ago my first priorities were to create a viable unit which would provide me and my family with an income sufficient to live on, while causing minimum environmental damage. This involved a schedule of fencing, reseeding, some field drainage, increasing stock numbers, and a programme of building to enable me to conserve grass as silage and feed that silage to stock housed in slatted-floored accommodation. There has been a conscious effort to maximise animal production from grass without massive inputs of bag nitrogen. This has been achieved by keeping stocking rates at a reasonable level, matching peak forage requirements to peaks of grass production and encouraging clover in grass swards. Careful integration of cattle and sheep grazing with silage making helps to keep livestock parasite burdens down, and preventative medicine is practised wherever possible.

All the farm woodland was fenced off to prevent stock access, and a start made at linking blocks of woodland by means of "wildlife corridors", often following steep-sided streams. Woodland management was fairly haphazard, with some thinning of plantations, the clear-felling of one block of Sitka Spruce and the removal of dead softwoods to provide firewood. Hedge maintenance was largely neglected, apart from cutting back of overgrown whin hedges, when the invasion of fields became too severe. A number of small ponds was created on the sites of silted-up flax dams, and many awkward corners were fenced off and planted with small clumps of trees and shrubs. Through involvement with FWAG, I became increasingly interested in a whole-farm approach to nature conservation, and by the time the ESA was enlarged to include our area a farm plan was well advanced. Thus the designation of the ESA gave me the impetus to continue the development of a whole-farm approach, putting into practice the ideas that I had been developing in earlier years.

FARMING WITHIN THE ESA

The operation of the ESA involves three management tiers : compliance with farming prescriptions to qualify for basic annual payments, caring for particular habitats such as woodland, heather moorland, and ancient monuments to receive higher levels of payment, and an optional enhancement tier involving regeneration and creation of various environmental features, both natural and man-made. These can be considered separately.

Farming Prescriptions

These generally coincide with my own approach to farming in an environmentally conscious way and present little or no problem. The following prescriptions are examples:-

Stocking density. I had attained a stocking density that seemed sustainable and was limited in any case by quota and Extensification Premium constraints.

Fertiliser usage. Fertiliser usage has been dropping in recent years as grassland management improved and a greater reliance was placed on the contribution of clover to nitrogen requirements.

Land reclamation/Drainage work. I have no wish to carry out land reclamation work, and am fortunate in needing no new drainage systems.

Application of herbicides. Herbicides have always been applied to grassland only as spot treatments when weed levels have passed a low threshold.

Silage effluent. Great care has always been exercised in the disposal of silage effluent, the bulk of it being diverted into a slurry tank while a pump empties a small reservoir that traps a leak at the rear of the silo. The use of a fine-chop forage harvester has given the opportunity for ensiling partially wilted grass, thereby reducing effluent production.

Retention of boundary features. Sod banks have always been maintained in reasonable order since they help to provide shelter, and when topped by a fence create excellent stockproof barriers. Hedge maintenance has been poor, but the Enhancement Plan has provided the opportunity for a programme of regeneration.

Protection of Sensitive Habitats

Woodland. All woodland on the farm was already fenced off with the exception of two clumps of mature trees in the field that lies in front of the house. These are considered to be parkland trees and therefore not treated as woodland. Preliminary management plans have been drawn up in consultation with staff of DANI's Forest Service, and work will begin in 1997 on creating a wider diversity within plantations in terms of both species and age structure.

Ancient Monument. The remains of a 15th century church give their name to the farm, and are a Scheduled Ancient Monument. Under the scheme, cattle have been prevented from approaching the surviving gable by means of an electric fence. Sheep, which pose no threat to the masonry, are allowed access under the wire, thus preventing the site from becoming overgrown. Discussions with the Environment and Heritage Service concerning maintenance of the church are ongoing, and it is hoped that some repointing work may be carried out during 1997 to prevent further deterioration.

Enhancement Plan

The greatest changes to farm practice have been achieved under the Enhancement Plan tier of the ESA agreement. Work has been undertaken under a number of headings:-

Hedge planting. A series of new thorn hedges has been created as field boundaries where only fences existed previously. Initially only small lengths were undertaken so that techniques could be perfected and management implications fully understood.

Hedgerow regeneration. Old, overgrown thorn hedges are being progressively coppiced, any gaps being planted up with a mixture of hawthorn and blackthorn. Future management will then be simply a matter of trimming on a two- or three-year cycle. Whin hedges are also being coppiced, and the regrowth will then be flailed regularly to prevent excessive encroachment into the fields.

Tree planting. A number of small, awkward or unproductive corners have been fenced off and planted with trees.

Wildlife corridors. A series of 10m wide strips connecting larger blocks of unfarmed land have been fenced off to create wildlife corridors. These have been planted with trees and shrubs, predominantly small, native, wind-tolerant species such as Birch, Alder and Rowan, depending on soil type.

Traditional farm buildings. As yet no work has been undertaken under the ESA scheme on old buildings in the farmyard, but repairs to slate roofs are intended, with replacement of some doors and windows in traditional style.

Creation of reed-beds. Consideration is being given to the creation of a reed-bed in an area where storm water from the farmyard emerges in a field before soaking away.

EFFECTIVENESS OF THE ESA

After only 3 years work at Magherintemple farm, the effects of the ESA designation are clearly visible. These will be even more apparent within a very few years as trees and hedges grow up, creating the intended mosaic of wildlife habitats linked together by linear features such as hedgerows and wildlife corridors. This should create a pleasing patchwork-type landscape which should also benefit livestock and managed grass by providing valuable shelter in a very exposed situation. Magherintemple is of course only one small farm in a large ESA, and major changes to the landscape can only be achieved by persuading a significant proportion of farmers to participate in the scheme. At present nearly 60% of the total ESA area is covered with about 500 farmers involved at some level, though uptake of the enhancement tier is slower. With a preponderance of small, tightly stocked farms, part of the problem lies in a reluctance to take land out of production and endanger qualification for the Extensification Premium top-up to Suckler Cow and Beef Special Premia. This inevitably limits the creation of wildlife corridors and the planting of trees on a scale that is likely to have a significant effect on wildlife or landscape.

This conflict between different grant schemes highlights the problems of the present piecemeal approach to policy-making. As reform is forced on the CAP by the conditions of GATT, the opportunity should be seized to develop a unified and carefully thought-out approach to environmentally-based grant aid for agriculture. A single scheme with a comprehensive menu of tiers and options should be available to all farmers, taking account of the differences between regions and flexible enough to allow for individual tastes. The ESA schemes, along with other measures such as Countryside Stewardship and Tyr Cymen, provide a foundation for an approach that with vision and adequate funding could be built on to give effective nationwide coverage.

Calcareous Grasslands in the ESAs

C.W.D. GIBSON[1], R.G. .JEFFERSON and H.J. ROBERTSON[2]
[1]Bioscan (UK) Ltd, Standingford House, Cave St, Oxford OX4 1BA
[2]Nature Conservancy Council for England, Northminster House, Peterborough
PE1 1UA

ABSTRACT

This paper examines the potential and actual achievements in improving biodiversity in the lowland calcareous grassland ESAs, against current knowledge of calcareous grasslands and the wider framework of habitats in which they occur (their landscape ecology).

The present ESA framework addresses only part of the needs of calcareous grassland fauna and flora. It currently makes no attempt to link the grasslands to other habitats such as the low-intensity arable land, which were typically found in the same areas. Further, knowledge of the specific effects of the framework is limited as ESA monitoring has concentrated on vegetation communities rather than key fauna. Much of our knowledge of the needs of key species and communities comes from outside the ESA system.

Nevertheless, the ESA framework has provided some benefits, not least in preventing further decline in existing ancient grassland and helping to provide links between isolated patches. Arable reversion to grassland in the ESAs has arguably created a more favourable farming context which should facilitate the grazing management of existing areas of semi-natural calcareous grassland. Further, the ESA system has only been operating for a short time compared to the time expected for grassland restoration to occur. The current system is of value in itself, besides providing a foundation for possible future systems to promote the full range of landscapes typical of calcareous grassland areas. Judgement of the ESAs and their future development however needs to be based on proper monitoring, targeted at species and communities of known importance.

INTRODUCTION

Reasons and origins - calcareous grassland biodiversity

Like the majority of British biotopes valued for their biodiversity, calcareous grasslands are an expression of long periods of using the land in ways which are now often uneconomic. It is not their landscapes or their wildlife which are redundant: it is the economic framework in which the landscape and wildlife developed and by which it was maintained. Indeed modern British society places perhaps a higher value on this landscape and wildlife than ever before. This is one of the main reasons why such schemes as the Environmentally Sensitive Areas have been put in place.

The patterns of land use which produced the biodiversity in British calcareous grassland did so in a sense by accident. Biodiversity was not their purpose, instead they were driven by imperatives for human survival at least as strong as the temporary problems in the present century which generated our subsidised intensive agriculture. Past land use was not steady either (Keymer and Leach, 1990): it was driven by the vagaries of climate and the changing needs of people through such events as the Neolithic revolution, the Roman occupation which produced Britain's first significant urban economies, the aftermath of the Black Death and the late-mediaeval wool boom, and Napoleonic and subsequent wars producing drives to increase home food production from arable farming.

'Traditional' farmers made their environmental mistakes as well. Perhaps the ecological consequences were less marked, because serious ecological mistakes were more quickly rewarded by human starvation and disease than they are today, but some of the mistakes were on a spectacular scale. The best known was the erosion of an average of a foot (30cm) of topsoil from the Cotswolds associated with Iron Age farming (Robinson and Lambrick, 1984).

Taken together however, these past patterns revealed Britain entering the 18th century with calcareous grasslands being one of the most diverse biotopes in Britain, since acknowledged by their status as a Key Habitat in the UK Biodiversity Action Plan (The UK Steering Group, 1995). This applied both on the small scale such as the large number of plant species which coexist in small areas of grassland turf, and on a larger scale with for instance a distinctive invertebrate (McLean, 1990) and bird fauna including even 'steppe' species like the great bustard (Fuller, 1982). Despite enclosures, collapse of farming economies with the availability of cheap food imports from the British empire and elsewhere, and gradual intensification of farming practices, this biodiversity in its greater part persisted well into the 20th century (Keymer and Leach, 1990). The few complete extinctions, such as the great bustard (*Otis tarda*), were of species needing large areas of extensively managed habitat, free from human predation and disturbance.

This persistence was due to the local survival of more traditional ways of using the land and to the ability of feral rabbit grazing to replace many of the effects of stock grazing. A great pulse of local extinctions followed the simultaneous collapse of rabbit populations after myxomatosis and subsidised conversion of farmland to intensive arable in the 1950s. This included national extinctions of species such as the large blue butterfly (*Maculinea arion*) and near-extinction of many others such as the stone curlew (*Burhinus oedicnemus*), wart-biter (*Decticus verrucivorus*) and field cricket (*Gryllus campestris*).

Despite the wide variety of microhabitats upon which such threatened species depended, there is a common theme, now backed by ample research results (reviewed in Gibson, 1995) which shows the essential features which allowed traditional land uses to produce such a high biological diversity across calcareous grasslands. The essential features, in comparison to subsidised post-1945 agriculture, were as follows.

1.   Low-intensity agricultural land use

This means minimising inputs from external sources such as fertilisers, but *not* necessarily under-utilisation of the land's inherent productivity. For instance large blue butterflies need habitat which is grazed to near its limit but without external inputs (Thomas, 1994).

Modern agriculture depends on using the land as a substrate for high external inputs and cropping at as high an intensity as possible, whether the crop is forage grass or food crops.

2. Nutrient sources, not sinks

Calcareous grasslands were often used as nutrient sources for arable land elsewhere in the same system. The best known is the downland system where sheep were shepherded on the down in the day and folded to dung on arable land or in shelter at night (Rackham, 1986). However any system which produces meat or wool (both protein) from pasture without fertilising it will produce and maintain the low nutrient status associated with calcareous grassland biodiversity.

Modern agriculture uses external nutrient sources freely, avoiding the need for an approach based on local sources and sinks.

3. Intermittent cultivation

In parts of the Breckland shifting cultivation was a common practice (Dolman and Sutherland, 1991). Elsewhere parts of the chalklands went in and out of arable use according to changes in farm economics and labour. Without the use of fertilisers and pesticides, this favoured the many species dependent on soil disturbance or patches of bare ground.

Until the advent of set-aside, modern agriculture favoured the use of fields for a similar purpose for as long as possible.

4. Spatial-temporal continuity

Whatever the use of any particular area, few of the traditional land uses were wholly inimical to calcareous grassland wildlife. Further, very many areas were never or rarely cultivated, allowing pasture successions to continue for centuries or longer. Although many organisms doubtlessly occurred in discrete colonies as today, movement between colonies or establishment of new colonies was easier.

In contrast modern agriculture surrounds surviving patches of calcareous grassland with habitat which is completely unsuited for most species, making the surviving patches into true 'islands'.

Many other features arise from the above four key differences between ancient and modern calcareous grassland areas, such as the modern drift towards autumn sowing (Ward and Aebischer, 1994) because, with the right chemical and machinery inputs to hand, it is usually more reliable and efficient. Without these inputs the balance shifts to spring sowing, which coincidentally favours a greater variety of fauna (Green, 1988; Potts, 1991).

Intentions behind ESAs

The ESA programme is designed to reverse some of the perceived harm to calcareous grassland wildlife from intensive agriculture. This paper reviews experience to date against the yardstick of the 'key features' laid out above. First the potential for this particular programme is assessed, followed by the actual achievements in practice. Finally we suggest ways to improve performance, either by better implementation of the existing programme, or by modifying it. The scope covers only the lowland calcareous grasslands, effectively those within Breckland, the Cotswolds, the South Downs and the South Wessex Downs ESAs, because upland systems containing calcareous grassland are described elsewhere.

POTENTIAL ACHIEVEMENTS OF THE ESAs

Three changes in the pattern of calcareous grasslands have been repeatedly identified as particularly damaging to biodiversity (Keymer and Leach, 1990; Sumption and Flowerdew, 1985) and as contributing to the extinction of particular species (e.g. Thomas 1983; 1994). These are:

1   The loss of appropriate management, usually grazing, on surviving semi-natural patches.

2   The physical destruction of semi-natural grasslands by their conversion to modern arable or improved sown grasslands.

3   The consequent isolation of surviving patches.

The potential of the ESA framework or any similar scheme for maintaining and enhancing our surviving biodiversity needs to be judged against its capability to address these three problems, via the four key mechanisms identified in the Introduction.

1   The ESA protocols provide explicitly for restoring grazing to unmanaged semi-natural grasslands. They acknowledge that this must be done by low-intensity means, without extra inputs. However they are not able to ensure that such areas act as nutrient sources. Indeed grazing semi-natural grasslands in conjunction with improved grasslands may make the semi-natural areas into nutrient sinks, if animals are allowed to feed preferentially on improved grasslands (ADAS, 1996) but rest and dung on the semi-natural patches. There are too few semi-natural patches left in most areas for intermittent cultivation to be appropriate on the timescales concerned, although such methods are being used for nature reserve management in Breckland.

2   The protocols again provide explicitly for attempts to reconstruct permanent grasslands on modern arable land, but not for the low-intensity arable which can aid species associated with intermittent cultivation. The need for source-sink manipulation has been recognised in experiments and monitoring but not in the protocols themselves.

3   Links between surviving patches are addressed by the encouragement of arable reversion. Should this succeed, in the long term it would help to reverse the effects of fragmentation.

4   The overall continuity of calcareous grasslands in both time and space can be aided, in the long term, by the combination of the first three features above. However, it can only be achieved if mechanisms such as the ESA framework continue to be applied over a period of decades or centuries.

The potential of the ESA framework is therefore considerable in theory. Its major limitation is its inability to achieve the full source-sink relationships of traditional low-intensity agriculture. Whether or not this is important can only be judged against the results achieved so far.

SCIENTIFIC ASSESSMENT OF THE EFFECTS OF ESAs

The assessment of the ESA programme is limited by the short time for which the programme has been in operation compared to the long timescales for natural development of calcareous grassland plant and invertebrate communities (Wells *et al.*, 1976; Gibson and Brown, 1991; Gibson *et al.*, 1992; Sterling *et al.*, 1992; Gibson, 1995) and the restricted scope of monitoring which has taken place. Within these limits, some of the possibilities and achievements of the scheme can be seen, especially in groups such as birds which might be expected to respond quickly.

Vegetation regeneration of existing semi-natural grasslands

The ESAs considered here encompass many of the semi-natural calcareous grassland types of lowland Britain defined as National Vegetation Classification communities CG1-CG7 (Rodwell, 1992). The area of semi-natural calcareous grassland within these ESAs amounts to a maximum of 8000 ha which is about 20% of the total of lowland calcareous grassland in England (English Nature, unpublished). While the absolute take-up rates of ESA on different NVC communities of interest is unknown, it is clear from the limited monitoring data available (ADAS, 1996) that the ESA scheme has resulted in significant benefits.

ADAS(1996) have shown that under ESA grassland management in the South Downs the abundance of plant species suited by grazing, low nutrients and calcareous soils in semi-natural calcareous grasslands has been at least maintained in previously undergrazed unimproved grasslands. Unfortunately the species suited to calcareous conditions actually decreased in previously 'well-grazed' unimproved grasslands. The period of the studies encompassed seven years, long enough for a variety of annual weather types to have been encountered, and the cause of the changes needs further investigation.

The same study encompassed a range of grasslands from the unimproved types to species-poor improved leys. Overall, there were very few other statistically significant changes in major categories and the few that did occur were small. This shows clearly that the ESA regime is weak in causing change in grasslands which are already established. In part this is to be expected, especially in grasslands which have been improved by fertiliser additions, because in the mesotrophic grasslands where the only research has been done it typically takes 10-20 years before the effects of a new low-intensity regime become apparent (Oomes, 1990; Olff and Bakker, 1991; van der Woude *et al.*, 1994). The failure of calcareous grassland species to thrive better in previously well-grazed grasslands is however of concern, because it is the predicted outcome if the failure to provide positive nutrient removal (source-sink relationship) were important.

Vegetation monitoring on arable reversion

Vegetation monitoring of arable reversion areas in the South Downs (ADAS, 1996) shows a pattern which clearly reflects that expected from previous studies of ex-arable grasslands and reviewed by Gibson (1995). This review indicated that, if any other than species characteristic of calcareous grasslands are sown, then species diversity remains low, with few calcareous grassland species appearing even when potential sources are nearby. There is an initial flush of diversity, mainly associated with species which emerge from the buried seed bank and including some of nature conservation interest, but this is quickly swamped by the growth of a few vigorous grass and sometimes herb species (*e.g.* white clover *Trifolium repens*).

In contrast, areas sown from the beginning with a richer mixture including calcareous grassland herbs both remain more diverse (ADAS, 1996) and may remain more readily colonised by further calcareous grassland plant species (Charles Flower, personal communication). The best results of all have been obtained from areas stripped of turf to produce drastic nutrient reduction in the substrate used for development. This is not grant-aided within the ESA protocols but is beginning to be used as an experimental technique (Gibson, 1995).

The ESA monitoring results available are scientifically interesting in that they reinforce earlier findings and reviews (Tansley and Adamson, 1925; Hope-Simpson, 1940; Bullock *et al.*, 1994; Gibson, 1995). This is frustrating in practical terms because it means that (assuming the intention that ESA prescriptions should enhance biodiversity) the lessons of past work have been little used in determining ESA tiers. Even work reaching the same conclusions before the ESA protocols were finalised (e.g. Wells *et al.*, 1976; Gibson and Brown, 1991) merely conferred experimental validation on conclusions which were evident from work commenced in the 1920s (Tansley and Adamson, 1925) and whose results were clear before the middle of this century (Hope-Simpson, 1940). Subsequent experimental work has demonstrated the same features unequivocally and led to a better understanding of the mechanisms (Lloyd and Pigott, 1967) but has not changed the basic conclusion, apparent from 1940, that chalkland biodiversity can only be generated and maintained on substrata impoverished in major nutrients.

Effects on fauna

At the start, basic ESA monitoring concentrated on vegetation communities, an unfortunate limitation in view of the importance of these habitats for faunal biodiversity (Fuller, 1982; McLean, 1990). Nevertheless, there have been a number of studies on fauna in regenerating or newly-managed calcareous grasslands independent of the ESAs and the first results of explicit ESA studies are beginning to emerge.

Studies upon birds (e.g. Green, 1988) and butterflies (e.g. Thomas, 1994) have demonstrated unequivocally that success can be achieved with calcareous grassland fauna provided there is a good understanding of the ecology of the species concerned and the management required. In contrast to the restoration of chalk grassland at the community level, good results with particular species can be achieved remarkably quickly.

Despite this, proper scientific study to inform management is essential. The history of

121

the Large Blue butterfly in Britain is a key demonstration of this principle (Thomas, 1994). For over 100 years, nature reserves established especially for this species merely hastened local extinctions. By the early 1970s, the species was critically endangered, and its ecology was understood well enough to place management of its remaining sites on a 'semi-informed' basis: a little more sophisticated than the ESA protocol which allows grazing to be restored to surviving semi-natural grasslands. With hindsight, this level of understanding was not good enough and the correct management was understood just too late to save the species from extinction. Once enough understanding had been gained, a sustained success in reintroducing the butterfly and spreading it to new sites was initiated (Butterfly Conservation, 1995). Part of the earlier problem was the difficulty for workers to comprehend the extreme severity of local 'overgrazing' which was needed to create the right conditions for the butterfly's specific ant host.

Understanding the ecology of each of the thousands of animal species dependent on calcareous grassland is a daunting task but, as with the Large Blue, it is likely that management regimes directed at a relatively small number of key species of interest will bring many more in their train. Martin Warren, in his paper at this symposium, has given further examples of this type.

Many if not all of the species involved need more than one type of habitat structure. Management needs to be flexible to respond to different years' weather and sometimes to maintain a mosaic of grassland structure in the same area (e.g. Cherrill and Brown, 1990).

ESA management may be aiding many of these species, but this is unknown without specific monitoring. A major benefit of the ESA framework is the increase in scale of operations beyond what is possible on smaller isolated nature reserves or other land designated for nature conservation and attracting specific grant aid.

On the largest scale the results are equivocal. Populations of 'dry grassland' birds, even small passerines such as the corn bunting (Ward and Aebischer, 1994), operate over larger areas than most invertebrate species. In this particular case, studies of corn bunting have found it difficult to link population changes to any change in habitat management specifically attributable to ESAs. This may be because these birds ideally require spring-sown crops which are not targeted as an ESA protocol, or it may be merely that the studies have been unable to link population and land use changes on a smaller scale to the take-up rates of the ESA tiers.

In arable reversion, even in areas sown with indigenous grasses alone, it also appears that the potential for linkage of existing habitats is being realised. In the course of her work on butterflies in the South Wessex Downs ESA, Annabel Hoare (personal communication) has found that selected specialist species of butterfly such as Common Blue *Polyommatus icarus*, Marbled White *Melanargia galathea* and occasionally even the much more demanding Adonis and Chalkhill blues (*Lysandra bellargus* and *L.coridon*) are moving over the reversion areas as well as more ubiquitous grassland species such as Meadow Brown *Maniola jurtina*. The same species do not move over species-poor pastures resulting from ESA management of existing improved pastures or other methods of arable reversion.

Achievements to date

ESA management is providing a significant benefit particularly to those existing unimproved calcareous grasslands which fall outside the potential sources for other incentives such as are available in designated SSSIs, although prescriptions may need modifying to maximise the benefit, such as increasing grazing levels in some semi-natural grasslands. This is because ESAs at least allow the management of such areas to be maintained or reinstated. The benefit for fauna is however uncertain because of the lack of monitoring, and the overall benefit may be limited by the ways in which ESA management can be implemented.

In arable reversion, the only direct ecological benefit is found when relatively species-rich mixtures have been sown without any of the modern improved grassland varieties. Even here, studies outside ESAs show that the benefit may be difficult to maintain in the long-term without more drastic techniques to reduce the available nutrients. However even the sowing of grass mixes poorer in plant species may occasionally be able to improve linkage between existing habitats and enhance the potential for management.

In other cases of lowering management intensity of species-poor pastures, and arable reversion techniques using modern agricultural species or grass-only mixtures, there has been no detectable ecological benefit as yet. Such benefit would be expected to take at least 15-20 years to emerge. Over shorter time periods, any funds devoted to such management ends cannot be regarded as being employed for promoting grassland biodiversity although they may improve the landscape to some observers.

OPPORTUNITIES TO INCREASE ESA BENEFITS IN FUTURE

Time-scale of recovery

The natural development of calcareous grasslands from arable land took at least a century even when ample sources of plant and animal species were available for colonisation nearby (Gibson and Brown, 1991). The Dutch experience on mesotrophic grasslands, the only one in modern times where people have had the patience to wait and to carry out appropriate studies, shows that merely lowering the inputs on 'modern' farmland will start to have an influence after 10-20 years.

In the ESAs the basic tiers do just this: inputs of fertiliser and pesticide are lowered or prevented without any other special measures. Not surprisingly, after less than 10 years, no significant effect has appeared. This is frustrating for those who want quick results, but immaterial against the background of the real timescales on which species-rich communities are established.

In view of this, the temptation to give up too soon must be resisted. Instead, a long-term view of monitoring recovery is required, and factors promoting recovery investigated. The persistence of low-level and low-cost, but perhaps ultimately effective, means must be encouraged so that they are applied for long enough to test whether or not significant improvements in biodiversity can be attained.

Targeting effort in the existing system

Statistics on the rates at which the available 'tiers' of ESA are taken up are difficult to obtain. Nevertheless, it is clear that not all the land eligible for the different grants and incentives is actually placed in new management regimes. The reasons for this are complicated. In part, there are real or imagined fears that the ESA grants will not compensate properly for the loss of farming income. There are also problems of information exchange and the inertia in any system which is voluntary and changes established practice.

More needs to be made of the success of particular components of the present system. ESAs are rarely 'news'. The small successes of even the cheaper tiers of arable reversion need to be better monitored and more needs to be made of the results. The increase of even our commonest species of butterflies is worthwhile. The hope of increasing linkages between scattered populations of our rarest ones such as the Adonis Blue is a significant achievement. Farmers in particular, and the ESA framework as a whole, need to be congratulated on these achievements. Other animals and plants are no doubt following these trends, which people happen to have studied. Monitoring is not merely a luxury: it shows the extent and limits of the positive achievements which have been made and, properly exploited, demonstrates to the public at large that the subsidies which they are paying are being well spent. Monitoring needs to be targeted at species and communities of particular nature conservation value, such as those defined within the NVC and within the UK Biodiversity Action Plan.

A broader perspective - towards landscape ecology

The ESA framework is a 'piecemeal' approach to lowering the intensity of agriculture. Natural areas containing calcareous grasslands also contained other habitats important for biodiversity in the past. So far, only the grassland component of this landscape of many habitats has been addressed in the ESA prescriptions. The important role of cultivation in 'Natural Areas' supporting calcareous grassland has been ignored. This low-intensity cultivation is of little use for the many species associated with ancient pastures, but is of great importance for a number of other calcareous grassland species, ranging from plants such as the various fumitory species scattered as rare 'weeds' across the southern limestones to birds such as corn bunting and stone curlew.

These species continue to lie outside the ESA system, although they are becoming foci of local 'Biodiversity Action Plans' and a few are maintained within SSSIs and other protected areas. Relatively small changes to the ESA prescriptions could be used to encourage spring-sown crops and low-intensity arable production which would be of disproportionate benefit to biodiversity, encouraging the rich variety of species which depend on habitat disturbance but which cannot survive the particular disturbances of autumn sowing and intensive arable cultivation, characteristic of modern subsidised agriculture.

Leaving aside the many decades of waiting needed for significant results to appear from lowering the intensity for agriculture, there are a number of ways in which resources could be focused more effectively on calcareous grassland regeneration.

For instance, arable reversion a long way from potential sources of characteristic species will not be colonised for a very long time. Conversely, if expensive means of restoration with many sown species were concentrated near to surviving ancient grassland patches, it is clear that both plants and invertebrates (*e.g.* A.Hoare work cited above) could colonise much more quickly. This gives an opportunity to concentrate funds where they will quickly and significantly improve biodiversity, as in 'prime biodiversity areas' (Batten *et al.*, 1996). Such concentration should not be at the expense of the large-scale landscape benefits which ESAs can bring.

The most useful role of ESAs is to extend habitats rich in biodiversity gradually into the wider countryside where there is good hope of doing so, and so complement specific management of nature reserves.

New forms of integrated landscape management?

A widespread return to a real or imagined past is not feasible. Here as elsewhere the reasons include the expense of recreating past systems, our incomplete knowledge of how they worked and not least their inefficiency for achieving our goals. Mediaeval or earlier farmers were not farming for biodiversity; they were farming for survival. Modern farmers are farming for economic survival, a lesser but nevertheless effective means of concentrating the mind than that which faced our ancestors. We have decided, for whatever reason, that biodiversity is a desirable goal and that we wish to pay to ensure that as much as possible of the landscape and ecology of the past is preserved. Many people believe that this is sensible for sustainability as well as aesthetic or other reasons.

For these reasons, grants should foster systems which work in their entirety, rather than merely making sure that the Adonis Blue survives in a nature reserve. This is the point of the ESA system, but it has been designed as a series of piecemeal operations ('Tiers') rather than as a subsidy for low-intensity farming systems from which the conservation of biodiversity in a sustainable manner falls as a matter of course.

Such new integrated systems are our greatest challenge. We know that the old systems (even if we know what they were) are uneconomic or impractical in a modern environment. Our real challenge is to find new systems which repeat the key features of the old (such as source-sink design within the compass of a single holding) without incurring the costs of running a museum. The ESA framework for calcareous grasslands is our first approximation to this: it is worth doing because of the successes of each part of its piecemeal approach, but it is unable to make a system which works as a whole unit because it is designed to address particular problems, not set up as a sustainable system which conserves our calcareous landscape biodiversity.

Should we be able to design such systems, they would be the natural development from the ESA framework. The key concept of the ESAs is in their promotion of biodiversity in the wider countryside, not just in nature reserves. Any true replacement must exploit the ability to transfer nutrients from one part of the chalkland or similar ecosystem to another, to incorporate arable cultivation into the overall scheme, and to maintain the whole so that real farmers can make a living out of a low-intensity agricultural holding.

125

REFERENCES

ADAS (1996) *Botanical monitoring of grassland in the South Downs ESA; 1987-1995.* ADAS report to the Ministry of Agriculture, Fisheries and Food, April 1996.

BATTEN L., KIRBY K., MARSDEN J., WILKINSON M. and WHITMORE M. (1996) England: Natural areas and prime biodiversity areas. In NOWICKI P., BENNETT G., MIDDLETON D., RIENTJES S. and WALTERS R. (Eds). *Perspectives on ecological networks*, pp. 70-91. European Centre for Nature Conservation: Man and Nature Series, volume 1.

BULLOCK, J.M., CLEAR HILL, B., DALE, M.P. and SILVERTOWN, J. (1994) An experimental study of the effects of sheep grazing on vegetation change in a species poor grassland and the role of seedling recruitment into gaps. *Journal of Applied Ecology*, 31, 493-507.

BUTTERFLY CONSERVATION (1995) *Species Action Plan: Large Blue* Maculinea arion. Colchester, Butterfly Conservation.

CHERRILL A.J. and BROWN V.K. (1990) The habitat requirements of adults of the wart-biter *Decticus verrucivorus* (L.) (Orthoptera: Tettigonidae) in southern England. *Biological Conservation*, 53, 145-157.

THE UK STEERING GROUP (1995) *The UK Steering Group Report.* London, HMSO.

DOLMAN P.M. and SUTHERLAND W.J. (1991) Historic clues to conservation. *New Scientist*, 1751, 40-43.

FULLER R.J. (1982) *Bird Habitats in Britain.* London, T & AD Poyser.

GIBSON C.W.D. (1995) *Chalk grasslands on former arable land: a review.* Peterborough, Bioscan (UK) Ltd, Blue Circle Industries plc, English Nature special publication.

GIBSON C.W.D. and BROWN V.K. (1991) The nature and rate of development of calcareous grasslands in southern England. *Biological Conservation,* 58, 297-316.

GIBSON C.W.D., HAMBLER C. and BROWN V.K. (1992) Changes in spider (Araneae) assemblages in relation to succession and grazing management. *Journal of Applied Ecology*, 29, 132-142.

GREEN R.E. (1988) Stone curlew conservation. *RSPB Conservation Review*, 2, 30-33.

HOPE-SIMPSON J.F. (1940) Studies of the vegetation of the English chalk. VI. Late stages in succession leading to chalk grassland. *Journal of Ecology,* 28, 386-402.

KEYMER R.J. and LEACH S.J. (1990) Calcareous grassland - a limited resource in Britain. In HILLIER S.H., WALTON D.W.H. and WELLS D.A. (Eds). *Calcareous grasslands - ecology and management*, pp. 11-17. Huntingdon, Bluntisham Books.

LLOYD P.S. and PIGOTT C.D. (1967) The influence of soil conditions on the course of succession on the chalk of southern England. *Journal of Ecology*, 55, 137-146.

MCLEAN I.G.F. (1990) The fauna of calcareous grasslands. In HILLIER S.H., WALTON D.W.H. and WELLS D.A. (Eds). *Calcareous grasslands - ecology and management*, pp. 41-46. Huntingdon, Bluntisham Books.

OLFF H. and BAKKER J.P. (1991) Long-term dynamics of standing crop and species composition after the cessation of fertiliser application to mown grassland. *Journal of Applied Ecology,* 28, 1040-1052.

OOMES M.J.M. (1990) Changes in dry matter and nutrient yields during the restoration of species-rich grasslands. *Journal of Vegetation Science*, 1, 333-338.

POTTS G.R. (1991) The environmental and ecological importance of cereal fields. In FIRBANK L.G., CARTER N., DARBYSHIRE J.F. and POTTS G.R. (Eds). *The Ecology of Temperate cereal fields.* Oxford, Blackwell Scientific Publications.

RACKHAM O. (1986) *The History of the Countryside.* London, Dent.

ROBINSON M.A. and LAMBRICK G.H. (1984) Holocene alluviation and hydrology in the Upper

Thames basin. *Nature*, 308, 809-814.

RODWELL, J.S. (1992) *British Plant Communities: Volume 3: Grasslands and Montane Communities*. Cambridge, Cambridge University Press.

STERLING P.H., GIBSON C.W.D. and BROWN V.K. (1992) Leaf miner assemblies: effects of plant succession and grazing management. *Ecological Entomology*, 17, 167-178.

SUMPTION K.J. and FLOWERDEW J.R. (1985) The ecological effects of the decline in Rabbits (*Oryctolagus cuniculus* L.) due to myxomatosis. *Mammal Review*, 15, 151-186.

TANSLEY A.G. and ADAMSON R.S. (1925) Studies of the vegetation of the English chalk. III: The chalk grasslands of the Hampshire-Sussex border. *Journal of Ecology,* 13, pp. 177-223.

THOMAS A.S. (1963) Further changes in vegetation since the advent of myxomatosis. *Journal of Ecology*, 51, pp. 151-186.

THOMAS J.A. (1983) The ecology and conservation of *Lysandra bellargus* (Lepidoptera: Lycaenidae) in Britain. *Journal of Applied Ecology*, 20, pp. 59-83.

THOMAS J.A. (1994) The ecology and conservation of *Maculinea arion* and other European species of butterfly. In Pullin, A.S. (Ed) *Ecology and conservation of butterflies*, pp. 180-197. London, Chapman & Hall.

VAN DER WOUDE B.J., PEGTEL D.M. and BAKKER J.P. (1995) Nutrient limitation after long-term nitrogen fertiliser application in cut grasslands. *Journal of Applied Ecology,* 31, 405-412.

WARD R.S. and AEBISCHER N.J. (1994) Changes in corn bunting distribution on the South Downs in relation to agricultural land use and cereal invertebrates. Peterborough, *English Nature Research Reports* No. 129.

WELLS T.C.E., SHEAIL J., BALL D.F. and WARD L.K. (1976) Ecological studies on the Porton Ranges: relationship between vegetation, soils and land-use history. *Journal of Ecology,* 64, 589-626.

Farming on the South Downs

C. W. PASSMORE

Applesham Farm, Coombes, East Lancing, West Sussex BN15 0RP

ABSTRACT

The consequences of certain traditional farming practices on the South Downs are explained, together with the various Tiers in the South Downs ESA management prescriptions. The enterprises at Applesham Farm are described, and the main changes in grassland management resulting from joining the Scheme are discussed. While the Tier 1 objectives to maintain existing chalk downland have been met successfully, Tier 3B intentions to promote reversion from ley/arable to permanent grassland have posed problems in weed control and parasitic worm infestations. Public access and increasing rabbit populations also cause concern. In the future, management prescriptions must recognise the importance of low-intensity mixed farming in maintaining habitat and wildlife diversity.

INTRODUCTION

The South Downs consist of a range of chalk hills, about sixty miles long, stretching from Old Winchester Hill in Hampshire to the White Cliffs of Beachy Head in East Sussex. Most of the soils are calcareous loams, but there are considerable areas of flinty clays and loams overlying the chalk rock. These soils were usually acid, but have been dressed with chalk and are now neutral.

The South Downs are designated an area of outstanding natural beauty and in 1986 were included in the first six Environmentally Sensitive Areas in the UK. For several centuries most of the downs have been farmed in fairly large units of several hundred acres, part as open downland grass and part as arable crops. Large flocks of sheep were kept. These grazed the downland grass by day and were usually folded on arable crops by night. This continual transfer of fertility to the arable land helped to create and maintain the calcareous grassland, very low in plant nutrients, but very high in plant diversity with up to 40 plant species recorded per square metre.

SOUTH DOWNS ESA

The characteristic open rolling downland and river valleys that cross the Downs provide valuable habitats for wild flowers and insects associated with traditional chalk grassland as well as breeding sites for many species of birds. There is a wealth of archaeological interest, such as old settlements and remains of extensive field systems. Historic field barns, livestock enclosures and flint walls all add to the interest of this unique area.

Without agriculture, this landscape and much of the wildlife would not survive.

Fig. 1   South Downs ESA: Tiers and Payments

Tier 1 - Permanent Grassland on the Chalk £40 per ha	Tier 4A - Winter Stubbles with Undersowing £110 per ha
Tier 2 - Permanent Grassland in the River Valleys £40 per ha	Tier 4B - Winter Stubbles without Undersowing £90 per ha
Tier 3A - Arable Reversion to Chalk Grassland £290 per ha	Tier 4C - Conservation Headlands £80 per ha
Tier 3B - Arable Reversion to Permanent Grassland £250 per ha	Public Access Tier £170 per ha

APPLESHAM FARM

My farm lies within an area of outstanding natural beauty with panoramic views of the sea and inland Downs and within the boundaries of the South Downs Environmentally Sensitive Area.

Soil type :   Mainly flinty Icknield, Coombe and Charity loamy soils overlying chalk,

Topography: Mostly rolling chalk Downland. Fields, divided by fences, average 16 ha (39 acres), ranging from 8.5 ha to 28 ha (21 to 70 acres). The chalk escarpment covers 28 ha (70 acres).

Farm activities: Livestock: 400 breeding ewes + followers
                                        100 suckler cows + followers
                Arable: 175 ha (430 acres)
                Grass/clover leys: 83 ha (205 acres)
                Permanent pasture: 44 ha (110 acres)
                Traditional downland pasture: 30 ha (70 acres)

Livestock enterprises at Applesham Farm take the form of a 100-head suckler herd, comprising both Friesian x Hereford and 50 pedigree Limousin cows, and a flock of 400 breeding ewes.

Suckler calves are weaned at the end of October and finished for beef on the farm over winter, with surplus pedigree Limousin bulls and heifers sold for breeding. The cows are out wintered on the leys and Downland banks.

Ewes and lambs are turned on to the first year leys which provide nutritious grazing relatively free of parasitic worms. Cattle mop up any surplus herbage and graze the second year leys which also provide conservation cuts of hay and silage. The third year leys are grazed by both sheep and cattle before being ploughed up for wheat.

The livestock and arable enterprises are fully integrated on the light, free-draining soils of the Downland with a rotation that allows three or four years of cereals followed by three years of grass and clover leys established by under sowing the last of the cereal crops.

Catch crops of Italian ryegrass, mustard and forage rape are slotted in where possible to provide additional stock grazing. Cereal stubbles are similarly grazed before being ploughed up for the following crop along with any surplus straw. By incorporating a large proportion of white clover - up to 50% - in the ley mixtures, the pasture provides a high quality diet at relatively low cost for young lambs and calves throughout the summer, as well as feeding the grass and building up soil nitrogen reserves for subsequent cereal crops.

ESA Downland management

The 28 ha (70 acre) bank is entered into Tier 1 of the Environmentally Sensitive Area scheme (maintaining existing chalk downland). Although this spectacular escarpment which sweeps for 1700 metres along the south-west border of Applesham Farm, rising 70 metres above field level in places, is maintained in an unimproved state, it does contribute to the cropping rotation on the farm. The bank is divided so that when adjoining fields are down to leys it is grazed year-round for three years. This keeps coarse grasses and scrub invasion in check. When the adjacent fields grow cereals, the lack of summer grazing allows wild flowers and grasses to bloom and replenish the seed stock. The bank is then grazed for a short period between harvest and autumn ploughing, which removes excess vegetation.

Some 35 ha (86 acres) of steeper, less fertile land has been converted from arable production to chalk downs under Tier 3B of the ESA scheme by sowing to a grass mixture. This area is grazed alternately by the farm's sheep and cattle to keep the pasture 'clean'. Effective management of all the land covered by the ESA scheme rules, now about one-fifth of the farm, relies to a large extent on the performance achieved on the rest of the farm, for example to provide sufficient winter fodder and bedding straw for livestock, to allow movement of livestock off the designated areas for the benefit of wildlife at sensitive times, or to allow for a variable stocking rate in line with seasonal herbage growth.

Some effects of the scheme on grassland management of Applesham Farm

Tier 1   Management remains as before, with no changes.

Tier 3B.   This land was in the grass ley/arable rotation. Now it is in permanent grass. No fertiliser, dung or slurry can be used, no rolling or harrowing is allowed and no cutting until 1st July (previously 15 July). Production has decreased each year. Grass growth is less even over the field. Mowing is impractical, owing to the large number of

130

flints (rolling is not allowed), and spring growth is reduced. Spear and nodding thistles are a problem. Delaying mowing until after the July dead-line is too late, as thistles have already seeded by then. Creeping thistles are a new problem, previously controlled by spraying the cereal crops. Weed wipers can be used, but the grass has to be grazed very short for them to be effective.

Our system of rotating sheep and cattle to avoid dosing for parasitic worm control could now break down owing to the larger area of permanent grassland. We have no parasites resistant to any of these products at present.

Some benefits of the South Down ESA Scheme

Payments under the scheme are encouraging the conversion of marginal arable land to grassland, on the High Downs, thinner soils and steeper land.

The new arable Tier 4B is encouraging.

Some effects of the restrictions of the scheme to Farmers in the area

The scheme is resulting in a gradual decline in soil fertility, and decreasing animal production owing to lower herbage *growth* and lower herbage *quality*. This is causing a lowering of farm output (*i.e.* income and profit). Other effects include:

1. Increase in 'Tor' grass (*Brachypodium pinnatum*).
2. Wormer resistance following an increasing reliance on their use.
3. Greater reliance on livestock enterprises, close to large urban populations which demand access, and resent fences, though these are essential for good livestock management. Fences are therefore cut or demolished by off-road vehicles. Sheep are worried by dogs. There is also a big increase in rabbit populations, causing much damage to some very valuable, botanically diverse downland turf.

CONCLUSION

Overall the South Downs scheme has been a success. For the first ten years the main objective has been to preserve the remaining chalk grassland (Tier 1), secondly to encourage the conversion of some arable land into grassland (Tiers 2 + 3A + 3B).

This year two new tiers have been added, winter stubble with under-sowing (Tier 4A) and fallow winter stubble (Tier 4B). These new Tiers recognise the importance of maintaining a large and more diverse wild bird population and represents a new bold step in the right direction.

The authorities are at last beginning to recognise the importance of low-intensity mixed farming, with arable cropping, grassland and livestock, to the farming economy of the area. In addition it supports a *much greater diversity* of wildlife (both fauna and flora) than do exclusively arable or exclusively grassland systems.

Mixed farming needs much more emphasis in the future, so as to maintain and sustain the viability of this type of farming and increase the diversity of wildlife. To achieve this it will be necessary for environmental and Government bodies to be made much more aware of the complexity of this issue, and learn much more about how farms actually work!

Grassland Management to Promote Soil Biodiversity

R.D. BARDGETT, R. COOK[1], G.W. YEATES[2], L. DONNISON[1],
P. HOBBS[3] and E. McALISTER
School of Biological Sciences, Stopford Building, University of Manchester,
Manchester M13 9PT
[1]Institute of Grassland and Environmental Research, Plas Gogerddan, Aberystwyth,
Dyfed SY23 3EB
[2]Landcare Research, Palmerston North, New Zealand
[3]Institute of Grassland and Environmental Research, North Wyke, Okehampton,
Devon EX20 2SB

INTRODUCTION

Soil biotic communities play a key role in grassland ecosystems by regulating the dynamics of organic matter decomposition and plant nutrient availability. It has been argued, and in some cases demonstrated, that different approaches to soil and land management affect the structure and activities of these communities (*e.g.* Bardgett, 1996). It is also becoming evident that those systems which have a soil community that bears the closest resemblance to natural ecosystems may require fewer inputs because greater reliance can be placed on ecosystem self-regulation (Yeates *et al.*, 1997).

The aim of this study was to assess the impacts of changes in grassland management, as prescribed in Environmentally Sensitive Areas (ESAs), on the structure and diversity of soil communities of grassland systems. In particular, we aimed to test the hypothesis that soil communities that develop under ESA management are abundant, diverse and "stable" (*sensu* Pimm, 1991) and therefore, due to enhanced nutrient conservation and reliance on ecosystem self-regulation may require fewer management inputs.

MATERIAL AND METHODS

Measurements were made on a range of paired, adjacent permanent grassland sites which were under traditional management (no fertilizer) or improved management (100-200 kg fertilizer N ha^{-1} an^{-1}). Details of the sites are shown in Table 1. At sites 1 and 3, random soil cores (3.5 cm diameter, 5 cm depth) were taken, passed through a sieve (<6mm) and analyzed for microbial biomass and community structure using phospholipid fatty acid analysis (Bardgett *et al.*, 1996). Fatty acids i15:0, a15:0, 15:0, i16:0, 17:0, i17:0, cy17:0, 18:1⍵7 and cy19:0 were chosen to represent bacterial biomass and 18:2⍵6 was used as an indicator of fungal biomass. The ratio of 18:2⍵6:bacterial PLFAs was taken to represent the ratio of fungal:bacterial biomass in soil (Bardgett *et al.*, 1996). The abundance of fungi and vesicular-arbuscular mycorrhiza (VAM) were measured at sites 3, 4 and 5 by ergosterol analysis and VAM spore counts, respectively. At site 2, nematodes were extracted from soils and counted, and identified on the basis of feeding groups (Yeates *et al.*, 1997). The diversity indices for nematodes were calculated according to Yeates *et al.*, (1997).

132

Table 1.   Description of study sites and their management. All sites were grazed by cattle and/or sheep. Sites 3,4 and 5 were all traditionally managed *Anthoxanthum odoratum - Geranium sylvaticum* meadows. Site 3 was within the Pennine Dales Environmentally Sensitive Area.

Site	Location and description
1.	Clay loam soil, IGER North Wyke, Devon.
2.	Clay loam, sandy and loam soil , Dyfed, Wales.
3.	Brown earth soil, Upper Teesdale, County Durham.
4.	Brown earth soil, Ravenstonedale, Cumbria
5.	Brown earth soil, Dolgellau, Wales.

RESULTS

Total microbial and fungal biomass were greater under management systems without fertilizer application (Table 2). The ratio of fungal:bacterial biomass was also significantly greater in grassland sites without fertilizer applications (Table 2).

Table 2.   Grassland management and soil microbial characteristics at sites 1 and 3.

	North Wyke		Teesdale	
	No Fert	Fertilized	No Fert	Fertilized
Microbial biomass (μg C g^{-1} soil)	1713	1125[***]	2246	2062[**]
Fungal PLFA (nmol g^{-1} soil)	1.64	0.69[***]	8.02	5.29[***]
Fungal:bacterial PLFA	0.03	0.02[***]	0.10	0.06[***]
Coefficient of variation of microbial biomass (*CV*)	33	52	n/a	n/a

[***] $P < 0.001$.

Figure 1.   Relationship between total VAM spores and fungal biomass, measured as ergosterol, in a range of soils from fertilized and unfertilized meadow grasslands. a and b mark outliers from the relationship.

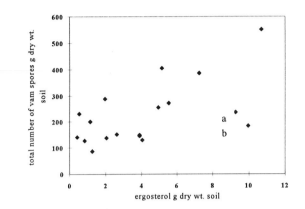

Figure 2.   Effects fertilizer management on VAM spore counts at sites 3,4 and 5.

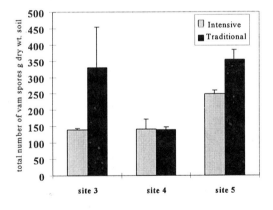

For sites 3, 4 and 5 there was a significant positive correlation (r = 0.7, P <0.001) between fungal biomass, measured as ergosterol, and VAM spore counts (Figure 1). VAM spore counts were significantly lower in fertilized than adjacent unfertilized grasslands (Figure 2). At site 2, numbers of fungal- and plant-feeding nematodes were significantly greater in unfertilized than adjacent fertilized grasslands (Table 3). Nematode diversity, as measured by the Shannon-Weaver Index (H′) was somewhat higher (P<0.1) in unfertilized grasslands (Table 3).

Table 3.   Grassland management and nematode community structure at site 2.

		Management	
Nematodes (10^3 m^{-2})	Fertilized	Unfertilized	SED
Bacterial feeders	930	1110	99
Fungal feeders	260	570	49[***]
Plant feeders	2000	2600	195[**]
Predators	77	36	12[**]
Omnivores	150	190	26
Diversity index (H′)	0.63	0.72	0.05

**, *** $P<0.01$, $P<0.001$.

DISCUSSION

The results of this study show that soil microbial biomass is higher in unfertilized than intensively managed, fertilized grassland. They also suggest that differences in microbial biomass are associated with shifts in microbial community structure. In particular, we found that the abundance of fungal fatty acids and the ratio of fungal:bacterial fatty acids were greater in unfertilized than fertilized grasslands. This indicates that the larger microbial community of unfertilized grassland is dominated by fungal decomposition pathways. In contrast, the lower microbial biomass of fertilized systems appears to be dominated by bacteria. The finding that fungal-feeding nematodes were more abundant in unfertilized than fertilized grasslands also supports the view that soils of low-input systems are dominated by fungal decomposition pathways.

Data from three of the sites showed a positive correlation between fungal biomass, measured as ergosterol, and VAM spores. In view of this, it is likely that differences in fungal biomass between sites were attributed in part to changes in the abundance of VAM. Additional evidence for this comes from the finding that numbers of VAM spores were lower in the fertilized, than adjacent unfertilized grasslands. This is in agreement with other workers who have shown that a substantial part of the fungal biomass of traditionally managed meadows are VAM fungi (*e.g.* Read and Haselwandter, 1981) which are sensitive to fertilizer applications (Sparling and Tinker, 1978). Since these fungi have been shown to promote seedling establishment and plant species diversity (Grime *et al.*, 1987) it is possible that reductions in VAM in fertilized grasslands contribute to observed declines in plant species diversity (Bardgett, 1996). Therefore, the recovery of plant species diversity in improved meadows may be linked to the development of VAM fungi in soils. Further studies are required to substantiate these claims.

It has been suggested that temporal variability of a given group of organisms is a measure of its "stability" (Pimm, 1991). This is partly because if organisms are more resistant to disturbance, they will fluctuate less in response to changes in environmental conditions. A common index of temporal variation is the Coefficient of Variation (Pimm, 1991; Tilman, 1996). We found that the CVs for measures of soil microbial biomass at site 1 were consistently lower in the unfertilized than in the fertilized grasslands (Table 2). This suggests that the soil microbial community of the unfertilized grassland was more "stable", and hence more resistant to disturbance than that of the intensively managed, fertilized sites. The finding that the diversity of nematodes was somewhat higher in the unfertilized fields tends to support the hypothesis that diversity of soil communities is positively associated with its stability. Such findings are consistent with studies of above-ground diversity-stability relationships (*e.g.* McNaughton, 1988) and, of course, have implications for both the functioning of grassland systems and their response to management and global change. However, further studies are obviously required to substantiate these broad findings.

CONCLUSION

This study tends to corroborate the existence of bacterial- and fungal-based compartments (*sensu* Moore *et al.,* 1996) in microbial communities of managed grasslands. Intensively managed grasslands appear to encourage the "fast cycle" dominated by labile substrates and bacteria, while less productive, unfertilized soils are more "stable" and are dominated by the "slow cycle", more resistant substrates and fungi. These findings are also consistent with Odum's theory (1969, 1985) that communities become more diverse and "stable", and that larger organisms dominate during successional development of communities; fungi are several orders of magnitude larger than bacteria. Overall, these findings support the thesis that biotic communities that develop in less intensively managed grassland soils have more resemblance to those of natural ecosystems. As a consequence, they may require fewer management inputs due to greater reliance being placed on ecosystem self-regulation.

ACKNOWLEDGEMENTS
We thank MAFF and BBSRC for funding this work.

REFERENCES
BARDGETT R.D. (1996) Potential effects on the soil mycoflora of changes in the UK agricultural policy for upland grasslands. In: Frankland, J.C., Magan, N and Gadd, G,M, (Eds.), *Fungi and Environmental Change, Symposium of the British Mycological Society*, Cambridge University Press. pp 163-183.
BARDGETT R.D., HOBBS P.J. and FROSTEGÅRD Å. (1996) Changes in soil fungal:bacterial ratios following reductions in the intensity of management of an upland grassland. *Biology and Fertility of Soils* 22, 261-264.
GRIME J.P., MACKEY J.M.L., HILLIER S.H. and READ D.J. (1987) Floristic diversity in a model system using experimental microcosms. *Nature* 328, 420-422.
McNAUGHTON S.J. (1988) Diversity and stability. *Nature*, 333, 204-205.
MOORE J.C., DE RUITER P.C., HUNT W.H., COLEMAN D.C. and FRECKMAN D.W. (1996) Microcosms and soil ecology: critical linkages between field studies and modelling food-webs. *Ecology* 77, 694-705.
ODUM E.P. (1969) The strategy of ecosystem development. *Science* 164, 262-270.
ODUM E.P. (1985) Trends expected in stressed ecosystems. *Bioscience* 35, 419-422.
PIMM S.L. (1991) *The Balance of Nature*. University of Chicago Press, Chicago.

READ D.J. and HASELWANDTER K. (1981) Observations on the mycorrhizal status of some alpine plant communities. *New Phytologist* 88, 341-352.

SPARLING G.P. and TINKER P.B. (1978) Mycorrhizal infection in Pennine grassland. I. Levels of infection in the field. *Journal of Applied Ecology* 15, 943-950.

TILMAN D. (1996) Biodiversity: population versus ecosystem stability. *Ecology* 77, 97-107.

YEATES G.W., BARDGETT R.D., COOK R., HOBBS P.J., BOWLING P.J. and POTTER J.F. (1997). Faunal and microbial diversity in three Welsh grassland soils under conventional and organic management regimes. *Journal of Applied Ecology*, 34, 453-470.

The Impact of Grassland Management on Threatened Butterflies in ESA's

M. S. WARREN and N. A. D. BOURN

Butterfly Conservation, PO Box 444, Wareham, Dorset, BH20 5YA

INTRODUCTION

Over three-quarters of Britain's 59 resident butterfly species breed in grassland habitats over all or part of their range. Recent research has shown that their populations are extremely sensitive to grassland management and respond rapidly to changes in grazing regimes (*e.g.* Thomas, 1984). They are thus useful barometers of the impact of grassland management within ESA's and probably reflect changes that may be occurring in a wide range of other invertebrates (*e.g.* Fry and Lonsdale, 1991; Thomas, 1991).

Of the 44 butterflies that breed in lowland grassland, almost half are in steep decline (*i.e.* >25% decline in 25 years), two are extinct, and eight are highly threatened (most >50% decline in 25 years, Warren *et al.,* in press). Butterfly Conservation has drawn up detailed Action Plans for these declining species and summary plans for the five most threatened species are included in the recent Biodiversity Steering Group report (DOE, 1995). Three major threats are identified in these plans: 1) Continuing loss of unfertilised, flower-rich grasslands; 2) Problems of ensuring appropriate habitat management on remaining grasslands; and 3) Problems associated with habitat fragmentation and isolation of surviving habitat patches. The latter is now thought to be a significant problem for threatened butterflies which now exist as metapopulations covering networks of comparatively small sites, connected by occasional dispersal, within which there are local extinctions and colonisations (Gilpin and Hanski, 1991; C. D. Thomas, 1995).

A variety of actions are needed to tackle these threats, ranging from research to improve our knowledge of species requirements, improved measures for habitat protection and management. Because grassland habitats are now so highly fragmented in Britain, measures on small isolated nature reserves are rarely enough and such protected areas continue to loose rare butterflies at an alarming rate (J. A. Thomas, 1983; C. D. Thomas, 1995, Warren, 1993). All the plans recognise that agri-environment schemes such as ESA's and Countryside Stewardship can play a fundamental role in tackling all three major problems and they may be the only mechanisms that can encourage appropriate conservation action on a sufficiently large scale. Nature reserves and other protected sites can play a crucial complimentary role in safeguarding important colonies and maintaining large populations which help ensure metapopulation survival in the long term.

ESA COVERAGE AND ECOLOGICAL BACKGROUND TO KEY SPECIES

A significant proportion of colonies of threatened grassland UK butterflies now occur within ESA boundaries and the remainder breed in habitats covered by other agri-environment schemes (Table 1). The survival of these butterflies therefore depends heavily on the take-up of such schemes and the subsequent impact on habitat suitability. For grassland butterflies, a key factor determining habitat suitability is turf height which in turn depends on grazing levels (*e.g.* Butt, 1986). Some downland species like the Adonis blue *Lysandra bellargus* and silver-spotted skipper *Hesperia comma* require very short turf while others like the marsh fritillary *Eurodryas aurinia* require taller vegetation (Table 1). Other declining butterflies like the Duke of Burgundy *Hamearis lucina* and dark-green fritillary *Argynnis aglaja* prefer even longer turf and some scrub.

Table 1. Summary of threatened grassland butterflies in the UK and their coverage by ESAs. The species included are priorities taken from the short and middle lists of the UK Biodiversity Report (DoE, 1995). NB Most sites not within ESAs are eligible for other agri-environment schemes such as Countryside Stewardship (England); Tir Cymen and Habitat Scheme (Wales); and Countryside Premium Scheme (Scotland).

Species	Habitat	Turf height required (cm)	Management required	% colonies within ESAs
Silver-spotted skipper	chalk downland	1-4 (sparse)	heavy grazing	17
Adonis blue	chalk downland	1-3	heavy grazing	*c.* 50
Silver-studded blue	heathland + calc. grassland	3-10	grazing/burning/ cutting	< 10
Large blue (reintroduced)	coastal + calc. grassland	1-4	heavy grazing	57
Marsh fritillary	damp + calc.grassland	7-20	light/mod. grazing (cattle or ponies)	28
Heath fritillary	moorland edge (Exmoor only)	5-15	light/mod. grazing (+ periodic burning?)	53
High brown fritillary	bracken slopes	-	cattle/pony grazing preferable	59
Pearl-bordered fritillary	bracken slopes + rough grassland	-	cattle/pony grazing preferable	not known

A number of threatened fritillary butterflies also breed in unimproved grassland that has a good cover of bracken *Pteridium aquilinum*, often in bracken/grass mosaics that are maintained by stock grazing, usually including cattle or ponies. On marginal hill land and lower slopes where the soils are only mildly acidic (pH 5-6), such habitats can contain an abundance of the larval food-plants, violets (usually common dog-violet, *Viola riviniana*), as well as other plants typical of a vernal woodland flora (Warren and Oates, 1995; Warren,

1995). Important butterflies include the highly threatened high brown fritillary *Argynnis adippe* and pearl-bordered fritillary *Boloria euphrosyne* (Table 1) and declining species like the small-pearl bordered fritillary *Boloria selene* and dark-green fritillary. These species were formerly widespread in coppiced woodland but have become increasingly reliant on non-woodland habitats as this traditional practice declined during the present century.

CASE STUDIES ON THE MARSH FRITILLARY

The impact of ESAs and other land enhancement schemes has recently been examined for the marsh fritillary in England (Bourn and Warren, 1995). This species is threatened throughout Europe and is protected under the Bern Convention and the EC Habitats and Species Directive. In Britain, the marsh fritillary's range has declined by over 62% although it is still quite widespread in parts of SW England and Wales (Warren, 1994). Several ESAs have been identified as key areas for the species, including Dartmoor, Blackdown Hills, Exmoor, Somerset Levels and Hills, South Wessex Downs (England), Preseli, Ynys Mon (Wales), Argyll Islands (Scotland), and West Fermanagh (N. Ireland) (Barnett and Warren, 1995).

The marsh fritillary breeds in two distinct types of habitat: damp, neutral or acidophilous grassland; and dry calcicolous grassland (mostly chalk grassland). In both habitats the main food-plant is devil's-bit scabious *Succisa pratensis* although other plants are used occasionally on calcicolous grassland. It lays its eggs in large clusters and females select larger plants, typically those growing where turf height is 8-20 cm (Warren, 1994). The species is therefore very susceptible to high grazing levels and most colonies occur where there is light, often extensive cattle grazing, or where grazing has recently been abandoned. Few sites are sheep grazed, probably because these animals are highly selective feeders and graze the food-plant preferentially rendering it unsuitable for egg-laying.

The study found that even though many of the schemes had been introduced very recently, several important sites had been entered into agreements notably within Countryside Stewardship and the Dartmoor and South Wessex Downs ESAs (Bourn and Warren, 1996). However, the impact on individual populations was variable: on some sites, the schemes had maintained populations and habitats extremely well while on others the quality of the habitat and hence the size of the population had fallen considerably. The most common problem arose through the introduction of heavy grazing, which was considered necessary to control scrub and coarse grasses when restoring neglected sites. While this may bring about the most rapid botanical benefits, the sudden change can be disastrous for butterflies like the marsh fritillary which require an intermediate length turf and is likely to be harmful to other invertebrates which also need structural diversity (*e.g.* Fry and Lonsdale, 1991; Kirby, 1992).

Another problem was that the stocking rates required to maintain a suitable sward structure varied considerably from site to site, in response to factors such as location and soil productivity. For example, a stocking rate that may be highly suitable on sheltered sites with good grass growth, can be far too high on exposed or very wet sites. In addition, selective grazing was found to be detrimental on a few sites where cattle had grazed herb-rich parts of a field very heavily, thereby eliminating suitable food-plants, while coarser herb-poor vegetation was untouched. This problem is due partly to the use of modern breeds which are more selective and reluctant to eat coarse vegetation.

Some of the most beneficial effects were where existing grazing regimes had been recognised as being suitable for a range of important wildlife species and perpetuated under ESA agreements. In South Wessex Downs ESA this has led to the very effective conservation of many key sites not only for the marsh fritillary but also for other threatened species like the Adonis blue and Duke of Burgundy.

DISCUSSION & CONCLUSIONS

General impact on threatened butterflies

Agri-environment schemes appear to be attractive to farmers, with widespread uptake, (Morris and Potter, 1995) and have generally been successful in slowing the recent rapid loss of unimproved grassland and beginning the process of habitat restoration. However, our preliminary study shows that their impact on marsh fritillary populations has been variable. We are aware of only one marsh fritillary colony becoming extinct through a site entering a land enhancement scheme but several have been reduced to critically low levels due to inappropriate management, usually over grazing. This is a particular problem in restoring neglected sites where high grazing levels are considered both necessary to control the scrub and desirable on botanical grounds. However such grazing regimes are disastrous for the marsh fritillary which needs intermediate turf height, and is no doubt damaging for many other invertebrates which also need structural diversity in the sward.

Within the ESA's there appears to have been relatively little impact on marsh fritillary colonies yet, because most of the relevant areas were only designated in the last few years (Bourn and Warren, 1996). Many of the sites entered have had little or no effective restriction or management change but some have been brought back into management.

An important distinction of the ESA's is the whole farm approach which, where applied imaginatively can link areas of semi natural habitat and generally improve the environment of the farm. This is already being achieved by encouraging downland restoration in strategic areas within the South Wessex Downs ESA. The direct benefit to the marsh fritillary and other priority butterflies is likely to be marginal for many years, but the measures will undoubtedly help maintain the viability of populations and metapopulations in the long term. Little comparative information is available on other priority butterflies and the impact is likely to be highly variable between species, according to how closely their habitat requirements match those being encouraged within ESAs. It is clearly important that this impact is monitored so that schemes can be improved as they develop.

Monitoring

With the exception of a butterfly monitoring programme on the South Wessex Downs ESA, none of the agri-environment schemes in our study monitored invertebrates (Bourn and Warren, 1996). Data on marsh fritillary populations (largely gathered by volunteers) have demonstrated that monitoring is vital for schemes which have a widespread impact on the breeding habitats, especially invertebrates which are strongly influenced by vegetation structure (Thomas, 1984; Kirby, 1992). There is a strong case for targeting additional monitoring at biodiversity priorities such as the marsh fritillary, as they are within management grants administered by the Dartmoor National Park. Clearly, more resources need to be allocated to the biological monitoring of invertebrate populations generally so that the schemes can be adjusted for this major group and help achieve biodiversity targets set out in the steering group report (DOE, 1995).

Maintaining environmentally beneficial farming systems in the long term

While historical reasons for decline continue to be important for threatened butterflies, a crucial factor determining their future survival is how appropriate agricultural systems can be maintained in the long term. Many unimproved, rough grassland sites are unsuitable for commercial breeds and appropriate grazing regimes can presently be impractical for the farmer. ESA's thus have an important role in maintaining whole agricultural systems that will encourage sustainable management for biodiversity.

The need for targeting and specialist advice

Our study on the marsh fritillary has also highlighted the fact that stocking rates need to be highly flexible and adapted to the specific nature and productivity of the sites concerned. We are therefore keen to stress the need for more widespread monitoring programmes with appropriately qualified staff. It may also be far preferable to specify grazing limits with respect to turf-height rather than stocking rates, as this would automatically take account of site productivity and would maintain better structural diversity in the sward for invertebrates like the marsh fritillary.

There is a close similarity between total areas eligible for schemes and the proportion of marsh fritillary sites entered, which suggests that the general habitat approach is picking up many important butterfly sites. However, in very few cases have the presence of marsh fritillary had any affect on the type of regime paid for under the scheme which probably explains the rather mixed affect on populations. There is no doubt that the management schemes which have worked best for the marsh fritillary are those that have had trained personel and a commitment to monitor and assess their biological impact. We consider that the scheme run by the Dartmoor National Park, now run in collaboration with the ESA, is an exemplary model of how biodiversity targets can be attained at the landscape scale while catering for individual priority species.

REFERENCES
BARNETT L.K. and WARREN M.S. (1995) Species Action Plan: marsh fritillary *Eurodryas aurinia*. Butterfly Conservation. Wareham, Dorset.
BOURN N.A.D. and WARREN M.S. (1996) The impact of land enhancement schemes on the marsh fritillary butterfly, *Eurodryas aurinia:* A preliminary review in England. Butterfly Conservation. Wareham, Dorset.
BUTTERFLIES UNDER THREAT TEAM. (1986) *The management of chalk grassland for butterflies.* Peterborough, NCC.
DEPARTMENT OF THE ENVIRONMENT. (1995) *Biodiversity: The UK steering group report.* London: HMSO.

FRY R. and LONSDALE D. (1991) *Habitat conservation for insects - a neglected green issue.* Middlesex: The Amateur Entomologists' Society.

GILPIN M. and HANSKI I. (1991) *Metapopulation dynamics: Empirical and theoretical investigations.* London. Academic Press.

KIRBY P. (1992) *Habitat management for invertebrates: a practical handbook.* Bedfordshire, Royal Society for the Protection of Birds.

MORRIS C. and POTTER C. (1995) Recruiting the New Conservationists: Farmers' Adoption of Agri-environmental Schemes in the UK. *Journal of Rural Studies*, 11, 51-63.

THOMAS C.D. (1995) Ecology and conservation of butterfly metapopulations in the fragmented British landscape. In: Pullin A. S. *Ecology and Conservation of Butterflies.* pp. 46-63. London. Chapman and Hall.

THOMAS J.A. (1984) The conservation of butterflies in temperate countries: past efforts and lessons for the future. In : Vane-Wright R. I. and Ackery P.R. (Eds). *The biology of butterflies.* pp. 333-353. Symposium of the Royal Entomological Society, 11, London: Academic press.

THOMAS J.A. (1991) Rare species conservation: case studies of European butterflies. In: Spellerburg, I.F., Goldsmith, F.B., and Morris, M.G. (Eds) *The scientific management of temperate communities for conservation* pp. 149-197. Oxford: Blackwells.

WARREN M.S. (1993) A review of butterfly conservation in central southern Britain: 1. Protection, evaluation and extinction on prime sites. *Biological Conservation*, 64, 25-35.

WARREN M.S. (1994) The UK status and metapopulation structure of a threatened European butterfly, the marsh fritillary *Eurodryas aurinia. Biological Conservation*, 67, 239-249.

WARREN M.S. (1995) Managing local microclimates for the high brown fritillary, *Argynnis adippe.* In: Pullin A.S. *Ecology and Conservation of Butterflies.* pp. 198-210. London. Chapman and Hall.

WARREN M.S. and OATES M.R. (1995) The importance of bracken habitats to fritillary butterflies and their management for conservation. In: Smith R. T. and Taylor J. A. (Eds) *Bracken: An environmental issue.* pp. 178-181. International bracken group special publication 2. Aberystwyth, University of Wales.

WARREN M.S., BARNETT L.K., GIBBONS D.W. and AVERY M.I. (in press). Assessing national conservation priorities: and improved red list of British butterflies. *Biological Conservation.*

The Selection of Grazing Marshes by Breeding Birds

S. PEEL [1], T.P. MILSOM [2] and S.D. LANGTON [2]

[1] ADAS Bridgets, Martyr Worthy, Winchester, SO21 1AP

[2] Central Science Laboratory (MAFF), Sand Hutton, York, YO4 1LZ

INTRODUCTION

Wet grazing marsh is a key habitat for wildlife, particularly birds, and is currently subject to a Biodiversity Action Plan (Anon, 1995). The largest area of grazing marsh in England and Wales is in North Kent, but between 1935 and 1982 this area fell by 40%, mainly by conversion to arable. ESA designation provides an opportunity to reverse this trend and to increase the wildlife value of the remaining grassland.

Marshes vary due to their surface topography, wetness, accessibility, fertility, cutting/grazing management, and type of livestock. The relationships between these factors, and their consequences for wildlife, are poorly understood since the extensive grazing of lowland wet grasslands, particularly on marine clay soils, has received little research effort. Yet soil conditions, and the timing and severity of grazing, have a profound influence on the structure and composition, and hence the conservation value, of such swards. Guidelines for farmers need to allow flexibility to respond to changes in soil conditions and herbage growth, and be compatible with the requirements of livestock production systems.

The management of the North Kent ESA is currently being addressed by a project with the following objectives:

(i)   To characterise the management of grazing marshes in the North Kent ESA, and assess the scope for flexibility in existing regimes.

(ii)   To assess the impact of management on sward height and structure, and the consequences for field selection by birds.

(iii)   To construct models of the relationships between grazing regime, site factors and selection of fields by birds, to predict the consequences of changes to management and habitat.

(iv)   To suggest new guidelines to improve wildlife value whilst enabling viable livestock production systems to be practised.

METHODS

A case study approach has been adopted. On each of 19 holdings, interviews were held throughout 1995 and 1996. The farmer, and grazier where necessary, were asked in detail about past and present management at both the whole farm and individual field (marsh) level. Each field was surveyed, between late March and early May, and again between late May and early June in both 1995 and 1996, to assess its physical and sward characteristics. The total number of fields surveyed in 1995 was 528, covering exactly 3000 ha. This represented 40% of the grassland area within the ESA boundary. Two thirds of the fields were in ESA agreement; of the remainder the majority were in English Nature management agreements. Sward height was measured using the HFRO swardstick (Hodgson et al., 1986); giving an accuracy of better than ± 1.0 cm. Sward heterogeneity was expressed by estimating the frequency and size of 'tussocks', a tussock being defined as any area of sward more than 50mm above the surrounding sward. In North Kent tussocks are similar in composition to the rest of the sward, rather than being comprised of *Juncus, Deschampsia* or other unpalatable species. Observations of bird numbers and breeding behaviour were made on every marsh on three occasions between March and May in both 1995 and 1996, using the mapping method (Bibby *et al.*, 1992). The relationship between the distribution of birds and grazing marsh habitat were modelled using a Generalised Linear Mixed Modelling (GLMM) procedure which allowed for the spatial arrangement of the fields in our sample (Breslow and Clayton, 1993)

RESULTS
Physical and sward features
On average there were 28 fields per holding, each of 5.7 ha. Forty-one per cent of fields were less than 4 ha and 40% were between 4 ha and 8 ha. Only 37 fields - 7% of the sample - were greater than 12 ha in size.

The North Kent marshes are almost entirely flat. However, topographical features, on a scale of a few centimetres to a metre or two, are an essential characteristic of the marshes. Much of this relief is due to old water channels, or rills, formed when the land was saltmarsh, and 57% of the fields had many or abundant rills assessed both in the field and from aerial photographs.

Table 1.   Sward height.

| | | Percentage of fields | | |
| | 1995 | | 1996 | |
Sward height (cm)	April	Nov	April	May/June
>2	7	<1	7	<1
2-4	29	10	46	18
4-6	24	23	28	29
6-8	16	33	14	15
8-10	14	24	4	14
10-12	5	6	<1	7
12-14	3	2	<1	3
14-16	<1	1	<1	3
16-18	0	<1	0	2
18-20	<1	0	0	1
>20	1	<1	0	7
	100	100	100	100

Winter 1994/5 was very wet, and in April 1995, 67% of fields had some standing water.

On 14% of fields it covered 5% or more of their surface area. By May/June 29% of fields still had some standing water, though on the majority of these it covered <1% of the surface area. Although winter 1995/6 was drier, the spring was cold so drying took place more slowly. Consequently the proportion of fields with standing water in 1996 was similar to 1995.

In April 1995 the mean sward height was 6.1 cm. Table 1 shows that on 60% of fields sward height was less than 6 cm, the minimum height normally recommended for growing cattle. In April 1996 mean sward height was 4.5 cm, even shorter than April 1995, with 81% less than 6 cm and 53% less than 4 cm, the minimum height normally recommended for ewes with lambs. A further assessment was made between mid-May and mid-June. Mean height had increased to 8.6 cm.

Assessments of tussock size and frequency are indicative of sward heterogeneity and hence the complexity of the habitat. Tussock frequency is shown in Table 2.

Table 2.   Tussock frequency.

Frequency	(ground covered by tussocks)	Percentage of fields				
		1995			1996	
		April	May	Nov	April	May
None	(0)	17	14	16	21	21
Sparse	(<5%)	6	7	12	24	21
Occasional	(5-15%)	21	22	25	24	29
Frequent	(15-35%)	44	43	34	19	17
Abundant	(>35%)	6	9	9	4	1
Localised*		6	5	4	8	11
		100	100	100	100	100

* Tussocks restricted to only part of the field.

There was a wide range of tussock frequencies throughout the study period. On the majority of fields throughout 1995 they were either frequent or occasional. In 1996 frequency had declined, and there were more fields where tussocks were sparse or absent. The size of the great majority of tussocks was between 50 and 200mm above the height of the surrounding sward. However, size declined following the dry summer of 1995, only showing some sign of increasing again by May 1996.

Effect of management on swards

There were very highly significant differences ($P<0.001$) in April 1995 between the heights of swards that farmers stated had been regularly grazed by different species of livestock prior to the study. Cattle grazed swards were more than twice the height of those grazed by sheep, with mixed grazing intermediate. The effect of grazing remained very highly significant even when the differences between farms were removed. This relationship was repeated even more strongly in April 1996.

146

Type of livestock also affects sward structure. Under sheep-only grazing almost 50% of swards had no tussocks whereas under most other combinations of livestock tussocks were absent from only 10% of swards. Furthermore on cattle grazed swards more than 60% of swards had large or medium-sized tussocks, whereas under sheep less than 10% fell in these categories, the great majority of tussocks being small.

Fields were categorised by previous history of supplementary feeding; on only 10% of fields where no feeding was practised were there no tussocks in April 1995. Where feeding was carried out, even in some years only, almost 50% of fields had no tussocks. A similar trend was apparent in April 1996 when feeding over the previous winter was examined.

Breeding birds

The quality of the marshes as breeding habitat for ground-nesting species varied considerably; in 1995, 73 fields (17%) held no birds at all, whereas the greatest number of species breeding in any one field was 14. The relationship between the number of species per field in 1995 and habitat variables above was modelled using a Poisson GLMM procedure. The model predicted that the fields **least** likely to hold any breeding birds at all tended to be small (<4 ha), dry by early June, adjacent to roads, under national grid powerlines, with very short swards in April (<2 cm) which lacked tussocks. In contrast, those fields holding the **greatest** number of species tended to be large (>12ha), distant from roads, not under powerlines, with the bottoms of rills and hollows still wet in June, and with moderately tall swards in April (>10cm) which comprised many tussocks.

The relationships between the distribution of selected breeding bird species in 1995 and the habitat variables were modelled using a binomial GLMM procedure.

Table 3. Factors affecting distribution of bird species : binomial Generalised Linear Mixed Models (GLMM).

	Lapwing		Redshank		Skylark		Meadow pipit	
	1995	1996	1995	1996	1995	1996	1995	1996
Sward height (cm)	*	*					**	**
Frequency of tussocks	*		*		***	**	**	**
Abundance of rills	(*)	***						
Field area (ha)	***	***	***	***	***	***	***	***
Wetness of rills in May/June			**	**				
Distance to road			(*)	*	***	**	**	**
Type of boundary					***	***	***	***
Presence of power lines					**	***	***	

Notes: (*) $0.1>P>0.05$; * $P<0.05$; ** $P<0.01$; *** $P<0.001$

Models were constructed for the four most widespread bird species, including lapwing (*Vanillus vanellus*) and redshank (*Tringa totanus*) which are key indicators for the North Kent ESA. They were then refitted to the data for 1996.

Eight habitat variables were included in the habitat selection models (Table 3). Seven occurred in more than one species model. Though the explanatory power of field area was very strong in all the models, the effect was probably stochastic due to the unequal size of the sampling units. Larger marshes are more likely to be occupied by chance than smaller ones.

The models implied that height and structure of the grass swards were important determinants of the suitability of the fields for the four bird species, though this needs to be confirmed by behavioural studies and experiment. For all four bird species, fields with a greater frequency of tussocks were more likely to be occupied. Tussock size did not appear in any model but it was correlated with frequency. Sward height was significant for lapwing, which preferred short swards (<2 cm in April), and meadow pipit (*Anthus pratensis*) which preferred taller swards (>10 cm). The combination of terms describing sward structure was the same in the 1995 and 1996 models for skylark (*Alauda arvensis*) and meadow pipit. For lapwing and redshank however, tussock abundance was significant in 1995 but not in 1996 due to the fact that both species occupied a higher proportion of fields which lacked tussocks in the second year. The distributions of lapwing and redshank in April 1996 were, however, positively correlated with the abundance of tussocks the preceding November.

Rills are a prominent feature of the surface topography of many grazing marshes and they contain most of the spring flood water. Even so, the abundance of rills, as a factor positively related to bird settlement, was only included in the models for lapwing.

The maintenance of high water levels in spring is perceived to be an important issue in the management of marshes for nesting birds. However, of the four most widespread species, a significant preference for field wetness in June was shown only by redshank.

FURTHER DEVELOPMENT OF ESA GUIDELINES

The modelling identified eight habitat variables which appear to influence the pattern of settlement by ground nesting birds. Two of the variables, (sward height and frequency of tussocks) can be manipulated within the current ESA prescriptions. Surface wetness can also be manipulated, and is encouraged by higher payments, but North Kent has very low annual rainfall (c.550mm) and very limited groundwater reserves so that there may be little prospect of increased wetness on the majority of fields. A further two variables, (the size of fields and types of boundary) could be manipulated but only by using drastic land management such as hedge removal, which would contravene the spirit, if not the letter, of the ESA prescriptions. The density of rills could probably be increased although the techniques for doing this are still at the experimental stage. The proximity of marshes to roads and National Grid powerlines lie beyond the control of individual landowners. Given the combined effects of the five topographical and human disturbance variables and the limited scope for their manipulation, targetting of fields may well be desirable when applying management prescriptions for ground-nesting birds.

Within the ranges of sward heights and frequencies of tussocks encountered in the study, the models imply that the presence of tussocks, more than sward height, is an important determinant of the suitability of grazing marshes for ground-nesting bird species. A preliminary assessment of the relationship between the occurrence of tussocks and grazing regimes suggests that year-round sheep grazing is inimical to the development of tussocks; at present the grazing prescriptions do not specify the type of stock that can be run on the marshes. The results also suggest that supplementary feeding leads to the absence of tussocks.

The ESA scheme might be further developed by the formulation of a grazing management plan for each holding. This would classify and prioritize each field according to its potential for enhancement of habitat for birds or other wildlife, as well as its value and limitations for grazing of cattle or sheep. The plan would take into account the timing and intensity of grazing, type of livestock, provision of supplementary feed and the need to gather stock. This could be supported by the development of sward-based guidelines for management. Some re-organisation of the tier structure of agreements might also be considered; if reduced grazing pressure is required on marshes with most wildlife potential, then increased grazing pressure and limited fertilizer inputs might be allowed on those with little potential. Levels of payment would need to reflect the differences in the extent of income foregone.

ACKNOWLEDGEMENTS

This project is funded by the Conservation Management Division of MAFF Countryside Group. We thank Bill Parkin, Julie Bishop, Justin Hart and Niall Moore for undertaking the great majority of the fieldwork. We also thank the RSPB and the Kent Trust for Nature Conservation for provision of bird data.

REFERENCES

ANON (1995), Biodiversity Steering Group Report Vol. 2; Action Plans, HMSO, London.
BIBBY C.J., BURGESS N.D. and HILL D.A. (1992). *Bird census techniques*. Academic Press, London.
BRESLOW N.E. and CLAYTON D.G. (1993). Approximate inference in generalised linear mixed models. *Journal of American Statistical Association,* 88, 9-25.
HODGSON J., MACKIE C.K., and PARKER J.W.G. (1986). Sward surface heights for efficient grazing. *Grass Farmer*, 24, 5-10.

Conservation and Management of *Molinia* and *Juncus* Pastures in Wales, with Reference to Agri-Environment Schemes

T. H. BLACKSTOCK, D. P. STEVENS and M. J. M. YEO
Countryside Council for Wales, Penrhos Road, Bangor, Gwynedd LL57 2LQ

INTRODUCTION

Wet pasture habitats, characteristically with communities dominated by *Molinia caerulea*, *Juncus acutiflorus* and other tall *Juncus* species, have become a focus of increasing conservation attention in the lowlands of western Britain. Such wet grassland is widely distributed in the Atlantic fringes of Europe, but in many regions its constituent communities have become extremely scarce, primarily due to agricultural intensification (e.g. Sissingh, 1978). On the Devon Culm Measures in south-west England, it is estimated that there has been a reduction in the cover of wet pasture complexes of almost 90% since 1900, with some 3,600 ha surviving in the early 1990s (Wolton, 1994). The need to provide enhanced conservation measures has most recently been recognized in a special conservation plan for *Molinia* and *Juncus* pastures formulated as part of the UK Biodiversity Action Plan (UK Government, 1995).

In Wales, *Molinia* and *Juncus* communities are widely distributed in both the lowland agricultural zone and the unenclosed uplands. They commonly occur on peaty gleys or shallow peat soils, in moist acidic to mildly base-rich conditions, but may also develop over deep peats. This habitat is accorded protection in Environmentally Sensitive Areas (ESAs) and other agri-environment schemes, as well as in special conservation sites. In this brief review, variation in the cover and conservation significance of wet pastures in Wales is assessed; farming and conservation management are considered in relation to possible future refinements in ESAs and similar schemes.

WET GRASSLAND COVER IN WALES

A substantial body of data on the distribution and abundance of *Molinia* and *Juncus* wet grassland in Wales has been recorded during survey work in the 1980s and 1990s by the Nature Conservancy Council (NCC) and its successor body the Countryside Council for Wales (CCW). Following a survey of plant community cover in the major upland ranges, a comprehensive survey of lowland habitats (adopting the classification in NCC, 1990) is almost complete. From the latter findings, semi-natural lowland grasslands are selected for more refined community-based survey and inventory; sites with 0.5 ha or more of scarce communities or at least 5.0 ha of more common communities are included. Community classification follows the new National Vegetation Classification, and wet pasture types (characterized in Rodwell, 1991) in Wales are outlined in Table 1.

Table 1.   *Molinia* and *Juncus* pasture communities in Wales. Community nomenclature and codes follow Rodwell (1991).

Community	Number of sub-communities	Frequency	Distribution
Juncus subnodulosus-Cirsium palustre fen-meadow (M22)	3	Rare	Restricted to lowland base-rich fens and grasslands
Juncus effusus/ acutiflorus - Galium palustre pasture (M23)	2	Frequent	Widespread rush-pasture in the lowlands and sub-montane zone
Molinia caerulea-Cirsium dissectum fen-meadow (M24)	2 (+ distinctive intermediate stands)	Occasional	Confined to mildly base-rich wet grasslands and fens in the lowlands
Molinia caerulea-Potentilla erecta pasture (M25)	3 (+unclassified spp-poor stands)	Frequent	In western wet grass-land and fen complexes, extending from the low-lands to the sub-montane, especially abundant in the mid and south Wales uplands
Molinia caerulea-Crepis paludosa pasture (M26)	1	Very rare	Found only in a handful of lowland and upland fringe sites in north Wales

Overall, some 31,000 ha of lowland wet pasture have been recently mapped in the Welsh lowlands; this mostly comprises 'marshy grassland', together with a small amount of 'wet modified bog' (*sensu* NCC, 1990). For the uplands the equivalent figure is 49,000 ha which includes large expanses of species-poor *Molinia* vegetation and is mostly based on data following Ratcliffe and Birks (1980), as well as some survey using NCC (1990). In both cases, the data refer mainly to communities in Table 1.

Broad-scale geographical variation in the cover of wet grasslands in the lowlands is summarized for 12 survey areas in Fig.1. There is a preponderance of lowland wet pasture in western districts, with far less in the eastern borders; the west part of the south Wales coalfield has an especially high concentration. Within the uplands, there is similarly low cover in the east, but *Molinia* cover increases from north to south showing an inverse pattern to trends in the extent of near-natural blanket bog habitat (Yeo, in press).

Fig. 1.   Cover of lowland wet pasture habitat in 12 survey areas in Wales.

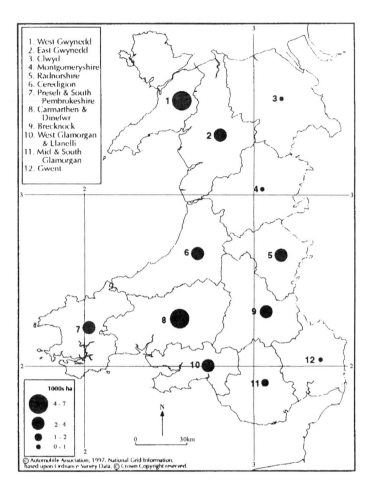

CONSERVATION ASSESSMENT

Molinia and *Juncus acutiflorus* communities in the north-west Atlantic zone have distinctive floristic features which distinguish them from analogous wet grasslands in Continental Europe and the Iberian Peninsula (de Foucault and Géhu, 1980). Examples of Atlantic taxa characteristic of Welsh wet pastures are given in Table 2, which also includes certain scarce British plant species found in this habitat. Many of these restricted species appear to have a moderately wide ecological range in western Britain and are not normally restricted to a particular community. But it is noteworthy that most of the taxa included in Table 2 are almost completely confined to lowland sites. Likewise, the least common communities are also absent from the uplands (Table 1).

Table 2. Examples of Atlantic and uncommon British plant species recorded from Welsh *Molinia* and *Juncus* pasture communities.

Atlantic taxa		
Carum verticillatum	*Genista anglica*	*Sibthorpia europaea*
Cirsium dissectum	*Hypericum undulatum*	*Wahlenbergia hederacea*
Dactylorhiza praetermissa	*Scorzonera humilis*	
Dactylorhiza purpurella	*Scutellaria minor*	
Other uncommon and rare British taxa		
Carex montana	*Osmunda regalis*	*Trollius europaeus*
Dactylorhiza incarnata	*Platanthera bifolia*	
Gymnadenia conopsea	*Scapania paludicola*	

The fauna of *Molinia* and *Juncus* pastures has not been thoroughly investigated, but preliminary survey work has demonstrated the presence of diverse and distinctive invertebrate assemblages in lowland Wales (Fowles, 1994). Various scarce and declining taxa have been reported, including the marsh fritillary butterfly (*Eurodryas aurinia*) which has undergone a substantial range-contraction in Britain over the last 150 years (Warren, 1994). Wet pastures are also important bird habitats, especially for breeding waders (Smith, 1991).

Oceanic examples of *Molinia* and *Juncus* pasture are thus of particular conservation concern in view of their restricted and diminishing European distribution, and their associated range of rare and scarce taxa. On the other hand, this type of wet grassland can replace other less modified communities, including wet heath (Blackstock *et al.*, 1995) and rare forms of rich-fen vegetation (Meade and Blackstock, 1988) in the lowlands. There has also been extensive replacement of blanket mire and wet heath communities in the uplands by impoverished *Molinia* stands, especially in mid and south Wales (Yeo, in press). Overall then, it is in the lowlands that *Molinia* and *Juncus* pastures, with their specialist flora and fauna, assume greatest conservation significance.

Two additional features of lowland *Molinia* and *Juncus* wet pastures need to be taken into account in conservation and restoration schemes. Most of the surviving examples occur in small stands, and individual sites may exhibit considerable small-scale heterogeneity. This is reflected in high community diversity in some local sites, as in Brecknock, for example, where even very small (<5 ha) wet pasture systems usually have more that one vegetation type (Fig. 2). In many cases, *Molinia* and *Juncus* pasture is accompanied by dry grassland, flush, heath, scrub and bracken communities.

WET PASTURE MANAGEMENT IN LOWLAND WALES

Little detailed information is available on present land management practices associated with wet pasture, and even less has been documented on historical management activities. A useful

Fig. 2.   Relationship between community diversity and area at lowland damp pasture sites in Brecknock.

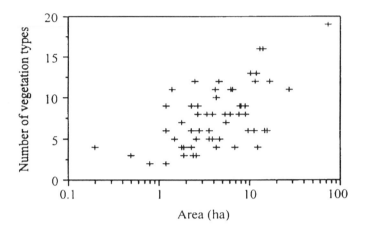

attempt was recently made by Lyons and Jones (1992) to glean information about agricultural land use for this habitat from past and current farmers at 35 Sites of Special Scientific Interest (SSSIs) in Ceredigion. Their findings are outlined in Table 3, and it should be emphasized that the results indicate trends from anecdotal sources rather than a fully accurate comparative data-set. The immediate impression is that there was formerly much more varied activity than today when most sites are primarily used as rough grazing for cattle and horses, and less so for sheep, with associated activities almost restricted to occasional ditch maintenance. In the past, parts of the wet pasture sites were more frequently burnt (mostly during the winter to remove litter), *Juncus* stands were often cut (in late summer with the cut material used for bedding), and scrub clearance has also been commonplace. Peat cutting took place up to the early part of the 20th century. Ploughing and reseeding were reported for dry sections of 14 sites, which had also received fertiliser application and often lime; these mostly represent earlier attempts at grassland improvement during the first half of the 20th century. Absence of recent agricultural intensification has undoubtedly been beneficial from a conservation standpoint, but cessation of scrub clearance and perhaps other activities may be detrimental.

The comparative uniformity of modern management is further indicated by analysis of treatment recorded at quadrat samples from *Molinia* and *Juncus* communities at lowland sites in different parts of Wales (Table 4). As sites were sampled with varying intensity, the data again suggest trends rather than absolute frequencies. But there is a high degree of consistency among the major types of *Molinia* and *Juncus* pasture; in each case cattle are the most frequent livestock, followed by horses, while sheep are somewhat less frequent. Hay making and other activities are infrequent. The commoner *Juncus-Galium* and *Molinia-Potentilla* pastures in particular are occasionally unmanaged.

The similarity in management between the main communities also points to ecological factors rather than present-day treatment effects as major controlling influences. Analysis of soil data from a range of lowland sites across Wales has revealed correlation between community type and gradients of base-enrichment and to a lesser extent major nutrients (N and P), but none of the vegetation types is associated with fertile soils (Stevens *et al., 1994*).

Table 3. Past and present management practices on *Molinia-Juncus* pastures in Ceredigion. All locations are Sites of Special Scientific Interest. Data summarized from Lyons and Jones (1992).

Management	Number of sites (n=35)	
	Past	Present (post 1990)
Burning	20	3
Peat cutting	13	-
Scrub clearance	16	1
Juncus cutting	16	-
Mowing	13	4
Ploughing	14	-
Reseeding	14	-
Fertiliser application	17	1
Liming	9	-
Ditch maintenance	22	11
Livestock - Cattle	31	27
- Horses	27	24
- Sheep	22	19

CURRENT CONSERVATION MEASURES

Although development of active conservation measures for lowland *Molinia* and *Juncus* pasture habitats in Wales and elsewhere has been relatively tardy in comparison with many other habitats, there has been significant recent progress. Wolton (1994) reported that approximately 50% of the remnant cover of wet pasture on the Culm Measures in south-west

England is protected, principally under a Wildlife Enhancement Scheme in SSSIs and through Countryside Stewardship measures.

Information for Wales is summarized in Table 5. By 1994, somewhat under 2,000 ha was within 250 SSSIs across lowland Wales where the habitat is targeted for selection, whereas over 16,000 ha was within less than 40 upland SSSIs mostly selected for the presence of different moorland habitats (Blackstock *et al.*, 1996). Over 3,000 ha is managed under Tir Cymen, a 'whole-farm' agri-environment scheme developed by CCW for three trial districts (CCW, 1996). Unfortunately, protected habitat cover specifically for wet pastures is not currently available for the six ESAs in Wales, nor for the Habitat, Moorland and Organic Aid Schemes.

Table 4. Management (% frequency) recorded for quadrat samples of lowland *Molinia* and *Juncus* communities at localities in south (Gwent and Glamorgan), central (Brecknock and Dinefwr) and north (Anglesey, Arfon and Dwyfor) Wales, by NCC and CCW (1987-93).

	Juncus-Cirsium meadow (M22)	*Juncus-Galium* pasture (M23)	*Molinia-Cirsium* meadow (M24)	*Molinia-Potentilla* pasture (M25)
Pasture	74	83	88	78
Cattle (C)	33	39	36	32
Horse (H)	15	16	17	18
Sheep (S)	7	10	12	14
C + H	-	5	5	4
C + S	15	5	9	7
H + S	-	1	3	2
C + H + S	4	-	1	1
Hay cutting	26	3	4	1
Burning	-	2	1	5
Unmanaged	-	11	6	14
No. of samples	27	396	572	564
No. of sites	12	204	196	204

DISCUSSION

ESAs and similar schemes which integrate modern farming and wildlife conservation potentially have a key role in the survival and possible expansion of lowland *Molinia* and *Juncus* pastures in Wales and other parts of their European range.

Proposals for promoting conservation of 13,500 ha of this wet pasture habitat are put forward in the UK Government's (1995) Habitat Action Plan by further protection of existing stands in special conservation sites and by the extension of agri-environment measures; it is also proposed that a further 500 ha should be newly established. Attention is mostly directed at lowland sites; in the uplands conservation measures more often aim to reduce the extent of *Molinia* vegetation and to restore bog and heath communities. Major features of Welsh wet pastures that need to be taken into account in conservation schemes include the following.

- Fragmentation and isolation of surviving examples in the lowlands.
- Small-scale ecological diversity in lowland wet pasture complexes.
- Association of wet pasture with cattle and horse grazing.
- Increasing management neglect.
- Low levels of soil fertility.
- Unfavourable expansion of *Molinia* grassland in moorland habitats in the uplands, and rich fens and wet heaths in the lowlands.

Table 5.   Wet pasture in SSSIs and under Tir Cymen management in Wales. Data from Blackstock *et al.* (1996) and CCW (1996).

Sites of Special Scientific Interest (SSSIs) in 1994

	No.sites	Cover of marshy grassland (ha)
Lowland SSSIs	255	1,802
Upland SSSIs	38	16,688

Tir Cymen in April 1996

	Cover of lowland marshy grassland (ha)
Meirionnydd	1,500
Dinefwr	1,520
Swansea	154

Localized measures for nature conservation are increasingly being advocated for agri-environment schemes. In Wales, it would be especially appropriate to provide strong and wide-ranging incentives for lowland *Molinia* and *Juncus* pastures in their western and other strongholds (Fig.1). Even within particular districts, specific habitat provisions may be favourably localized within selected catchments.

Research requirements to develop favourable wet grassland management and manipulation are considered by Tallowin and Mountford (this volume). Experimental attempts at habitat restoration and development of *Molinia* and *Juncus* pastures from agricultural land have begun in Britain, but are less advanced than in the Netherlands, especially for *Cirsio-Molinietum* grasslands which were often traditionally managed for hay but have dwindled considerably. Soil acidification, eutrophication and drainage influence restoration potential. Turf-stripping ('sod cutting') and manipulation of drainage systems have proved successful in some circumstances in restoring *Cirsio-Molinietum* from agricultural land and other habitats, but in other cases unsuitable hydrological conditions and high P levels have proved intractable (Jansen *et al.*, 1996; Jansen and Roelofs, 1996). Proximity of propagule sources, or seed-bank availability, to provide inocula for community development can also be critical (Berendse *et al.*, 1992). An experimental approach, supported by CCW, at restoring wet grassland from improved agricultural pasture is being undertaken adjacent to a *Molinia-Juncus* mosaic at Rhos Llawr-cwrt National Nature Reserve (W.A. Adams and G. Roughley, in progress); reduction in soil fertility is being attempted by cutting and removing vegetation, herbicide application to remove *Trifolium repens* (and restrict N-fixation), and addition of $Al_2 (SO_4)_3$ to reduce P availability.

ACKNOWLEDGEMENTS

We gratefully acknowledge the contribution of our colleagues to the recent programme of CCW vegetation survey in Wales. We particularly thank Clare Mockridge and Carrie Rimes for helping to collate data, and Keith Jones and Mary Roddick for preparing figures.

REFERENCES

BERENDSE F., OOMES M.J.M., ALTENA H.J. and ELBERSE W.Th. (1992) Experiments on the restoration of species-rich meadows in The Netherlands. *Biological Conservation, 62*, 59-65.

BLACKSTOCK T.H., STEVENS J.P., HOWE E.A. and STEVENS D.P. (1995) Changes in the extent and fragmentation of heathland and other semi-natural habitats between 1920-22 and 1987-88 in the Llŷn Peninsula, Wales, UK. *Biological Conservation, 72*, 33-44.

BLACKSTOCK T.H., STEVENS D.P. and HOWE E.A. (1996) Biological components of Sites of Special Scientific Interest in Wales. *Biodiversity and Conservation, 5*, 897-920.

COUNTRYSIDE COUNCIL FOR WALES. (1996) *Tir Cymen - Four Years' Achievement.* Bangor: Countryside Council for Wales.

DE FOUCAULT B. et GEHU J-M. (1980) Essai synsystematique et chorologique sur les prairies à *Molinia coerulea* et *Juncus acutiflorus* de l'Europe occidentale. [A synsystematic and chorological account of *Molinia caerulea* and *Juncus acutiflorus* meadows in western Europe]. *Colloques Phytosociologiques*, 7, 135-164d.

FOWLES A.P. (1994) *Invertebrates of Wales.* Peterborough: Joint Nature Conservation Committee.

JANSEN A.J.M., DE GRAAF M.C.C. and ROELOFS J.G.M. (1996) The restoration of species-rich heathland communities in the Netherlands. *Vegetatio, 126*, 73-88.

JANSEN A.J.M. and ROELOFS J.G.M. (1996) Restoration of *Cirsio-Molinietum* wet meadows by sod cutting. *Ecological Engineering*, 7, 279-298.

LYONS J. and JONES R.W. (1992) *Ceredigion Grassland SSSI. Survey of Past and Present Management and Photomonitoring.* Dyfed Wildlife Trust.

MEADE R. and BLACKSTOCK T.H. (1988) The impact of drainage on the distribution of rich-fen plant communities in two Anglesey basins. *Wetlands, 8*, 159-177.

NATURE CONSERVANCY COUNCIL. (1990) *Handbook for Phase 1 Habitat Survey.* Peterborough: Nature Conservancy Council.

RATCLIFFE D.A. and BIRKS H.J.B. (1980) *Classification of Upland Vegetation Types in Britain.* Peterborough: Nature Conservancy Council.

RODWELL J.S. (Ed) (1991) *British Plant Communities. Vol.2. Mires and Heaths.* Cambridge: Cambridge University Press.

SISSINGH G. (1978) Le *Cirsio-Molinietum* Sissingh et de Vries (1942) 1946 dans les Pays-Bas. [*Cirsio-Molinietum* Sissingh and de Vries (1942) 1946 in the Low Countries]. *Colloques Phytosociologiques*, 5, 289-301.

SMITH K.W. (1991) Breeding waders of damp lowland grassland in Britain and Ireland. *Wader Study*

Group Bulletin, 61 (Supplement), 33-35.

STEVENS P.A., BRITTAIN S.A., HUGHES S., SPARKS T.H. and WORTH J. (1994) *Soil/Plant Interactions in Lowland Grassland*. Bangor: Institute of Terrestrial Ecology.

UK GOVERNMENT. (1995) *Biodiversity: the UK Steering Group Report*. London: HMSO.

WARREN M.S. (1994) The UK status and suspected metapopulation structure of a threatened European butterfly, the marsh fritillary *Eurodryas aurinia*. *Biological Conservation*, 67, 239-249.

WOLTON R.J. (1994) Conservation of the Culm Grasslands of South-west England. *Grassland Management and Nature Conservation, Occasional Symposium of the British Grassland Society,* No.28, pp. 320-322.

YEO M.J.M. (in press) Blanket bog degradation in Wales. In: Hulme P.D., Tallis J.H. and Meade, R. (Eds). *Blanket Mire Degradation*. Aberdeen: Macaulay Land Use Research Institute.

Multi-site Experiments on the Restoration of Botanically Diverse Grassland in ESAs

R. PYWELL, S. PEEL*, A. HOPKINS† and J. BULLOCK‡

Institute of Terrestrial Ecology, Monks Wood, Abbots Ripton, Huntingdon,
Cambridgeshire, PE17 2LS
*ADAS Bridgets, Martyr Worthy, Winchester, Hampshire, SO21 1AP
†IGER, North Wyke, Okehampton, Devon, EX20 2SB
‡Institute of Terrestrial Ecology, Furzebrook, Wareham, Dorset, BH20 5AS

INTRODUCTION

In the last fifty years there has been a marked intensification of agricultural management practices throughout Western Europe which has caused the degradation, fragmentation and loss of many species-rich grasslands (e.g. Fuller, 1986). Large areas have been cultivated and planted with arable crops or have been re-seeded with rye-grass and clover mixtures. At the same time productivity has been increased by under-drainage, and the application of fertilisers and herbicides. This has allowed earlier, repeated cutting for silage and stocking rates to be increased.

Recent changes in rural land use polices offer opportunities and financial incentives to restore diverse grassland communities on productive farmland through schemes such as the Environmentally Sensitive Areas (ESAs: Anon, 1986). Previous studies have demonstrated that the natural colonisation of such sites by desirable plant species can be a slow and unreliable process, especially when these species are absent from the seed bank and the surrounding landscape (e.g. Berendse et al., 1992: Bakker, 1989; Hutchings and Booth, 1996). In order to accelerate the re-assembly of species-rich grassland communities on such sites it may be necessary to deliberately re-introduce seed of the appropriate species, either into gaps created in grassland swards (Wells et al.,1989) or to a prepared seed bed on ex-arable land (Wells, 1989). The successful establishment of diverse grassland is dependant on a variety of environmental factors which vary at a local and region scale, including soil type, fertility and climate. It is therefore important to test the efficiency of habitat restoration methodologies over a wide a range of such variables.

This paper describes the preliminary findings from a series of multi-site experiments which compare different techniques for the restoration of species-rich grassland on former arable land and productive grassland.

METHODS

Grassland diversification experiments

Improved, permanent pastures were selected within each of the following six ESAs: South Downs, South Wessex Downs, Pennine Dales, Radnor, Blackdown Hills and Somerset Levels. The swards were relatively homogeneous and species-poor. Previous management included annual mowing, but without intensive fertiliser application or recent re-seeding. Each site was mown and the herbage removed. A total of six treatments were applied to plots measuring 6 m by 4 m in a randomised block design with four replicates. Each plot was separated by a 1 m guard row. The treatments involved different methods of disturbance followed by the introduction of seed of the desired species: 1. control; 2. seed drilling using a rotary strip-seeder with blades at 230 mm spacing; broadcast-sowing following 3. light harrowing; 4. partial rotovation to give c.50% bare ground; and 5. complete turf removal to a depth of c.30 mm using a horticultural turf cutter; finally 6. transplantation of container-grown plants (plugs) into the existing sward. Treatments 1. to 5. were applied in August 1994, treatment 6. was applied in October 1994.

The composition of the seed mixtures was based on the botanically diverse grassland communities described in the National Vegetation Classification (Rodwell, 1992) which were considered appropriate to the soil type, drainage and location of each site. Native seed of some species was not available from commercial suppliers. The seed mixtures typically comprised between 35 to 40 species, of which about 30% were grasses and 70% were forbs. The total seed rate used was 12.4 to 14.1 kg/ha of which forbs accounted for 80% by weight. Twelve forb species were introduced as plugs. These were planted in single species groups of three at a density equivalent to eight plants per m^2. The allocation of species to each patch was made on a stratified random basis. The plugs were planted into an area where a 150 mm diameter disc of turf had been removed to a depth of c.20mm. The sites were lightly grazed by sheep in October and November of that year, and again in the following spring. Livestock were removed by 15 April and hay was cut in July followed by aftermath grazing.

Arable reversion experiments

Cereal fields were selected in the following five ESAs: South Downs, South Wessex Downs, Suffolk River Valleys, Norfolk Broads and sites on both clay and limestone in the Upper Thames Tributaries. In September 1994 seven treatments were applied to plots measuring 10 m by 4 m in a randomised block design with four replicates. Each plot was separated by a 1 m guard row. These treatments involved different intensities of disturbance followed by the introduction of seed as either a simple mixture of grasses as recommended in the current ESA guidelines or as a complex seed mix based on the NVC. The ESA mix comprised 6 to 8 common grasses and was sown at 20 to 31 kg/ha. The NVC mix had a composition identical to that used for the grassland diversification experiments but the proportion of grasses was increased to account for c.80% of the total sowing rate of 24 to 28 kg/ha. Finally, the effects of companion species on seedling recruitment were investigated by sowing a tetraploid cultivar of westerwold's rye grass *(Lolium multiflorum)* sown at a rate of 20 kg/ha. The treatments were as follows: 1. control; 2. deep ploughing + ESA seed mix; 3. deep ploughing + NVC mix + companion grass; 4. deep ploughing + NVC mix; 5. minimal cultivation + ESA mix; 6. minimal cultivation + NVC mix + companion grass; 7. minimal cultivation + NVC mix. The seed bed was then harrowed and rolled. The herbage from two highly productive sites was cut and removed in the following April. All sites were cut in June to prevent the companion grass from persisting. In subsequent years the grass was cut in mid July and left for 2 to 3 days before removal. This was to allow some seed return. The sites have been grazed each autumn for 2-3 weeks by 6-12 sheep.

Monitoring

Prior to establishment, soil samples were taken from each site to estimate soil fertility. This exercise will be repeated at the end of the experiment. Seed bank determinations were made on the soil samples taken from the arable reversion sites. The fresh and dry matter production of each treatment is estimated each year at the time of hay cutting. Sub-samples of this material are sent for chemical analyses. The vegetation has been monitored in June of each year from three quadrats placed at random within each plot. The quadrats measure 400 by 400 mm and are divided into sixteen 100 by 100 mm cells. The presence of each species within each square is recorded. In addition the plots are searched for species present at low frequency.

RESULTS AND DISCUSSION

Grassland diversification experiments

The botanical diversity of the improved grassland sites at the start of the experiment was relatively variable with means of 9 species (South Wessex Downs) and 20 species (Radnor) per site (Table 1). With the exception of light harrowing (3) and plug planting (6), all of the disturbance treatments followed by the addition of a seed mixture significantly increased the number of species recorded compared to the control (1) in the first year. Turf removal and rotovation caused a significantly greater increase in diversity compared to the other treatments (Table 1). Overall the grassland of the Radnor site was significantly more diverse.

The number of species in the controls of the Radnor and Blackdown sites increased in the second year (Table 1). The controls of the other sites remained largely unchanged. The botanical diversity of the disturbance and seed addition treatments remained higher than that of the control. However, these differences were only significant at the $P < 0.05$ level for the turf removal treatment. The overall diversity of the sites was more variable in this year, with the Radnor, Pennine Dales and Blackdown Hills sites all being significantly more diverse compared to the others.

De-turfing is likely to make conditions more favourable for the establishment of the sown species by the removal of both established competitors and the seed bank of undesirable species, together with soil nutrient pools. Both de-turfing, rotovation and strip-seeding will have created many sites suitable for germination and establishment. The disturbance associated with strip seeding and rotovation treatments is likely to have increased the rates of soil nutrient mineralisation. This would have enable the established competitors to grow more rapidly and may account for the decline in the diversity of many of these plots in the second year. Conversely, light harrowing is unlikely to have created sufficiently numerous and long-lived gaps for germination. Finally, the probable reason for the failure of plug planting to increase diversity is that these species had not yet spread sufficiently within the grassland.

Table 1.   Mean number of species recorded in quadrats on the grassland diversification experiments. Means with the same letter were not considered to be significantly different ($P<0.05$) using the Student-Newman-Keuls test.

1995

Tr.	South Downs	South Wessex	Pennine Dales	Radnor	Blackdown Hills	Somerset	Mean
1.	11	9	15	20	12	17	14.0[d]
2.	19	15	15	24	17	18	18.2[bc]
3.	13	8	15	24	11	17	14.7[cd]
4.	20	17	22	31	18	18	21.0[b]
5.	21	29	19	33	25	24	25.5[a]
6.	13	12	17	26	15	18	16.8[cd]
Mean	16.5[b]	15.0[b]	17.2[b]	26.5[a]	16.3[b]	18.7[b]	

1996

Tr.	South Downs	South Wessex	Pennine Dales	Radnor	Blackdown Hills	Somerset	Mean
1.	11	8	16	28	16	15	15.7[b]
2.	12	12	19	39	18	14	19.0[b]
3.	11	8	18	34	17	15	17.2[b]
4.	14	12	23	38	21	17	20.8[b]
5.	30	29	22	43	36	24	29.0[a]
6.	9	10	18	35	20	16	18.0[b]
Mean	14.5[c]	13.2[c]	19.3[b]	36.2[a]	19.7[b]	16.8[bc]	

Arable reversion experiments

The number of species recorded in the controls of the arable reversion sites was considerably lower (4 to 7) than that recorded at the grassland diversification sites (Table 2). Over all sites the botanical diversity of the controls was significantly lower than all other treatments. Disturbance followed by the addition of the ESA seed mix (treatments 2 and 5) produced a grassland with significantly fewer species than the treatments involving the application of the diverse NVC seed mix. There were no apparent differences caused by the type of disturbance applied to the sites. Similarly, sowing a companion grass appeared to have no significant effects on plant diversity across all sites. There is evidence to suggest that this treatment had a negative effect on species recruitment at the Upper Thames clay site where there was a large seed bank of grass species already present (Manchester *et al.,*1997). There were significant differences in mean diversity between sites. The Norfolk Broads site was significantly more diverse and the Suffolk River Valleys was significantly less diverse than the other sites.

The mean number of species recorded in the controls in the second year increased slightly on some sites, but declined on the Norfolk Broads site (Table 2). Most of the significant treatment effects from the first year were carried over into the second year. Over all sites the controls and plots sown with the ESA seed mix were significantly less diverse than the plots sown with the NVC seed mix. Similarly, the companion grass had no significant effects on the number of species established. The pattern of mean diversity between sites remained the same with the Norfolk Broad site significantly more diverse than the others.

Table 2. Mean number of species recorded in quadrats on the arable reversion experiments. Means with the same letter were not considered to be significantly different ($P<0.05$) using the Student-Newman-Keuls test.

1995

Tr.	South Wessex	Upper Thames clay	Suffolk River Valleys	Norfolk Broads	South Downs	Upper Thames limestone	Mean
1.	6	4	7	7	5	4	5.6[c]
2.	10	10	10	13	9	12	10.6[b]
3.	14	10	13	20	19	20	15.9[a]
4.	14	18	14	19	19	21	17.5[a]
5.	10	10	10	13	9	11	10.4[b]
6	15	14	11	19	20	18	16.0[a]
7.	13	17	13	18	20	17	16.5[a]
Mean	11.9[bc]	11.9[bc]	10.8[c]	15.5[a]	14.4[ab]	14.7[ab]	

1996

Tr.	South Wessex	Upper Thames clay	Suffolk River Valleys	Norfolk Broads	South Downs	Upper Thames limestone	Mean
1.	6	4	9	5	10	9	7.0[b]
2.	9	8	5	9	6	8	7.4[b]
3.	13	11	10	17	19	14	14.0[a]
4.	12	14	10	17	18	15	14.3[a]
5.	8	7	7	9	4	8	7.2[b]
6	13	12	11	17	17	16	14.4[a]
7.	15	16	10	17	16	14	14.6[a]
Mean	10.7[b]	10.4[b]	9.1[c]	13.1[a]	12.6[a]	11.8[ab]	

The small number of species recorded in the controls suggested that there was little or no potential for the natural reversion of arable land to species-rich grassland on the sites studied. Disturbance followed by the sowing of a simple ESA seed mixture offered only a small enhancement of botanical diversity. However, the ESA mix recommended for the South Wessex Downs included some forb species. At this site there were smaller differences in the number of species recorded on plots sown with this mix and the NVC mix. On all other sites sowing the NVC seed mix caused the greatest increase in diversity. The abundant bare ground on most arable sites may account for the lack of differences in establishment caused by the two intensities of disturbance. Finally, the lack of any effect of the companion grass may be explained by the sowing of large quantities of grasses with the forbs. In conclusion, the treatments applied to the arable sites have increased botanical diversity to a greater degree than those applied to the grassland sites. This may be explained by the lack of an established sward of competitive grass species, and the greater opportunity to create microsites for germination and establishment on arable land.

ACKNOWLEDGEMENTS

This research was funded by the Ministry of Agriculture (BD0312). The authors are grateful to the numerous site owners and ESA Project Officers for their co-operation in the establishment and management of these experiments.

REFERENCES

ANON. (1986) *Environmentally Sensitive Areas: First report as required in Section 18 of the Agriculture Act 1986*. Ministry of Agriculture Fisheries and Food, London.

BAKKER J.P. (1989) *Nature Management by Grazing and Cutting*. Kluwer, Dordrecht.

BERENDSE F., OOMES M.J.M., ALTENA H.J. and ELBERSE W.TH. (1992) Experiments on the restoration of species-rich meadows in the Netherlands. *Biological Conservation*, 62, 59-65.

FULLER R.M. (1986) The changing conservation interest of lowland grasslands in England and Wales: a review of grassland surveys 1930-84. *Biological Conservation*, 40, 281-300.

HUTCHINGS J. and BOOTH K.D. (1996) Studies on the feasibility of re-creating chalk grassland vegetation on ex-arable land. I. The potential roles of the seed bank and the seed rain. *Journal of Applied Ecology*, 33,1171-1181.

MANCHESTER S.J., TREWEEK J.T., MOUNTFORD O.M. and PYWELL R.F. (1997) The success of nurse crops in the establishment of species-rich lowland wet grassland. In: R. Sheldrick (ed) *Grassland Management in Environmentally Sensitive Areas, Occasional Symposium of the Bristish Grasslands Society*.

RODWELL J.S. (1992*) British plant communities. Volume 3. Grasslands and montane communities*. Cambridge University Press, Cambridge.

WELLS T.C.E. (1989*) The establishment and management of wildflower meadows*. Nature Conservancy Council, Peterborough.

WELLS T.C.E., COX R. and FROST A. (1989) Diversifying grasslands by introducing seed and transplants into existing vegetation. In: G. P. Buckley (Ed). *Biological habitat reconstruction*. pp. 283-298. Bellhaven: London.

THE FUTURE

Chairman: Jim McAdam
Department of Agriculture for Northern Ireland

A Way Forward for Environmentally Sensitive Farming that Meets the Needs of Public and Farmer

C.H. BULLOCK[1] and H. L. MCHENRY[2]

[1] Macaulay Land Use Research Institute, Aberdeen, AB15 8QH

[2] Teagasc, 19 Sandymount Avenue, Dublin 4

ABSTRACT

Direct support payments to farmers are increasingly likely to be in the form of agri-environmental payments. This paper reviews the results of two studies undertaken in the Southern Uplands of Scotland, a contingent valuation survey of public preferences in relation to landscape changes potentially arising from reductions in grazing pressure, and a survey of farmers' attitudes to Environmentally Sensitive Area policy. It argues that payments for the preservation of wildlife habitats and flora are a laudable means of subsidising farming in the uplands. However, policy must also recognize that many farmers will continue to regard the environment as being peripheral to their role as producers of food. The full public benefits of agri-environmental policy will not be realized unless they have 'meaning' to farmers.

THE CURRENT STATE OF AGRI-ENVIRONMENTAL POLICY

Agri-environmental schemes, such as Environmentally Sensitive Areas (ESAs) and Stewardship, have become an increasing feature of support to agriculture. While these measures are currently supplementary to supported market prices, there are strong indications that the reform of the Common Agricultural Policy (CAP) that is expected to follow the next round of World Trade Organisation negotiations, will emphasize 'neutral' support policies that do not have an impact on output. Environmental payments are the most likely medium for this type of support. They can be argued to provide public benefits and, increasingly, have the support of the farming lobby.

However, those farming in Less Favoured Areas (LFA's) express concern at their dependency on existing structural payments such as Hill Livestock Compensatory Allowances (HLCAs). If environmental payments are to form a larger proportion of support to agriculture in the future, this feeling of dependency could be aggravated because many farmers would appear to regard environmental management as being peripheral to their perceived role as producers of food (McHenry, 1994). Farmers often give financial factors as their main reason for being unwilling to sign up to ESA prescriptions, but may actually be concerned at agreeing to long term management plans that involve restrictions on their perceived freedom as farmers. Other farmers, who are attracted by the financial payments, may be reluctant to commit much time to conservation in practice. In the long run this could undermine the durability of conservation management (Potter, 1996). While the national agricultural ministries and departments have been keen to flag the success of ESAs on the basis of numbers joining, these figures can conceal the true quality of environmental management and the fact that many farmers restrict conservation to unproductive parts of their farms.

Acceptance of environmental policies by farmers largely depends on how these policies are presented. McEachern (1992) found that farmers in the Yorkshire Dales often farmed according to what could be described as good environmental practice and believed themselves to be enhancing the environment where possible within the limits exerted by nature. However, many farmers with land in those marginal, *i.e.* upland environments, where 'nature' is most imposing, often get classified as 'laggards' precisely because their economic insecurity and small farm size does not permit them the luxury of being able to consider formal environmental agreements. In other cases, farmers' definitions of good environmental practice square uncomfortably with those of the policy makers. For example, prescriptions aimed at grazing extensification (reductions in grazing pressure) may have an untidy outcome whereas farmers often characterise their own environmental management as overcoming a 'robust' nature (Green, 1992) by 'taking in the wild' or creating 'neatness' (McEachern, 1992: McHenry, 1994).

In yet other cases, farmers emphasize their role as custodians of the environment (Cox *et al.*, 1985) as an excuse for carrying on as normal (McHenry, 1996). Farmer organizations have been keen to promote the concept of stewardship of the landscape as a natural extension of farmers' traditional role (Green, 1992). Indeed, this is a reasonable proposition that farming has been responsible for the heterogeneity and attractiveness of many of Britain's valued landscapes (Selman, 1996). On this basis much of the intensification, removal of hedgerows and drainage that has occurred in the last thirty years is sometimes argued to be a blip in the longer term contribution of farming to the landscape (McHenry, 1996).

Policy makers have embraced 'stewardship' as a means of pursuing conservation objectives through farming (SNH, 1994). Their enthusiasm represents an acceptance that 'the environment' needs appropriate packaging if it is to appeal to farmers who have their own definition of conservation and are suspicious of that held by other groups in society. There is, though, a risk that Stewardship could formalise, with specific payments, activities that were previously freely provided as an inherent outcome of efficient farming (Colman, 1994). Commoditizing the environment in this way could make conservation 'symbolic' (Cary, 1993) and undermine the gradual change in attitudes that has been sought by proponents of agri-environmental policy.

In practice, a twin approach may be necessary in the future. On the one hand, positive and adaptive management is necessary if the continuing fragmentation of habitats (Selman, 1996) is to be replaced by policies that enhance the environment. However, on the other hand, there needs to be a recognition that not all farmers will be receptive to the conservation policies that appear to promote wildlife habitat at the expense of farming. Fry and Herlin (1995) note that most European landscapes are cultural rather than natural and argue that the case for their preservation, and that of the associated communities, needs to be made more comprehensive to the general public. The livelihoods of these farmers might be better served by a rural policy that acknowledges the contribution that both farmers and prosperous communities have upon landscape. Current policy would appear to only recognize the value of wildlife habitats. The problems therefore are, firstly, to determine exactly what it is that *the public* actually values and, secondly, how to protect this without turning farmers into museum fixtures.

To illustrate some of the issues, we introduce the results from two surveys undertaken in the Southern Uplands of Scotland. The first is a contingent valuation survey undertaken in 1994/95 (Bullock and Kay, 1997) which set out to quantify the public's preference for different landscape scenarios that could arise from grazing extensification. This survey was supplemented by focus group discussions with local residents and interest groups, including farmers. The second is a qualitative survey of farmers attitudes to conservation schemes undertaken in 1993/94 (McHenry, 1994). Together, the studies indicate the factors that need to be considered by those responsible for devising agri-environmental policy. Firstly, we describe the case study area.

THE SOUTHERN UPLANDS

The Western and Central Southern Uplands ESAs were designated in 1993 and cover a large area (596,000 ha.) of moorland and rough grazing over 150 metres. Sheep farming is the principal land use with specialised sheep breeding being locally important. Many farmers are tenants, but the area also contains some very large estates on which sport shooting or forestry are important. The ESA has particularly focused on the protection of heather moorland and the few remaining areas of semi-natural woodland by providing payments to reduce grazing pressure through stock removal or stock management. Payments are also available for the muirburn (the encouragement of heather re-growth by periodic burning) and for the maintenance of traditional stone walls and farm buildings.

Productivity has increased due to supplementary feeding and the conversion of rough grassland and moorland to improved grassland. Traditionally, heather was valued by shepherds as a good source of winter fodder and shelter for hill sheep. Areas of native trees and scrub were also valued as shelter and for fuel. However, both have been lost as landowners have cut back on labour which had been used to shepherd stock around the hill. Sheep now tend to concentrate on the better grassland or around supplementary feed blocks. Localised over-grazing has followed, preventing tree regeneration and causing a reduction in the diversity of grassland vegetation. Elsewhere, the heather has gone ungrazed and unmanaged, the loss of its economic value having been exacerbated by the cost and inconvenience of muirburn.

The Western and Central Southern Uplands ESAs contain very similar prescriptions despite rather different conditions. In the west, large scale afforestation is controversial and is viewed by locals as a cause of depopulation. The west also receives higher rainfall which makes muirburn difficult without which the moorland can become economically useless. Neglect and poor burning often lead to an increase in the area of unpalatable *Molinia* grass. The east is drier and has experienced a greater contrast between areas of agricultural improvement and neglect where reduced grazing has led to the dominance of poor *Nardus* grasses. In both areas, as elsewhere in Britain, there are few remnants of the semi-natural systems that Webster and Felton (1993) believe should form the core areas of conservation interest that need to be preserved. The reality is that these areas are simply farmed less intensively than lowland areas while natural features have lost their significance to the farm operations.

THE CONTINGENT VALUATION SURVEY

A contingent valuation (CV) survey was undertaken to estimate the public's willingness to pay (WTP) for grazing policies in the Central Southern Uplands. The survey consisted of a main postal survey of 1,500 members of the public living in southern Scotland and an in-person survey of 150 visitors conducted at the Grey Mare's Tail, a waterfall and popular beauty spot owned by the National Trust for Scotland. These were supplemented by smaller surveys of local birdwatchers and ramblers as well as by focus group discussions. The latter were held with local residents and interest groups in order to explore those issues that were important in relation to the ESA.

The questionnaire took the form of a pamphlet which contained straightforward information about how grazing extensification could bring change to the upland landscape.

A discrete choice with payment card follow-up was selected as the format for the valuation question. Respondents were first asked if, in principle, they were willing to pay for the (grazing extensification) policies that would bring about landscape change. They were then asked if they were willing to pay a particular bid level representing a presumed policy cost. These bids were randomly allocated from one of fifteen cost levels between £5 and £190 per household per year. Finally, depending upon the discrete response (*i.e.* *yes* or *no*) they were asked to select a follow-up bid from a card listing a wide range of possible amounts.

Landscape scenarios

As sheep are the dominant enterprise, extensification has the potential to affect the whole landscape. Three colour scenarios of possible change applied to a single anonymous locality were produced. These were simply entitled A, B and C, but represent:

- Landscape A: 'Policy-off'. A landscape with levels and coverage of grazing at the higher end of current practice in which there is very little heather or scrub.
- Landscape B: 'Policy-on - extensified'. This landscape is similar to that which might be expected to result from extensification following ESA designation. There is little erosion and more diversity than in A.
- Landscape C: 'Policy-on - very extensified'. In this scenario there has been a much greater level of extensification and some removal of stock. As a result there is considerable regeneration of heather, trees and scrub.

All three pictures were combined with a detailed map and basic information on vegetation change, time scale, wildlife effects and possible employment implications. Easy-to-understand symbols demonstrated the relative numbers of sheep and variety of birdlife, mammals, insects and flora typically found in such upland landscapes.

Three questions related to the respondent's perception of the *status-quo* and changes to it. The first of these asked the respondent which landscape he/she considered to be 'more typical' of the Central Southern Uplands. A later question asked the respondent to rate his/her relative *preference* for each landscape using the question, "which of the three landscapes would you most like to see and visit in Southern Scotland?". Together, answers to these questions indicated whether or not the respondent considered change to the illustrated landscapes to represent *preservation* or *enhancement*. The third question followed the valuation question and asked whether the respondent would like the policy to produce "no", "some" or "many" more landscapes like Landscape C.

Discussion of the CVM Survey results

A number of models were run drawing upon the sixteen variables provided by responses to individual questions. On the basis of the best-fitting model, the mean 'willingness to pay' (WTP), derived from responses to the follow-up question, was £55 per household per annum (confidence interval; = £48,£62) for the postal sample and £49 (£41,£57) for the Visitor Subset. Aggregated to the level of the population of Southern and Central Scotland, these estimates imply that annual public benefits exceed policy cost by £32 million, a sizeable margin.

The analysis of responses indicated a clear desire for policies that would create a more extensified landscape involving an increase in the cover of heather and, especially, trees. For most respondents this represented an enhancement on the current more intensively grazed landscape. Landscape C was considered an enhancement on A by 88% of the sample and this preference was particularly apparent amongst those respondents who perceived the current typical landscape in the Central Southern Uplands to resemble the open landscape (A). This relationship was also evident from the significance of this interaction in the analysis of WTP responses. Respondents who regarded the current landscape to resemble A (43%) had a higher median WTP of £62 per household per annum for a policy that would change the appearance of the landscape than were those respondents who regarded B as typical (37%) for which WTP was £45. The results were mirrored by the Visitor Subset who were willing to pay £77 where they regarded the current landscape to resemble A (48%), but £43 where they regarded B as being more typical (30%).

By contrast, for the Yorkshire Dales, Garrod and Willis (1991) found a preference amongst the majority of respondents for today's farmed landscape for which the average WTP of both residents and visitors was £24 per household per year. Wild and unmanaged alternative landscapes were less popular, although those who did prefer them were WTP a higher amount. They explained their results as evidence of a *status-quo* bias, a common observation amongst psychologists who, in experiments, have found that wherever the outcome of a change is not known with certainty, subjects prefer to stay with the *status-quo* (Samuelson and Zeckhauser, 1988).

One explanation for the difference between the results for the Central Southern Uplands and the Yorkshire Dales survey is that, the latter sought a WTP to *preserve* the *status-quo*. The Southern Uplands survey let the respondent decide which landscape resembled the *status-quo*, the responses being split between A and B. Most CV applied to landscape have implied that inaction could lead to a deterioration of the *status-quo*, (e.g. Willis *et al.*, 1993; Hanley *et al.*, 1996). As the Dales are a National Park and could be described as an example of a "prototypical" landscape (Purcell, 1987), i.e. a landscape that has an important cultural heritage and acts as a reference point, it is unlikely that many people would prefer a different landscape. *Status-quo* bias would have reinforced this outcome.

The Southern Uplands arguably have a less distinct identity. The population is more sparse and the area dominated by single-feature land use types (MLURI, 1988). The survey was principally concerned with the landscape and mentioned, but did not emphasize, farmers and the farming system. Nevertheless, it was surprising how few visitors commented on the role of farming even when prompted. Moreover, many respondents considered change to be an 'enhancement' for which they were WTP.

The focus group discussions

Naturally the Southern Uplands do have a more distinct identity for the people who live there. This was evident from the focus groups that were held before the CV survey in order to reveal issues that were regarded as important in relation to the ESA. Sessions were held with the Upper Tweed and Ettrick & Lauderdale Community Councils, a local branch of the Scottish Ornithology Club and invited farmers.

Predictably, the birdwatcher group placed particular value on natural features, especially the remnants of trees and scrub which exist as islands of biodiversity amongst the "depressing" monocultures of heather and conifer plantation. Indeed, they noted that the "only birds to be found in the hills are in the cleuchs (wooded gullies)". Participants in both the Council and Birdwatcher groups were dismissive of monocultures such as heather. Firm views were expressed, *i.e.* "we should be trying to see that different areas complement one another rather than producing heather *en masse*", "heather isn't natural", "hills covered in heather are no more attractive than hills covered in grass", "it also appears black except in August", "you've got the Highlands for heather - we don't want more here" and, from a birdwatcher, "pure heather leads to a thin spread of birds...which then get shot!". They did, though, recognize its relevance to farming, (albeit incorrectly) *i.e.* "heather is possibly better for the sheep than grasses if well managed and burnt - that's why so much is left".

Amongst members of the Council groups there was an awareness of the land as an productive asset: "nobody here wants all the land turned over to non-productive activities, we need an integration", "farmers are important for future management", "your pictures suggest a loss of employment because this depends on sheep" or "if people like what they see, then we should be seeking to enhance that scenery rather than to change it". The birdwatchers acknowledged the stewardship role of farmers, but cautioned that "there's a lot of creeping intensification going on" or "we need to educate farmers".

As with the public in general, opinions differed amongst the various participants. However, while most members agreed with the respondents to the survey that parts of the Southern Uplands could be "open and bleak" and in need of more broadleaf trees, there was also a recognition of the importance of farmers to the landscape.

UNDERSTANDING THE FARMER'S VIEW

We now discuss the qualitative study in order to examine the way in which farmers in the Southern Uplands give meaning to the changes occuring in agriculture and the growing importance of conservation issues. In-depth interviews with forty farmers were the main source of this data (see McHenry, 1994 for further discussion).

The study found that many farmers felt strongly that land should be used to its full agricultural potential and that any departure from this was wrong. Farmer A thought that conservationists wanted to leave the land 'in its natural state':

> Farmer A   *Well I wouldn't take stock off the.. to leave it to grow a wilderness. That is wrong I think.*

Neatness in the countryside was viewed as a good thing as it is evidence of the land being farmed in a productive manner and is an indication of the ways a farmer 'cares' for the land (Nassauer, 1988).

> Farmer B   *I do think extensive farming makes the countryside look worse but I mean to my eye well grazed, well farmed land looks good and set aside and under grazed grass and hobby farming looks bad.*

Here again there is evidence of the conflict of ideas between what conservationists want and farmers like. As long as farmers continue to see farming in terms of managing the landscape, the success of schemes which encourage scrub, undergrowth and uncultivated areas on the farm will be limited. Evidence that the countryside is being farmed and looked after comes from the general appearance of the farm showing that it is functioning and productive. This way of seeing the landscape is likely to affect farmers' reactions to conservation policies which encourage a less tidy appearance.

Suggestions of overgrazing aroused a very strong reaction from farmers. It was felt that such an accusation was tantamount to suggesting that farmers were not looking after the land. It was also seen as an attack on 'farming knowledge'. If voluntary conservation schemes are to attract farmers, it is clear that these schemes must make sense to them. Farmers perceptions of the benefits of conservation were varied, but it was clear that many of them saw it in a very instrumental way. There had to be some return from the market for their conservation, either from shooting, diversified enterprises or tourism.

For most farmers the attractions of the ESA were more agricultural than environmental. The main enticement to farmers was the chance to rebuild stone walls. The same has been found by Skerret *et al.* (1992) in Breadalbane ESA. It is ironic that this policy, which signals a move away from conventional farming, should support the rebuilding of stone walls which are a symbol of traditional farming ideals. It is also an example of agri-environmental policy subsidising an *agricultural* improvement.

The financial situation of the farmer was of course a major factor in the consideration of the ESA. This took account not only of direct costs, but also costs which might result from restrictions. These included non financial issues such as regulation and paper work.

In addition, there were very practical reservations about possible increases in vermin, or restrictions on vermin control. Uncertainty about what would happen in the future was also a major factor:

> Farmer C   *..it's total uncertainty that costs real money, bearing in mind you produce an animal until it's a piece of steak... Farmers [are] making policy for three years ahead...*

Adding to this uncertainty was a feeling that farmers had become even more dependent on government subsidies and direct support. This, combined with the perceived increases in bureaucracy and regulation facing farmers, had resulted in the feeling for many farmers that they were under the government's control.

> Farmer D   *That's the only thing about living off the subsidies and grants .. you are dependent on somebody else giving you them and you never know when they are going to be cut off...*

Because the ESA scheme is voluntary those who feel strongly about being dependent on the government and subsidies are not likely to join. The feeling of dependence arises as a result of other direct forms of support. Potter and Gasson (1988) in their study of land diversion from productive agriculture, found that far from regarding a land diversion payment as a useful additional source of income, constrained farmers feared the prospect of lower returns, reduced flexibility and increased bureaucracy.

CONCLUSIONS

Many farmers in the Southern Uplands have been prepared to learn more about the ESA scheme, either because they realize that incomes can be supplemented with ESA payments or because of the rising profile of conservation in agricultural support generally. Others have been constrained by their tenancy status or limited resources. However, most farmers considered their principal role to be that of food producer. Environmental management was regarded as being peripheral and farmers were not prepared to be disadvantaged by joining environmental schemes. The emphasis placed by the ESA on heather and grazing management was not shared by most farmers. The agricultural relevance of heather as potential fodder, and of the hill land generally, has diminished. Moreover, farmers did not rate highly the aesthetic value of heather and believed that its expansion would be regressive, akin to letting the land "go wild".

Large areas of heather were also given little value by the focus groups and by the public in the CV survey. Instead, the survey indicated a firm preference for increased landscape diversity, in particular increased tree cover. As there is currently little tree cover in the Southern Uplands, this indicates that the public were prepared to accept changes to the current landscape that they regarded as 'enhancement'. In other CV surveys, a stronger attachment to the *status-quo* has been evident. However, it is difficult to determine the extent to which the cultural element in the landscape has contributed to

175

this preference as the subject has not been dealt with specifically in any case. This would be an interesting consideration for future research. For instance, Ronningen (1993) notes that some social groups value the same landscape characteristics as farmers, for example 'neatness' and 'organization'.

There are farmers whose active interest in conservation (or self-preservation) will allow them to respond to the 'enhancement' measures that are becoming an increasing feature of agri-environmental policy. For other farmers who are preoccupied with the business of producing food, environmental measures should have a purpose that they can relate to, for example watercourse protection, shelter belts and beetle banks, rather than heather moorland. Yet others will restrict their interest to cosmetic environmental measures or those of direct benefit, *i.e.* stone walls. Although these measures have good uptake, it will eventually be necessary to decide if such 'soft' measures provide *real* public benefits.

REFERENCES

BULLOCK C. and KAY J. (1997). Preservation and Change in the upland landscape - the public benefits of grazing management. *Journal of Environmental Planning and Management* in press.

CARY J. (1993). The nature of Symbolic Beliefs and Environmental Behaviour in a rural setting. *Environment and Behaviour*, 25(5), 555-576.

COLMAN D.R. (1994) Ethics and externalities: agricultural stewardship and other behaviour: presidential address. *Journal of Agricultural Economics*, 45(3).

COX G., LOWE P. and WINTER, M. (1985) *Journal of Rural Studies*, 1, 173-183.

FRY G.L.A. and HERLIN I.S. (1995) Landscape design: how do we incorporate ecological, cultural and aesthetic values in landscape assessment and design principles? In Griffiths, G.H. (Ed). *Landscape Ecology: Theory and Application (proceedings of the fourth annual IALE(UK) conference held at The University of Reading.*, pp. 51-60.

GREEN B.H. (1992) Case study: agricultural plenty - more of less farming for the environment. In Berry, R. J. (Ed)., *Environmental Dilemmas: ethics and decisions*, Chapman & Hall, London, pp. 104-117.

HANLEY N., SIMPSON I., PARSISSON D., MACMILLAN D., BULLOCK C. and CRABTREE R. (1996) Valuation of the conservation benefits of Environmentally Sensitive Areas *Economics and Policy Series 2*, MLURI, Aberdeen.

McEACHERN C. (1992) Farmers and Conservation: conflict and accommodation in farming politics. *Journal of Rural Studies*, 8(2), 159-171.

McHENRY H.L. (1996) Farming and Environmental Discourses: a Study of the Depiction of Environmental Issues in a German Farming Newspaper. *Journal of Rural Studies*, 12(4), 375-386.

McHENRY H. L. (1994) Understanding the farmers view: perceptions of changing agriculture and the move to agri-environmental policies in Southern Scotland, PhD Thesis, Aberdeen.

MLURI. (1988) The Land Cover of Scotland. Macaulay Land Use Research Institute, Aberdeen.

NASSAUER J. I. (1988). The aesthetics of horticulture: Neatness as a form of care. *HortScience*, 23(6), 973-977.

POTTER C. and GASSON R. (1988). Farmers Participation in Voluntary Land Diversion Schemes: some predictions from a survey. *Journal of Rural Studies*, 4(4), 365-375.

POTTER C. (1996) Environmental reform of the CAP. In: Curry, N. and Owen, S. (Eds). *Changing Rural Policy in Britain: planning, administration, agriculture and the environment*, Countryside and Community Press, Cheltenham.165-183

PURCELL A.T. (1987). Landscape Perception, Preference and Schema Discrepancy. *Environment and Planning*, 14, 67-92.

RØNNINGEN K. (1993) Agricultural policies and landscape management. Some examples from Norway, Great Britain and Germany. *Norsk Geografisk Tidsskrift*, 47, 93-104.

SAMUELSON W. and ZECKHAUSER R. (1988). Status Quo Bias in Decision Making. *Journal of Risk and Uncertainty*, 1, 7-59.

SELMAN P. (1996). The potential for landscape ecological planning in Britain. *Changing Rural Policy in Britain: planning, administration, agriculture and the environment*. N. Curry and S. Owen, (eds)., Countryside and Community Press, Cheltenham. pp28-43

SKERRET S.J., PERKINS T.J., LILWALL N.B. and TODD E.C. Socio-economic Evaluation of the Breadalbane Environmentally Sensitive Area Scheme, 1987-1990. *Paper presented to 30th EAAE Seminar "Direct Payments"*, Chateau d'Oex, France.

SNH. (1994). Agriculture and the Natural Heritage. Scotland's Natural Heritage: the magazine of Scottish Natural Heritage.

WEBSTER S. and FELTON M. (1993). Targeting for nature conservation in agricultural policy. *Land Use Policy*, 10(1), 67-82.

WILLIS K.G., GARROD G.D. and SAUNDERS C.M. (1993). Valuation of the South Down and Somerset Levels and Moors ESAs by the General Public. Centre for Rural Economy, University of Newcastle upon Tyne.

Cost Benefit for the Taxpayer?

R. CRABTREE and N. BARRON

Macaulay Land Use Research Institute, Aberdeen

ABSTRACT

This paper looks at the private and public costs and benefits of the Environmentally Sensitive Area (ESA) Scheme. The costs and benefits are assessed with reference to uptake rates, exchequer costs, impacts on farm income, farm practice and the local economy. Further investigations look at the provision of the environmental good associated with the scheme, and how the public perceives the 'value for money' aspects associated with the provision of this public good. Conclusions centre around the future for the ESA policy and how environmental measures can be successfully incorporated into the reform of the Common Agriculture Policy (CAP).

INTRODUCTION

The degradation of traditional environmental features is a by-product of the pace of agricultural technology and the economic pressures on farmers to adopt it. Concern amongst the public and environmental pressure groups about the extent of agricultural change in areas of high environmental value led to the introduction of Environmentally Sensitive Area (ESA) policy. By offsetting the financial pressures driving intensification and land use change, the ESA Scheme seeks to reduce the intensity of farming practices, protect the environment and enhance its quality. The incentive payments can be interpreted as payments from the taxpayer for an increase in the level of environmental goods produced from farming. The ESA Scheme, first introduced in 1986, has become the 'flagship' of the agriculture department's link with environmental issues; and by 1996, the 43 ESAs in the UK covered 15% of the total agricultural area (MAFF, 1996).

BENEFITS FROM ESAs

Economists conventionally use cost-benefit analysis to appraise major public investments. In this, the costs to society are compared with the societal benefits, where both costs and benefits are expressed in monetary values. Such an approach is difficult to apply to ESA policy. There are problems in valuing the public benefits from environmental change and calculating the cost to society of changing resource use in an agriculture greatly distorted by subsidies. In addition, with schemes that involve incentive payments it is the effectiveness of using public expenditure and not the social costs of a policy that are of paramount interest to policy makers.

Here we examine a number of aspects of the scheme all of which contribute to an overall assessment of 'value for money'. These aspects include uptake by farmers, environmental benefits, economic valuation of public benefits, public expenditure costs, and farm income effects.

Uptake by Farmers

A MAFF report from 1990 stated that in the first three years of the Scheme 5,100 farmers offered more than 250,000 hectares of land to the Scheme. By 1994 5,500 agreements were in operation covering more than 50% of the area deemed eligible for ESA payments by MAFF. A summary of he latest figures on the extent and number of ESAs in England are presented in Table 1.

Table 1.   Summary of ESAs in England (1996).

	Agreement Area (Ha).	Eligible Area (Ha).	Uptake Rate (%).	Total Payment (£m)
Mean	18636	42545	44	1.2
Median	12920	32307	40	0.8
Maximum	106538	219300	90	4.2
Minimum	949	3300	11	0.1

A review of the latest figures on the extent and number of ESAs in England (MAFF, 1996) show that the 22 ESAs cover 410,000 hectares, comprising 7,479 individual agreements. There is a large variation in the uptake rate of the individual ESAs. Observation of the 'raw data' does not give a true impression of the success of the scheme. West Penwith ESA is characterised as having the highest uptake rate (90% of the eligible area is under agreement), but only 6,255 hectares of land has a signed agreement; this compares with the Lake District ESA which has an uptake rate of 49%, but 106,538 hectares of land in the scheme. In such cases it is difficult to determine where the ESA Scheme will be most successful. There are no guidelines to determine what is or is not an acceptable uptake rate. Neither are figures available for the breakdown of uptake into the various tiers, so the divide between protection and enhancement cannot be truly appreciated.

This variation in uptake tends to be related to the specific prescriptions relating to these areas and the costs of compliance involved in joining the scheme. Higher compliance costs result in smaller income gains; this is especially true for areas which are seeking to convert arable areas back to grassland (for example, in Breckland the scheme seeks to revert arable land to heath; as compared to West Penwith where conservation is centred around maintaining Cornish hedges and moors). Similarly schemes involving structural changes (access, rebuilding of walls and traditional buildings etc.) require a high commitment of initial expenditure. The ESA Scheme in the Cairngorms has had very limited success in the maintenance of dykes due to the capital costs exceeding the compensation offered. Various studies have looked into reasons for interest in, and factors that limit participation in ESAs. Whitby *et al.* (1991), Carr and Tait (1991) and Brotherton (1991) found that major reasons for joining the ESA Scheme were to maintain or acquire additional income. If farmers are rational economists (profit maximisers) then entry to the scheme will be solely affected by the expected profit from entry to the scheme. Brotherton (1991) remarks that the effect of attitudes towards conservation is probably subservient to the power of financial attractiveness. Major conservation interests were expressed by part-time and semi-retired farmers who had substantial off farm incomes. Conservation and environmental interests were secondary, and usually were inspired ex-post to joining the Scheme, although a number of farmers felt that there was little distinction between conservation and farming. Some farmers were prepared to accept smaller compensation payments, suggesting over-compensation, with many farms having little or no reorganisation of practices in order to comply with the schemes prescriptions. Alternatively smaller payments may be accepted in exchange for the reduction in risk associated with entering a scheme for a guaranteed income. This argument is likely to become more important as agricultural price support is eroded through CAP reform. In UK agriculture the CAP remains the dominant policy and environmental schemes must provide large financial incentives if they are to negate the influence of the CAP towards relatively intensive land use practices.

Major disadvantages of the ESA Scheme from a farmer's perspective include the constraints on farm practices (cutting dates, fertiliser use), decrease in land fertility, erosion of owner autonomy, the change in rental and capital value, the decrease in income, and the constraint on stock numbers. Ideas proposed to increase the attractiveness of the scheme include higher payments, differentiated payments for different types of land, the relaxation and the elimination of constraints, boundary changes, and the longer duration of the scheme.

Environmental Benefits.

An ESA typically has 4 or 5 environmental objectives. These objectives, and the performance indicators against which they will be measured, are established in consultation with Government advisors. However, due to the short time since the introduction of most schemes, and the inadequacy of many of the environmental targets and monitoring mechanisms, the performance of many conservation schemes in meeting targets is difficult to assess (Birdlife International, 1996). Ecological changes occur over the long-term, and despite the monitoring reports, extensive information is not yet available to determine the success of the Scheme with respect to environmental factors. All that can be stated is that early indications suggest an increase in the diversity of species in the ESA agreement areas suggesting that the long term effects of the Scheme, with respect to environmental consequences will be positive. It is impossible to give an accurate assessment of such a long term policy in the period of time over which the policy has been in action and there is no guarantee that the specified environmental prescriptions will result in the regeneration of the desired environment.

A further difficulty in improving the environmental value of a region through the ESA Scheme is that the scheme is voluntary and agreements are signed for a relatively short (especially with respect to environmental changes) fixed period of time. If on the completion of the agreement market signals change (i.e. increased output prices), then the farmer is free to revert to more intensive agricultural practices and take the economic benefits associated with higher prices. The scheme involves no exchange of property rights, and hence there is no guarantee that the spending of public funds will bring about the long term agri-environmental improvements specified in the ESA aims and objectives.

Birdlife International (1996) judge environmental performance on two indicators, the success of the scheme in meeting environmental targets, and the effect that the scheme has had on influencing farmers' attitudes. They show that the scheme has been successful in yielding substantial conservation benefits (e.g. Somerset Levels) and that they have promoted a more sympathetic attitude to conservation amongst farmers. However, there are many important bird areas that are outside of the ESA boundary and hence are not protected by the scheme. In a study to look at how the design and implementation of schemes could be improved Birdlife International (1996) suggest that a more detailed scheme is required to look at the specifics of a continued decline in bird species, although they do suggest that ESAs should be remain as a core environmental scheme. They suggest that greater emphasis should be placed upon the enhancement, as opposed to conservation tiers of the ESA Scheme as those are the tiers that produce the greatest environmental benefits. Schemes should be designed with a greater amount of flexibility that allow the maximisation of conservation benefits but which also meet the agricultural requirements of the farmer.

Hughes (1994) has documented the existence of the 'halo' effect in the Cambrian Mountains ESA whereby management practices at one location lead to a spatial reorganisation of resources with undesirable ecological impacts at another location. MAFF has acknowledged the need to monitor the likelihood of a 'halo' effect arising from the schemes prescriptions. The natural progression of the ESA Scheme would seem to be whole farm conservation schemes which would eradicate this problem, and achieve the aim of more effective environmental protection and enhancement.

Economic Valuation of the Benefits from ESAs

The environmental benefits of ESAs occur primarily through protection and enhancement of habitats, landscapes and the archaeological heritage. These benefits are not priced through market processes and this contrasts with market goods for which prices are revealed through trade. Economists have developed a number of direct and indirect methods for attaching a value to the benefits received from environmental goods. Contingent valuation is the most widely applied direct method. It establishes a hypothetical market for the good in question and seeks to identify the public's maximum willingness to pay (WTP) to secure the environmental benefit or prevent the environmental loss.

Two major government-commissioned CVM studies have been undertaken on ESAs - by Willis et al. (1993) for the South Downs and Somerset Levels, and Hanley et al. (1996) for Breadalbane (Perthshire) and the Machair (Western Isles). Gourlay (1995) has also produced CVM estimates for Loch Lomond and Stewartry ESAs. In these studies the public were presented with scenarios (visual and textual descriptions) for the situation without an ESA policy (Policy-off) and with an ESA policy (Policy-on). In carefully structured interviews they were asked their willingness to pay to support the ESA policy. The production of such scenarios poses major problems since they require forecasts of how land use will change in both the absence and the presence of the ESA policy. There may well be environmental change in the absence of ESA policy and this means that the baseline for comparisons is not one fixed at the present. In the Scottish study photo-montage methods were developed to describe typical ESA landscape scenes, with both Policy-on and Policy-off montages differing from the current landscape. A series of such montages together with textual descriptions of expected changes provided the context in which respondents made their WTP decisions.

Results from these studies revealed that the WTP of residents to support ESA policy for a specified ESA varied from £13.0 to £27.5 per household per year, depending on the ESA in question. Visitor WTP were not comparable across the studies but Willis found mean visitor WTP of £11.8 and £9.5 for the two English ESAs. When aggregated up to account for the number of residents in an ESA area and the number of visitors each year, the value of the benefits was considerable (Table 2). The valuations are dominated by the general public's WTP because of the sheer number of households involved. Resident and visitor valuations make a relatively small contribution to the total except in area of high recreational use such as the South Downs.

Table 2. Aggregate WTP estimates for ESAs in England and Scotland (£m per year).

ESA	Residents (£m)	Visitors (£m)	General Public (£m)
Breadalbane	0.19	0.86	44.1
Machair	0.15	0.18	26.8
(Hanley et al., 1996)			
South Downs	0.26	48.4	31.1
Somerset Levels	0.10	10.7	41.9
(Willis et al., 1993)			
Loch Lomond	0.14	2.04	not estimated
Stewartry	0.18	1.47	not estimated
(Gourlay, 1995)			

These annual benefits from ESA policies greatly exceeded the Exchequer costs associated with payments to farmers and scheme administration. While reservations may be expressed about the reliability and interpretation of these environmental valuations, they do seem to indicate quite strong public support for ESA policies.

Exchequer Costs of the ESA Scheme

The public expenditure costs of ESA agreements differ between each designated area, due to particular distinctive landscape features reflected in the compensation payment and the level of uptake. Table 3 gives the costs of the ESA Scheme. Direct payments to farmers have increased from around £11 million in 1991/92, to approximately £32 million in 1996/97. This reflects the increase in the number and extent of ESAs over the last five years. Given that the scheme involves a standard payment, overhead costs are progressively declining in importance over time as a proportion of total ESA exchequer costs. In 1992/93 overhead costs represented 50% of total costs, this had fallen to 26% by 1994/95, and 19% by 1996/97. Total ESA Scheme costs have increased to around £40.5 million from £28.7 million in 1993/94. An increase in expenditure has also been seen in other agri-environmental schemes, yet there total value of £27.6 million is still well below the expenditure figure for the ESA Scheme.

Table 3. Historic and Forecast Uptake and Expenditure on ESAs.

	1993/94	1994/95	1995/96	1996/97
Area under Agreement (Ha)	266458	346391	409962	487922
Number of Agreements	4514	6141	7479	8556
Payments to Farmers (£m)	16.5	20.1	29.1	32.5
Overhead Costs (£m)	12.2	10.0	10.4	80.0
Total ESA Scheme Costs (£m)	28.7	30.1	39.5	40.5
Total other agri-environment 7627scheme costs (£m)	10.2	14.2	21.4	27.6

Source: Adapted from MAFF (1996).

The importance of the ESA policy in the MAFF budget can be seen in Table 4; this shows that the budget devoted to ESA payments is increasing, and is well in excess, in terms of magnitude, of any other environmental policy. Yet, as a whole the agri-environment programme takes up a fraction of the total CAP budget - around 0.6% of the total expenditure.

Table 4. Public Expenditure under the CAP and on National Grants and Subsidies (£m).

	1993/94	1994/95	1995/96
(A) Market regulation and other agricultural support measures under the CAP			
(i) Expenditure by the Intervention Board	1076.2	454.0	521.8
(ii) Expenditure by Agriculture and other Departments	648.9	1514.8	1750.3
Agri-environment and other measures			
of which: ESAs	13.1	10.8	16.2
Sub-total	18.8	29.6	33.7
(B) UK expenditure by Agriculture and other Departments			
of which: ESAs	10.2	22.1	37.0
Sub-total	75.0	80.4	100.4
TOTAL (A+B)	2684.8	2314.4	2853.4

Source: Adapted from MAFF (1995).

Farm Income Effects

The 'striking' conclusion of studies on the farm income consequences of ESA policy is the high proportion of the payments transferred to farmers which have not been offset by the costs involved in complying with the prescriptions, and have thus been reflected in the incomes of farmers (Colman, 1994). In general, the simpler the scheme and the greater the concentration on protection rather than enhancement, the greater the proportion of the payments retained by the farmer. This is a fairly intuitive conclusion: typically as the farm requires more reorganisation or investment to comply with the prescription, the more costs it will incur. In a similar argument, the farms that require the least reorganisation are the ones most likely to join. This would support the notion that lower tiers encourage protection, whilst higher tiers look towards enhancement and the additional capital costs associated with them. Initial compliance results in large income gains, with a low additionality to the environmental good, higher tiers offer smaller income gains, but with high additionality.

Hughes (1994) gives an example from the Cambrians, where the net value to farmers of the ESA Scheme was 60% of the gross annual value of ESA payments (i.e. approximately £2,200 per participant). This is a strong positive income effect, representing approximately 15% of the annual net farm income of the entrant farms. However, the distribution of payments was favoured towards larger farms, reflecting the bias of a policy that works on a per hectare base.

One of the major criticisms of the ESA Scheme is that many farms are getting paid for the continuance of existing farming practice. However, Colman (1994) justifies the ESA Scheme stating that initial minimum reorganisation of practices will encourage participation in the scheme and promote awareness of conservation, and as a result establish a basis from which greater change (environmental enhancement) can be developed. Certainly there has been a progressive shift in the ESA scheme from payments to protect existing biodiversity and landscape, to those that are specifically linked to environmental improvement. The additionality of the scheme and its cost effectiveness should increase as a result.

Other Economic Implications.

There are some wider economic implications of the ESA Scheme, all related to changes in farm incomes. These include:

- Some ESAs have caused a shift in agricultural enterprises and practices (shift to less intensive enterprises; move away from cattle towards sheep, and the associated reduction in the stocking rate).
- Change in national farm practices. Reductions in intensity leading to an increased demand for bought-in fodder; leading to changes in farm practices outside of the ESA boundary (cereal land diverted to fodder production etc.). These may have implications on the exchequer costs associated with supporting agriculture.
- Employment effect (increased demand for casual/contract labour - Colman (1994), Whitby et al. (1991)). Skerratt (1994) shows an increased demand for contractors to undertake conservation work in Breadalbane. However, the real impact on

- employment will be reduced as conservation works are completed.
- Enhanced rural development through the multiplier effect and links to the local economy.
- Increased supply of the public good associated with conservation; perhaps leading to enhanced recreational and leisure marketing opportunities.

Cost-Benefit and Future Development of ESAs.

On the rather limited evidence available it does seem that the ESA scheme has been broadly successful in protecting and enhancing areas of environmental sensitivity to agriculture. However, success has been variable. Where uptake has been low or where few additional benefits have been procured from the payments it would be difficult to argue that returns to public expenditure have been satisfactory. Undoubtedly the scheme has been most effective in areas of high environmental and cultural value where the risks of environmental degradation from changes in farm structure and management were high. But risks from changes to farming practice now seem much reduced and the main benefits from the scheme from now on are to be found where payments are directed at environmental enhancement. However, for the majority of farmers, the success of the scheme has been borne out of the increased opportunity for maintaining and improving incomes, as opposed to a new-found desire to conserve and enhance the environment.

The long-term environmental benefits associated with the provision of the public good cannot yet be fully appreciated, and there is evidence to suggest that the prescriptions laid down in the schemes guidelines are not those necessarily most favoured by society. For the ESA Scheme to be an effective element of policy much more needs to be known about the sorts of environmental investment valued by environmental interests and the public. For example, Gourlay (1996) has shown that the public do not rank stone wall building highly in their preferences for ESA expenditure, yet this absorbed 82% of the expenditure in the Stewartry ESA, and 57% in the Loch Lomond ESA. The structure of incentive payments needs careful investigation, since in order to be viable the ESA Scheme needs to encapsulate environmental changes that will not seriously affect the financial viability of the farm. This constrains the type of prescription that can realistically be introduced. Conservation depends upon the ability to fit the necessary constraints into routine farming practice; the degree to which these constraints are consistent with farming practices will determine the compensation levels required.

The ESA scheme is a spatially defined scheme, that is it is applied in selected areas. This makes eminent sense in England where there were distinct areas with environmental sensitivity to farming and there was a need to target policy to these as a priority. As such areas have been absorbed into the scheme the argument for a spatial approach declines. Indeed in Scotland where distinct sensitive areas cannot so readily be defined it has to be questioned whether the scheme was ever really appropriate.

The feasibility of supporting a spatially defined voluntary scheme, which may or may not produce the desired environmental outcome, has led to investigations into alternative mechanisms to provide the public good. Countryside Stewardship type schemes open to all farmers are an alternative to ESAs as an environmental measure for the future. These are targeted on securing high benefits to payments rather than targeting on distinct spatial areas. MAFF has now assumed responsibility for the original Countryside Commission scheme and its use as a vehicle for offering wider environmental opportunities for all farmers must be expected in the future. Even so, these schemes operate with little connection to international environmental priorities - for example for biodiversity, and it has to be expected that agri-environmental policy will be under pressure form the environmental lobby to contribute to wider environmental objectives in a more evident way.

Schemes in which farmers are paid production-decoupled payments to produce environmental goods fit well with likely future reform of the CAP. Franz Fischler has advocated a strong role for the existence of direct payments, stating that 'there are very good reasons for their existence which provide opportunity in rural areas for farmers and non farmers alike. The payments are there to recompense a very important service the agricultural community renders to society as a whole'. We may thus anticipate an extension of agri-environmental policy with opportunities for wider farm involvement. Establishing the structure of environmental priorities and payments will be a major challenge but, as Gardener (1996) predicts, in 10-20 years time environmental subsidies may well have replaced market support payments as the main supplement to farmers' incomes.

REFERENCES

BIRDLIFE INTERNATIONAL (1996). *Nature conservation benefits of plans under the Agri-environment Regulation (EEC 2078/92)*. Birdlife International European Agriculture Task Force.

BROTHERTON E. (1991). What Limits Participation in ESAs? *Journal of Environmental Management,* 32, 241-249.

CARR S. and TAIT J. (1991). Differences in the Attitudes of Farmers and Conservationists and their Implications. *Journal of Environmental Management,* 32, 281-294.

COLMAN D. (1994). Comparative Evaluation of Environmental Policies. In: Whitby, M. C. (ed.), *Incentives for Countryside Management: The Case of Environmentally Sensitive Areas.* CAB International, Wallingford.

GARDENER B. (1996). *European Agriculture: Policies, Production and Trade.* Routledge, London.

GOURLAY (1996). *Loch Lomond and Stewartry Environmentally Sensitive Areas: A study of Public Perceptions of Policy Benefits*, PhD Thesis, University of Aberdeen.

HANLEY N., SIMPSON, I., PARSISSON, D., MACMILLAN, D., BULLOCK, C and CRABTREE, R. (1996). *Valuation of the Conservation Benefits of Environmentally Sensitive Areas*, Economics and Policy Series 2, Macaulay Land Use Research Institute, Aberdeen.

HUGHES G. (1994). ESAs in the Context of a 'Culturally Sensitive Area'. The Case of the Cambrian Mountains. In: Whitby, M.C. (ed.), *Incentives for Countryside Management: The Case of Environmentally Sensitive Areas.* CAB International, Wallingford.

MAFF (1995). *Agriculture in the United Kingdom.* HMSO, London.

MAFF (1996). *United Kingdom: English Environmentally Sensitive Areas.* OECD Seminar on Environmental Benefits from Sustainable Agriculture: Issues and Policies. COM/AGR/CA/ENV/EPOC(96)121, Helsinki.

SKERRETT S.J. (1994). Socio-Economic Evaluation of the Breadalbane Environmentally Sensitive

Area Scheme, 1987-1990: Results and Critique. In: Whitby, M.C. (ed.), *Incentives for Countryside Management: The Case of Environmentally Sensitive Areas*. CAB International, Wallingford.

WHITBY M. (1994). What Future for ESAs? In: Whitby, M.C. (ed.), *Incentives for Countryside Management: The Case of Environmentally Sensitive Areas*. CAB International, Wallingford.

WHITBY M., SAUNDERS C. and WALSH M. (1991). *A Socio-Economic Evaluation of the Pennine Dales Environmentally Sensitive Area*. Report by the University of Newcastle upon Tyne.

WILLIS K.G., GARROD G., SAUNDERS C., and WHITBY M. (1993). *Assessing Methodologies to Value the Benefits of Environmentally Sensitive Areas*. Working Paper No. 39. ESRC Countryside Change Initiative, University of Newcastle upon Tyne.

WINTER M. (1996). *Rural Politics: Policies for Agriculture, Forestry and the Environment*. Routledge, London.

Impact of Environmentally Sensitive Areas (ESAs) on Farm Businesses

A. CLARK

NFU, 164 Shaftesbury Avenue, London WC2H 8HL

ABSTRACT

This paper discusses the broad policy and business context for Environmentally Sensitive Areas (ESAs). It is clear that many farmers have taken up agreements and a significant area is now enrolled; however, challenges await for the ESA programme. Using data drawn from an ADAS study of English ESAs, the paper discusses these challenges and identifies directions in which ESAs may evolve in the future. The paper also identifies the impact on farm businesses and contribution ESAs make to both environmental and socio-economic objectives. The paper concludes with a consideration of the marketing opportunities for ESA outputs and identifies a continuing need for applied research to ensure ESAs meet their objectives.

INTRODUCTION

Since their initial launch in 1987 Environmentally Sensitive Areas (ESAs) have steadily grown in number, area and prestige to the stage that they can now be considered as being at the core of the Government's agri-environment programme. ESAs are important: they have pioneered the UK's voluntary incentive approach towards countryside management; they are a role model for other schemes both here and the rest of Europe; and they were instrumental in shaping the EU's Agri-Environment Regulation 2078/92. In the UK there are now 43 ESAs with over 13,000 participants and an annual spend on farm agreements of £37Million (MAFF, 1996a). Over 3.3 million hectares (about 18% of the agricultural area) are designated under this programme. While the areas of ESA remains small when compared to the agricultural area as a whole (see Table 1), the publicity given to ESAs and their longevity ensures that when farmers talk about countryside schemes it is most often ESAs that they have in mind.

In this paper I wish to identify the characteristics of ESAs that make them attractive to farm businesses, what impact they are having on farm businesses across the countryside (in particular looking at their impact on farm management and support for the family farm), and finally look ahead to identify prospects for their future development. Examples are drawn from the English ESAs which were subject to a policy review during 1996 (ADAS, 1996a). While differences across the United Kingdom are found, the themes discussed are common to all ESAs.

Table 1.   ESA Designations and Agreement Areas in the UK (as at June 1996).

	England	Wales	Scotland	Northern Ireland	UK
Agricultural Areas (ha)	9371000	1493000	5270000	2347000	18481000
ESA Designated (ha)	1149217	519800	1439231	222000	3328248
ESA Agreements (ha)	426683	113543	362801	121000	1024027
Agreement /Agricultural Area (%)	4.55	7.60	6.88	5.15	5.54

ESAs - A WIDER CONTEXT

Before considering these aspects it is important to set ESAs in their policy and economic context. It is a truism that is frequently overlooked that agri-environment schemes do not operate in isolation of their political and business environment. The majority of farmers view ESAs and other conservation schemes not only as an opportunity to "do their bit for the environment" but also out of necessity as a business proposition: they are entirely correct to treat conservation schemes as an alternative "crop". Thus advocates of ESAs must be conscious of the economic environment and its implications for ESA agreements and recruitment. A prime example of this linkage has been the BSE crisis and the likely reform of the CAP Livestock regime it will precipitate.

ESAs do not exist in a policy vacuum: ESAs are one part of the UK's agri-environment package. Not only does this package include a range of alternative agri-environment schemes (at least 13 national schemes in England and Wales alone), it also includes information and advice on best practice (from FWAG and ADAS amongst others); environmental conditions attached to EU support payments; and a baseline of environmental regulation. Thus policy makers have a formidable battery of measures to support, encourage and cajole farmers to farm in an environmentally sensitive manner. It follows therefore that whilst ESAs are not the only solution to reconciling contemporary farm husbandry with environmental stewardship they are perhaps the most obvious.

Having said that, ESAs are an important exemplar of an approach that is likely to be of greater importance in the future. Many will be familiar with the pressures to liberalise world trade in agricultural commodities sponsored by the GATT Settlement and now within the World Trade Organisation. It seems likely to commentators (NFU, 1994; Buckwell, 1996) that a consequence of these developments will be pressure to "decouple" agricultural support from production within the European Union's CAP. Already the US Farm Bill has indicated how this process may take shape with "freedom to farm" backed by conditions on the environmental performance of farm businesses (for further details see Baldock and Mitchell, 1995).

In the EU, Commissioner Fischler also appears to have begun the process of preparing for further CAP reform with the "Cork Declaration" (European Commission, 1996) and focused discussion on the future of the Dairy and Livestock regimes. The Cork Declaration is of particular interest for it envisages a more broadly based agricultural and rural policy that gives greater emphasis to 'public goods' (conservation and a sustainable rural economy) that can be attained through targeted payments to farmers and land managers. Indeed the link between environmental management and employment generation is only now beginning to be explored but it can be anticipated that it will be of growing influence in the future reform of the CAP (Cuff and Rayment, 1997). It is in this policy context that ESAs are likely to find a reinvigorated future for, in the UK especially, agri-environment schemes are likely to provide the backbone of any EU-wide integrated rural development policy such as that proposed by Commissioner Fischler.

However, it would be a mistake only to view ESAs in the context of public policy. I believe that they may also have an increasingly important role in meeting, at least in part, the retailer's desire for more environmentally sensitively produced foodstuffs. Research by the Cooperative Wholesale Society (Shannon, 1995) shows clearly that consumers are becoming increasingly concerned about the source of their food and the nature of production though the extent of this interest may be limited. In this regard the NFU has witnessed a dramatic increase in the number of farmers responding to this demand as they join farm assurance schemes such as FABBL in recent years. I think we can anticipate that ESAs could play an influential role in meeting at least a proportion of the consumers' requirements for safe food and an assured source in the future.

Table 2.   Uptake of ESA Agreement in England (to February 1997).

	Hectares in agreement	Number of agreements	Proportion of eligible area%
Stage I	75,322	3036	51
Stage II	70,190	980	45
Stage III	205,159	2317	56
Stage IV	82,968	1865	32
Total	433,640	8198	

Source: MAFF personal communication

ESA STRUCTURE AND OPERATION

In general ESAs have been well received by farmers and land managers as participation within the programme demonstrates (see Table 2). The main features that have been central to their success have been those of voluntary participation, the combination of regularly reviewed management and capital payments, the flexible term of agreements, the tiered structure, and most crucially the presence of dedicated project officers. It is important that these characteristics be retained in the future. By way of explanation I would like to highlight the impact of several of these features for farm businesses.

- Incentive payments
- Tiered Structure
- Project Officers

Incentive Levels

Not surprisingly, incentive levels are frequently the subject of some contention between participants and the authorities. There is no question that for many incentive levels are a crucial attraction for participation on ESA agreements. Indeed the price sensitivity of agreement holders was demonstrated in ADAS's Economic Evaluation of Stage I ESAs (ADAS, 1996). This showed that even small reductions in payment levels would result in a significant loss in the number of agreement holders from the schemes, especially in the South Downs, Broads and Somerset levels ESAs, where alternative arable cropping regimes remain attractive. Similar responses can be expected in other ESAs. Conversely ADAS's survey also demonstrated that a substantial increase in payment levels would be required in order to attract more participants - clearly payment levels are finely balanced.

An important feature of the current arrangements for payment levels is their regular review. In each ESA payment reviews are held every two years. Conducted by ADAS on behalf of MAFF, these payment reviews consider both the cost of the environmental management required as a part of each ESA agreement and also the agricultural context in which ESA farmers are operating. Thus for example during the 1996 payment review of the Stage I ESAs, the NFU's submission to MAFF emphasised the relatively high costs of bought in fodder for agreement holders in the Pennine Dales ESA following two successive dry years in the Dales. Hence the biennial payment reviews are a two way process. Not only can MAFF alter the relative attraction of each scheme as a whole and tiers within each the scheme in response to area specific or nationwide changes in agricultural circumstances land managers too can benefit from changes in these incentive levels.

The calculation of payment levels on an area wide basis does not suit all farms. A consequence of averaging the cost of environmental management across all farms within an area is that some farms will find that they are under- compensated while others may be theoretically over paid. While the standard payment approach can result in such inequalities there appears no readily available or straightforward alternative. Some have advocated an approach based upon tendering for specific environmental outputs. Though tendering would require farmers to compete against one another as they put forward bids for the required management, in the NFU's view such an approach would not only be potentially divisive, resulting in wide differences in payments levels, it could also result in an opaque system of reward for environmental management - in stark contrast to the current system.

However, we must recognise that area payments do present problems for some categories of farm businesses, notably for tenant farmers and those on relatively small holdings. ESA agreements are based upon the area of land entered into agreement. Tenant farmers must have the security to commit themselves to the term of the agreement, as well as the ability to meet the Scheme's requirements. This is not always possible where seasonal grazing lets or short term farm business tenancies are an integral part of the farm business and the landlord fails to cooperate by putting together a practical management package to MAFF. Area payments also facilitate land to be taken in-hand rather than be let out.

It follows that the incentive to participate is smaller for those farm businesses with little eligible area, those on the margins of an ESA for example. For these businesses the benefit of taking up an agreement is often outweighed by the costs of participation and of adopting the required management practices. As a result a significant proportion of eligible area and many eligible holdings may find themselves effectively excluded from participation. The NFU is aware of three ESAs (Upper Thames, Pennine Dales and South West Peak) where this problem has been reported. Obviously the solution is not easy: some suggest a whole farm approach whereby farm businesses are entered as a whole even though only part of the farm falls within the ESA area; alternatively a minimum payment could be made for participation as is the practice within Tir Cymen.

Management Tiers

The tiered structure of ESAs has been refined since the programme was first introduced, however, it remains a core component of schemes. While entry into the basic tier is voluntary and most eligible land, subject to tests of value for money, would be accepted, higher management tiers place a greater emphasis on the Project Officer's discretion. It would appear that farmers welcome this approach. They may select the tiers most suited to their situation and opt at a later stage for more ambitious tiers as their knowledge and confidence grows.

Obviously as ESAs evolve, some pressure has been placed on raising the requirements for basic management tiers. This movement is not welcome for many businesses as it misreads the role of these basic tiers and places significant strains on the viability of participation. Our approach is that ESAs first objective should be to enrol a critical mass of farm businesses and support their efforts to conserve the existing farmed landscape. On the basis of this critical mass efforts can then be made to encourage and support change in desirable directions - but this latter role should not be confused with the distinct function of 'Tier 1' payments.

Indeed with the cessation of the Farm and Conservation Grant Scheme, in England there is a cogent argument for bringing in a management tier for countryside features complementary to existing 'Tier 1' land management and available to farmers within ESAs but without 'eligible' land.

Project Officers

The role of the ESA Project Officers has been critical to the success of the ESA programme. They are effectively the salespeople for ESA Schemes and the first point of contact with farmers collectively and individually. The NFU's own internal consultations clearly demonstrate that in ESAs Project Officers play an authoritative role in negotiating individual applications, introducing a degree of flexibility within the scheme guidelines, scheme development and in trouble shooting. These functions cannot be underestimated (NFU, 1996). Furthermore, as in the early days of ESAs, a Project Officers' personal character has changed farmers' opinions from one of scepticism to enthusiasm. A significant element of this success has been due to their accessibility to ESA farmers and empathy with local farming conditions and practices.

It is clear from these comments above that it is vital that good lines of communication are maintained both between farmers and their Project Officer and between the officer and MAFF centrally. We have found that the local ESA liaison groups have greatly assisted farmers to put across their concerns about farm businesses within each ESA.

THE IMPACT OF ESAs ON FARM BUSINESSES

There is little doubt that in some areas ESAs play an important role in the local farm economy. One would only have to consider the uplands of England where ESAs cover at least 30% of the LFA to appreciate the potential scale of this contribution. However, in lowland Britain ESAs may be less significant. It is appropriate to evaluate the socio-economic impact of ESAs to the local economy of both participating farm business and those beyond ESA designations.

Perhaps the most important factor in determining the motivation for farm businesses to take up an ESA agreement is the scale of payments offered (see Table 3). Within the Stage I ESAs the bulk of participants regard payment levels as crucial to their involvement. This was born out by the review undertaken in the Sussex Downs ESA (ADAS, 1996a). This found that 77% of participants cited payments as their most important reason for participating (compared with 45% of non-participants who felt payments were unattractive). Generally participants were more strongly motivated by care for the environment and the fact that the required management fitted well with their current practice.

Table 3.   Reasons for entering an ESA Agreement (% of respondents).

Reason	West Penwith	The Broads	Somerset Levels	South Downs	Pennine Dales
Payments	88	92	68	77	88
Eligible for grants	4	9	2	0	12
Care for the environment	48	59	32	63	25
Consistent reform system	40	69	58	40	23
Security of income	8	35	4	9	20
Project officer influence	10	10	14	7	1

An assumption generally made is that larger farm businesses have greater flexibility to join ESA agreements. While this theoretical position would appear to have some validity it does not always appear to always be the case. Comparing the scale of participating ESA farm businesses in the Broads with those in the Pennine Dales ESA, in the Broads businesses are noticeably larger than on average (204ha compared to the regional average of 82ha) whereas in the Pennine Dales participating businesses were smaller than on average (Table 4). It is notable, however, that only the Pennine Dales ESA exhibits this characteristic, which may have more to do with local circumstances of land tenure. Taken over the five ESA on average larger farm businesses do indeed find they have greater flexibility to commit to an ESA agreement than do smaller businesses.

Table 4.   Analysis of ESA and non-ESA average farms by area (ha).

	Participants	Non-participants
South Downs	290	102
Somerset Levels	75	55
West Penwith	81	29
Broads	204	82*
Pennine Dales	131	178

Note Norfolk MAFF census data

That being said it is not surprising, given the importance attributed to payment levels by farmers, that ESAs do contribute to farm business income. During 1996 farm businesses in the five Stage 1 ESA received an average of £3456 per agreement (MAFF, personal communication). The extent of the importance of these payments may be assessed in a number of ways: the impact of ESA payments on employment generation and the concerns of farmer should ESA payments be removed being but two. Obviously both measures are problematic as differentiating between impacts of the ESA as opposed to other factors. Nevertheless the ADAS Survey (ADAS, 1996a) does provide some indication of the response of farm businesses should ESAs be removed (see table 5 and 6).

Table 5.   Change in On-farm employment if ESAs were removed.

	Present	Without ESA	No.	%
South Downs	270	205	-65	-24
Somerset Levels	336	265	-71	-21
West Penwith	167	162	-5	-3
The Broads	1819	1652	-167	-9
Pennine Dales	283	270	-13	-5
Across ESA sample	2875	2554	-321	-20

Table 6.   Concerns if ESAs were removed (% of sample).

	South Downs	Somerset Levels	West Penwith	The Broads	Pennine Dales
Financial worried	25	25	32	11	16
Disappointed	19	24	14	25	46
Efforts wasted	26	8	18	11	23
Concern for environment	28	20	28	53	6
No concern	2	23	8	0	10

In terms of employment generation ESAs do appear to have an obvious beneficial impact. Not only does ESA management seek to maintain management practices such as stock husbandry or hay production which are often labour intensive, it also supports the management of features in ESAs. Payments to encourage the restoration of stonewalls or traditional farm buildings are notable examples. This generates employment potential not only for farm staff but also for more specialised trades within the local economy. It would therefore be a fair estimate of the contribution of ESAs to farm businesses to accept that up to 20% fewer employment opportunities would be generated in their absence. This finding finds strong endorsement from a recent study of Tir Cymen in Wales (ADAS, 1996b). This found that 62 person years of employment was generated by Tir Cymen on the 391 farms in agreement.

This marginal, though specific decrease in employment numbers is born out by the finding that a significant proportion of farmers would be concerned about the financial situation of their farm businesses in the absence of ESA payments (Table 6). It is likely that farm businesses would have to respond in a number of ways should environmental incentives were suspended. The most common response would be an intensification of the current enterprises, most obviously through increases in stocking density or resuming applications of artificial fertiliser and pesticides. Other businesses may revert from pastoral to crop based systems, though this transition would be hampered by the current eligibility for arable payments under IACS. Whatever the method of change, it is likely that an ending of ESA payments would result in dramatic changes not only for business structure but the environment as well.

Despite the beneficial impacts of ESAs there remains one business issue which has caused some farmers unease. This is generally termed the 'halo effect'. This effect is the perceived impact of payments of farm businesses who are not participants within the scheme.

For those outside eligible areas, or for business reasons those who choose not to participate, there is concern that the ESA programmes can affect their capacity to respond to the demands of the market and their ability to compete fairly for available resources. This feeling is especially acute in those areas with a high concentration of designations, the LFA being a good example. In such areas, in common with other approaches that use 'lines-on-maps' to define target areas, there is a widespread perception that ESA agreement holders may outbid non-participants for fodder, and grass keep due to the enhanced income they derive from ESA agreements. The recently high price of seasonally let land and fodder is often used as evidence for this concern.

In the NFU we are aware of some local examples where the available evidence to support this belief is convincing. However, this same evidence seems to suggest local rather than nationwide distortions are at work and that the impact of other factors, such as livestock extensification premia, need also to be considered. Clearly this is an issue which weighs on some farm businesses and is problematic for Government departments. If agri-environment schemes are to be extended countryside ways must be found that benefit the majority without harming the minority. To this end the NFU proposes that schemes should be open to all farm businesses wherever they farm rather than only in designated areas.

Having considered the business context for ESAs I now wish to turn my attention to the future challenges with which ESAs are presented.

FUTURE CHANGES FOR ESAs

If one is to look to the future I expect there are five key challenges that we may anticipate:

- Retaining and attracting a critical mass of participation;
- Steps to improve the ESA farmscape;
- The role of ESAs in Government's environmental policies;
- The context of changing market place demands; and,
- Demands for information on environmentally sensitive farm management.

Conserving the ESA Farmscape

As has been stated, a critical role of ESAs is their contribution to ensuring that the character and quality of the landscape remains largely unaltered at a time when the wider countryside continues to evolve (see, for example, Barr *et al.*, 1993). That being said it is not the role of an ESA to 'freeze' the landscape. Rather ESAs should foster and sustain farm management practices that have resulted in the traditional character for which they were originally designated. I believe this role will come under increasing pressure as the countryside beyond the ESA continues to change in response to pressures not only resulting from agricultural practice but also from the many other forces influencing our use and management of the countryside. Hence the challenge for the ESA programme will be to ensure that sufficient farm businesses participate in each programme so that the integrity of each ESAs landscape is conserved. I expect this will require efforts to broaden the base of positive conservation investment by more farmers in each ESA whether by opening conservation plans to agreement holders without land entered into the scheme or including specific management tiers for more intensively farmed land such as arable and improved grassland enterprises - as is already happened in the South Downs ESA.

Guiding Improvements in ESAs

Until the publication by MAFF of environmental objectives and performance indicators for English ESAs (MAFF 1994), there was little guidance towards the desired 'end-state' for each ESA. In this publication's place perhaps the best indication of success was a simple enrolment in each scheme. Clearly in the latter half of the 1990s this former approach was not satisfactory and I expect further strategic thinking to be undertaken to evolve a vision for each ESA. Perhaps the English Nature/Countryside Commission Character Map of England (EN/CoCo, 1996) may provide some regional guidance in this regard. Certainly a major component of the most recent round of ESA policy reviews has been greater clarity to scheme objectives and a commitment to develop targets of each scheme in consultation with local interests (for example MAFF, 1996b). This process is to be facilitated via discussions with the ESA Liaison Groups who will advise on priorities and suggest targets. I expect that in the future a growing challenge will be to set objectives for ESA schemes that enjoy widespread consensus and set a wide range of priorities.

Broader Environmental Policy Context

Few Government statements on the countryside do not now contain some references to need to encourage sustainable development or to conserve biodiversity. ESAs must now be viewed in the context of these core policy concepts, and are an important components of farmers' contribution to their achievement. In the NFU we concur with MAFF that the ESA programme will yield both significant benefits for biodiversity and also be practical examples of sustainable development in practice. It is therefore interesting to note that with the publication of the recent policy reviews for each ESA explicit mention was made of promoting biodiversity. Within each ESA lists of species that would benefit from greater flexibility of management are now included - strangely however few references are made to important habitats. The challenge for the future will therefore be to make this linkage between Government's environmental objectives more explicit.

Justifying ESA Schemes

Reference was made earlier to the pressures to liberalise world trade. Not only will these moves indirectly impact upon ESA programmes via a relative profitability of specific farming practices, it is also clear that the EU's agri-environment programmes will come under increasingly sceptical scrutiny by parties involved in the WTO discussions. At a recent OECD seminar on the environmental benefits of agriculture (OECD, 1996) markers have been put down by the Cairn's Group of nations (prominent free trade advocates including Australia, New Zealand, Argentina, Canada and the USA) that they will look closely at the benefits of environmental payments. These countries are wary of payments for environmental goods as, if poorly targeted, they would effectively be a support to domestic farming communities and potentially distort free trade. It is therefore a priority to ensure that ESA schemes not only meet the domestic and EU desire to see farmers provide environmental and public goods but also to ensure that our world trade partners perceive these payments as fully justified by the environmental benefits produced.

ESAs and Consumer Preference

It is evident to many farmers that consumers are increasingly conscious about methods of food production. Many farmers are responding to this concern by improving the traceability and market awareness of their output. A good example being the 'Fellbred Initiative' launched in 1996 and comprising a consortium of Cumbrian groups including many of the participants at this BGS conference. I do not expect every farmer to take the innovative steps of those in Cumbria for no other reason than there is an obvious limit to the number of 'niche' products with which consumers can be familiar. However, it would appear that producers within ESAs are uniquely positioned to benefit from consumers' newly found interest - they farm in areas that have a unique character, employ 'traditional' farming systems and use methods of production that are environmentally friendly.

197

Therefore the challenge for producers is to seize the opportunity of greener markets to add value to their ESA production systems.

New Information Requirements

When first launched little was known about the techniques required to sustain and recreate environmentally sensitive landscapes on the scale of whole ESAs. After ten years in many ways we can look back upon a macro scale land management experiment. Much has been learned about how land should be managed, and interestingly preconceptions about what is environmentally beneficial been challenged. For the farmers the main lesson has been that the path from a productive sward containing few species to a species-rich grassland is not going to be achieved swiftly or consistently. Improvement of grassland for agricultural reasons is better understood than is improvement for biodiversity. Thus as our objectives for ESAs grow more ambitious so will farmers requirements for information on both the status of current landscapes and habitats and also the evolution of these in desired directions. Therefore, I anticipate a continuing need for applied research, the development of new land management prescriptions and the effective monitoring of existing schemes to support the continued improvement of the ESA programme.

CONCLUSIONS

The NFU is a firm advocate of the ESA approach. The programme anticipated many of the core elements of agri-environment schemes both in the UK and abroad. ESAs also typify the European approach to nature and landscape conservation - that is farming in a manner that is compatible with both rural biodiversity and the viability of farm businesses. As we look to the future the main challenge will be to ensure that ESAs not only respond to the developing environmental agenda but also maintain the confidence of both farmers and the general public that real value is being delivered. To this end it is vital that farmers and researchers maintain a close dialogue that ensures the efficient transfer of new approaches and that there is ready awareness of the practical realities of ESA farming amongst policy makers and environmentalists alike.

REFERENCES

ADAS (1996a) Economic Evaluation of Stage 1 ESAs: Follow-up Study Report. ADAS, London.
ADAS (1996b) Socio-economic Assessment of Tir Cymen. CCW, Bangor.
BALDOCK D. and MITCHELL K. (1995) Cross-Compliance within the Common Agricultural Policy. IEEP, London.
BARR C.J., BUNCE R.G.H., CLARKE R.T., FULLER R.M., FURSE M.T., GILLESPIE M.K., GROOM G.B., HALLAM C.J., HORNUNG M., HOWARD D.C. and NESS M.J. (1993) Countryside Survey 1990 Main Report. DoE, London.
BUCKWELL A. (1996) Towards a Common Agricultural and Rural Policy for Europe. *1996 Asher Winegarten Memorial Lecture*. NFU, London.
CUFF J. and RAYMENT M. (1997) Working with Nature: Economies, Employment and Conservation in Europe. RSPB/Birdlife International, Sandy, Bedfordshire.
ENGLISH NATURE AND THE COUNTRYSIDE COMMISSION (1996) The character of

England: landscape, Wildlife and Natural Features. Cheltenham, England.

EUROPEAN COMMISSION (1996) Rural Europe - Future Perspectives: The Cork Declaration - A Living Countryside. *European Conference on Rural Development 7-9th November 1996*. Cork, Ireland.

MAFF (1994) Environmentally Sensitive Areas Scheme - Environmental objectives and performance indicators for ESAs in England. MAFF, London.

MAFF (1996a) Environmentally Sensitive Areas and other Schemes under the Agri-Environment Regulation. *Memorandum of Evidence Submitted to the House of Commons Select Committee on Agriculture*. MAFF, London.

MAFF (1996b) A consultation document from MAFF on proposals for the future of the Pennine Dales ESA. MAFF, London.

NATIONAL FARMERS UNION (1994) Real Choices. NFU, London.

NATIONAL FARMERS UNION (1996) ESAs and Other Agri-Environment Schemes.*Memorandum of Evidence Submitted to the House of Commons Select Committee on Agriculture*. NFU, London.

OECD (1996) Conclusions. *OECD Seminar on Environmental Benefits from a Sustainable Agriculture: Issues and Policies, 10-13th September 1996*. Helsinki, Finland.

SHANNON B. (1995) Agriculture and the Environment - a retailers view. *1st National FWAG Conference 30th November 1995*. NEC, Birmingham.

The Way Forward with Environmentally Sensitive Areas

R. J. WILKINS

Institute of Grassland and Environmental Research, North Wyke, Okehampton, Devon
EX20 2SB

ABSTRACT

An analysis of the strengths, weaknesses, opportunities and threats to the ESA scheme is made followed by consideration of future needs for support for environmental schemes, with reference to environmental aid schemes in Germany and Denmark. The possibilities for complete reliance on cross-compliance for achieving environmental goals are discussed and the attractions of countrywide schemes based on Countryside Stewardship or Tir Cymen are considered in relation to the development of the ESA scheme. It is concluded that there will be a continued case for Government support for environmental maintenance and enhancement and that the ESA scheme will continue to be particularly appropriate where discrete and coherent units of environmental interest and sensitivity can be identified. Increasing attention should be paid to environmental enhancement rather than maintenance, with a higher proportion of payments made to higher tier agreements. There is a case for extension of initiatives for environmental enhancement in other areas of the country. Cross-compliance cannot be used to offer spatially targeted environmental maintenance or enhancement.

INTRODUCTION

It is a daunting task to produce this final paper in the Conference, particularly as it is the fourth paper in a session entitled 'The Future', with many aspects of further possibilities having been detailed in the earlier contributions.

I will attempt to integrate some of the themes of the conference, highlighting challenges for policy makers, land managers and researchers. It is good to be dealing with a success story. Ever since its launch, the ESA scheme has been widely applauded throughout Society and by the farming industry (at least in areas designated as ESAs). Adoption rates have been high, major objectives have been satisfied and analyses have suggested large benefits in relation to the costs involved.

The framework of this paper is to undertake a SWOT analysis of the present scheme, consider future needs for support for environmental schemes, review briefly points from parallel schemes in other EU countries and consider three alternative models for the future. This is written from my background as a grassland scientist with interest in land-use issues, who has not been directly involved in the evolution or execution of the ESA policy.

THE PRESENT SCHEME

A SWOT analysis is given in Table 1. Many of the points have been covered in detail in other Conference papers. The overall aim of the ESA scheme was indicated by Swash (1997) as 'to maintain the landscape, wildlife and historic value of defined areas by encouraging beneficial agricultural practices'. It is thus a major strength of the scheme that appraisals discussed by Critchley (1997) and Swash (1997) conclude that the major objective of maintaining these values has been achieved. The retention of a high proportion of the extra grant income by farmers, as noted by Crabtree and Barron (1997),

Table 1. SWOT analysis of ESA scheme.

Strengths	Weaknesses
Success in arresting environmental degradation in designated areas.	Little environmental enhancement.
Increased income for farmers and rural communities.	Long-term benefits not ensured.
	Low adoption in some ESAs and for higher tiers.
Generally high adoption.	Only applies to part of country.
Employment generation.	Focuses on inputs not environmental outputs.
High perceived benefit:cost ratio.	
Voluntary principle.	Objectives not clear cut.
	Inflexible.
	Cost to exchequer.
	Little involvement of Society in scheme evolution.

Opportunities	Threats
Adoption of regulations and incentives to improve uptake and delivery.	Reduced willingness to pay by Government.
Development in wider geographical area.	Payments may not be acceptable in world trade negotiation.
Vehicle for foods with environmentally sensitive production methods.	Higher returns from other land uses may reduce uptake.
	Absorption within scheme for Integrated Rural Policy.

particularly for schemes involving maintenance rather than enhancement of the environment, and positive effects on employment (Clark, 1997), both indicate wider benefits for rural communities and economies. The results of contingent valuation exercises (Willis *et al.*, 1993; Hanley *et al.*, 1996) indicate a high ratio of perceived benefits to Exchequer costs for ESA schemes. This is extremely encouraging, but limitations to such studies are well recognized. I suspect that the 'willingness to pay' figures obtained from studies of ESAs (or other schemes to benefit the environment) are higher in studies carried out separately for particular ESAs and schemes, than if a comprehensive study were made, with individuals asked for reactions to all environmental schemes in the same exercise. Nevertheless the studies made have given very positive results. The voluntary principle was a key for successful scheme introduction, avoiding controversies of compulsory designation schemes such as that for Sites of Special Scientific Interest.

Any further development of the scheme should obviously seek to capitalize on the strengths whilst seeking to reduce areas of weakness. Whilst ESAs appear to have been successful in maintaining landscapes, there is, as yet, less evidence of environmental enhancement, despite the relaunch of schemes in 1992 and 1993 including greater emphasis on restoration and enhancement (Coates, 1997). Critchley (1997) says that 'Evidence of enhancement of grasslands within the ESA scheme is more limited, however, and where this has occurred, the changes are relatively small'. Swash (1997) refers to some examples of enhancement, but considered generally that wildlife conservation interest was being maintained.

In order to obtain enhancement it is, of course, necessary to (i) identify clearly the target, (ii) have the technical means for achieving that target and (iii) provide incentives for the land manager to seek to achieve the target. There is some concern as to whether the objectives in particular ESAs have been sufficiently clearly defined, with Bullock and McHenry (1997) stating that 'The problems therefore are, firstly, to determine exactly what it is that the public actually values, and, secondly, how to protect this without turning farmers into museum fixtures'. I have the impression that there was little direct involvement of society at large in the evolution of the ESA scheme and its prescriptions, and that a more participatory approach involving the various stakeholders may have advantage in the further evolution of the scheme.

The fear that the scheme rewards the management prescription (*i.e.* regulation of inputs) rather than directly rewarding the delivery of environmental goods (*i.e.* outputs) is recognised as a weakness (Coates, 1997). It is, however, a major challenge to devise an administratively acceptable scheme to give payment directly for outputs and it is likely that input control will remain the predominant feature. Accumulated experience and outputs from research and development should, however, progressively refine the procedures that can be followed to deliver environmental enhancement within farming systems. Papers from this Conference (*e.g.* Smith, 1997; Tallowin and Mountford, 1997) provide a strong basis for improving prescriptions for grassland management. Increased emphasis on achieving environmental enhancement produces a case for devoting a larger proportion of the resource to the higher tiers of the scheme as their regulations are designed for this purpose.

Flexibility, both through modification in the rules to incorporate new information, as discussed in the context of the Pennine Dales ESA by Howard (1997), and through consideration of special circumstances in particular situations, will be important for future success. Whilst Crabtree and Barron (1997) are correct to point out that the scheme does not guarantee any long-term benefits, because farmers are only bound by agreement for a 5 or 10 year period, it is difficult to envisage a situation in which voluntary agreements would be made for a longer period. For ensuring longer-term benefits there would probably be a need to divert more of the payment to 'capital' items or to move to a scheme with statutory land designation.

The opportunities for improvement in the scheme have largely been alluded to in the earlier discussion. I wish, however, to reiterate the point made by Clark (1997) that the ESAs do provide a vehicle for the labelling and marketing of agricultural products according to their production in an environmentally sensitive way. Whilst this was not a specific intention of the ESA policy, production within whole-farm ESA schemes could be an important selling point to a public increasingly concerned about food quality and methods of production.

The threats to the ESA policy arise largely from economic factors and the evolution of improved and more integrated schemes for delivery of rural policy. A current yardstick for appraising costs of the ESA scheme is the expenditure in relation to total CAP expenditure; Crabtree and Barron (1997), for instance, note that the expenditure on Agri-Environmental Schemes in aggregate is only 0.6% of CAP expenditure. However, CAP expenditure is currently astronomic, and with reduction in the general CAP support, the absolute costs of Agri-Environmental Schemes will come into increasing focus and tight scrutiny. The compatibility of these schemes with the deliberations and decisions of the Word Trade Organization was queried by Clark (1997). Whilst the pressure for improved and integrated rural policies, as reflected in the Conference (Coates, 1997), may provide a threat to the ESA scheme *per se*, its incorporation into a wider policy has the potential of increasing overall benefits from Exchequer support.

THE FUTURE NEED FOR ESA-TYPE POLICIES

There is need to reflect on whether the environmental features which ESAs were set up to protect are going to continue to be under pressure in the future and whether means other than Government payments could be used to deliver the required benefits.

In the short-to-medium term it is quite likely that the pressure to intensify agricultural production (or to maintain intensive systems) will reduce, because of continued concerns for over-production within the EU and adjustments to lower market prices. Indeed Crabtree and Barron (1997) indicate that 'risk from changes to farming practice now seem much reduced'. This, however, must be put against the appraisals of existing ESA schemes which indicate that even small reductions in payment levels will result in a significant loss in the number of agreement holders leading to the adoption of more intensive management practices and alterations in cropping. Possibly the pressures on farming systems and environmental sensitivity are higher in areas of England where there are a wider range of alternative enterprises and managements than in the generally more extensively managed areas in Scotland. A further factor is the longer term projection of increased real demand for food on a world basis (Pinstrup-Anderson, 1997) and increases in demand for land for fibre and biomass production. Such development would lead to pressures for intensive land use in Britain. Despite a possible short-term trend to extensification, there seems to be a persuasive case for continuing specific actions to protect and improve environmentally sensitive areas. This protection could, of course, be provided by statutory action, but the success of the voluntary principle involved in the

ESA scheme and concern for maintaining income levels in rural areas, are likely to favour continuation of ESA-type schemes.

We must consider, however, whether the market-place rather than the Exchequer could be used to achieve these objectives. Whilst there may be some possibilities for obtaining added value by marketing products from ESAs, as discussed above, and also for obtaining financial benefits from tourism stimulated by improved landscapes, it is probable that direct financial support to the land manager will be needed for sustaining or enhancing the environment in the long-term.

FEATURES FROM SCHEMES IN OTHER EU COUNTRIES

Schemes operating in different EU countries are reviewed in Baldock (1996). A major feature is the high diversity of agri-environmental schemes that are extant. I wish to draw attention to only two of these schemes. Firstly the MEKA scheme, which has operated since 1992 in Baden-Württemberg and directed to provide compensation for market relief and to maintain traditional landscapes. In this highly successful scheme, participating farmers are awarded points for maintaining or adopting specific farming practices, with farmers able to choose from a large number of possible measures and receiving payment for 'eco-points' up to a maximum amount per ha. This scheme suffers from the limitation, as with ESAs, of concentrating on inputs rather than outputs, it provides little focus on the pursuit of specific targets and is weak in situations where a series of actions (each with their own 'eco-points') are needed to deliver real benefits. It is, however, a transparent system with a higher level of flexibility than exists with the limited number of tiers in ESAs.

The second example, from Denmark, illustrates a higher local involvement in the evolution of a scheme. Each county was empowered to identify a maximum of 4% of the farmland as environmentally sensitive areas, with general guidelines on objectives being provided centrally. A consultation process was then carried out to identify specific objectives and areas, involving municipalities, farmers groups and local conservation bodies. Whilst the resulting scheme was scattered and fragmented, this participatory approach increased local 'ownership' and fully utilized local knowledge and views.

MODELS FOR THE FUTURE

This section considers three possible models for the maintenance and enhancement of the environment and landscape. All have been alluded to in the Conference. They are:
(i) the reliance on cross-compliance to achieve environmental protection and enhancement,
(ii) the establishment of a countrywide scheme developed from Countryside Stewardship,
(iii) the 'natural' development of the current ESA scheme.

The inclusion of cross-compliance provision within agricultural support schemes could be used to prevent environmental damage through ensuring, for instance, that stocking rates are below levels that would cause over-grazing and erosion and to ensure that actions are taken to prevent pollution of atmosphere and water. In essence it could achieve actions which are required generally for good husbandry and stewardship. It would, however, be an entirely inappropriate approach to ensuring spatially-targeted actions, an essential feature of the ESA scheme. Also the eventual elimination of agricultural support would bring with it the disappearance of the environmental protection mechanism.

Coates (1997) indicates that the environmental priorities for Countryside Stewardship are similar to those for ESAs. Although the scheme is available throughout England, it is targeted at particular landscapes and features. Tir Cymen is a parallel scheme in Wales and consideration is being given to the possibility of amalgamating Tir Cymen with the ESA scheme and extending coverage possibly to the entire country (Welsh Office Agriculture Department, 1997). Crabtree and Barron (1997) also query the relevance of the spatially defined ESA scheme to Scotland. Whilst accepting that there are distinct areas in England with environmental sensitivities to farming methods they maintain that '.... in Scotland where distinct sensitive areas cannot so readily be defined it has to be questioned whether the scheme was ever really appropriate.' If it were decided to extend ESAs more widely or to enhance the Countryside Stewardship/Tir Cymen-type schemes there would need to be a mechanism to limit total cost to the Exchequer. Appraisal of the ESA scheme indicates the high sensitivity of uptake to the level of grant offered. It would appear that for worthwhile benefits to be obtained from any nationally available scheme, there would need to be a cap on total expenditure, or limit to the area that could be included in the scheme. This cap could be applied at the national level or at the district level, giving the possibility of taking cognisance of particular pressures and opportunities more locally and introducing some local participatory element within the scheme's evolution.

The essential strength of the ESA scheme depends on the ability to identify areas of environmental significance that each represent a discrete and coherent unit of environmental interest which is dependant on the adoption, maintenance or extension of particular farming practices (Swash, 1997, from Harrison, in press). Once areas have been identified, the policy needs to have sufficient financial support to obtain a high level of participation to achieve environmental maintenance or enhancement throughout this area. Any proposals for new ESAs must fully consider these criteria. Possibly there is need to look again at some of the existing designated areas in this context.

Within justifiably discrete and distinct ESA areas, there will, as discussed earlier, be a need to progressively incorporate new technical information to improve the delivery of environmental benefits. For real environmental enhancement it will be necessary to increasingly target management for specific objectives in particular areas as discussed by Wilkins and Harvey (1994), probably involving further incentives for participation in higher tiers of the scheme. Where spatially distinct areas at risk cannot be identified, the operation of schemes based on Countryside Stewardship, but available to all farmers (up to a capped limit of participation) has much attraction, giving a wider potential for land managers to participate in Stewardship and consider, as noted by Clark (1997), conservation schemes as an alternative 'crop'.

REFERENCES

BALDOCK D. (1996) *Incentives for environmentally sound farming in the European Community*. Report of European Workshop, Otley, 1992. London: Institute for European Environmental

Policy.
BULLOCK C.H. and McHENRY, H.L. (1997) A way forward for environmentally sensitive farming that meets the needs of public and farmer. In: Sheldrick, R.D. (ed) *Grassland Management in the ESAs, Occasional Symposium of the British Grassland Society*, No. 32.
CLARK A. (1997) Impact of Environmentally Sensitive Areas (ESAs) on farm businesses. In: Sheldrick, R.D. (ed) *Grassland Management in the ESAs, Occasional Symposium of the British Grassland Society*, No. 32.
COATES D. (1997) UK policy for ESAs. In: Sheldrick, R.D. (ed) *Grassland Management in the ESAs, Occasional Symposium of the British Grassland Society*, No. 32.
CRABTREE B. and BARRON N. (1997) Cost benefit for the taxpayer. In: Sheldrick, R.D. (ed) *Grassland Management in the ESAs, Occasional Symposium of the British Grassland Society*, No. 32.
CRITCHLEY C.N.R. (1997) Monitoring methods. In: Sheldrick, R.D. (ed) *Grassland Management in the ESAs, Occasional Symposium of the British Grassland Society*, No. 32.
HANLEY N., SIMPSON I., PARSISSON D., MACMILLAN D., BULLOCK C. and CRABTREE R. (1996) *Valuation of the conservation benefits of Environmentally Sensitive Areas*. Economics and Policy Series 2, Macaulay Land Use Research Institute, Aberdeen.
HOWARD N.J. (1997) My experiences of hill farming in the Pennine Dales ESA. In: Sheldrick, R.D. (ed) *Grassland Management in the ESAs, Occasional Symposium of the British Grassland Society*, No. 32.
PINSTRUP-ANDERSON P. (1997) A vision of the future world food production and implications for the environment and grasslands. *Proceedings XVIII International Grassland Congress*, Winnipeg, 1997 (in press).
SMITH R.S. (1997) Upland meadow grasslands in the Pennine Dales Environmentally Sensitive Area (ESA). In: Sheldrick, R.D. (ed) *Grassland Management in the ESAs, Occasional Symposium of the British Grassland Society*, No. 32.
SWASH A. (1997) Environmentally Sensitive Areas and their grassland resource. In: Sheldrick, R.D. (ed) *Grassland Management in the ESAs, Occasional Symposium of the British Grassland Society*, No. 32.
TALLOWIN J.R.B. and MOUNTFORD J.O. (1997) Lowland wet grasslands in ESAs. In: Sheldrick, R.D. (ed) *Grassland Management in the ESAs, Occasional Symposium of the British Grassland Society*, No. 32.
WELSH OFFICE AGRICULTURE DEPARTMENT (1997) *Agri-environmental schemes in Wales. Consultative Paper*. Cardiff: Welsh Office Agriculture Department.
WILKINS R.J. and HARVEY H.J. (1994) Management options to achieve agricultural and nature conservation objectives. In: Haggar, R.J. and Peel, S. (eds) *Grassland Management and Nature Conservation, Occasional Symposium of the British Grassland Society*, No. 28, pp. 86-94.
WILLIS K.G., GARROD G., SAUNDERS C. and WHITBY M. (1993) *Assessing methodology to value the benefits of Environmentally Sensitive Areas*. Working Paper No. 39, ESRC Countryside Change Initiative, University of Newcastle upon Tyne.

POSTER PRESENTATIONS

Contributions arranged alphabetically by
Surname of First Author

An Environmental Information System for ESA Management

D. ASKEW

FRCA Leeds, Lawnswood, Otley Road, Leeds

INTRODUCTION

A vast amount of information relating to land under ESA agreement has been and continues to be generated. This ranges from ownership details of fields to detailed scientific monitoring data, including, for example, botanical species records. The ability to access and use this information effectively is one important aspect of ESA management. MAFF have funded the development by FRCA Leeds of a GIS (Geographical Information System) based environmental information system to provide, storage management and analysis capabilities of this information resource. Pilot systems have been developed for the Lake District and Pennine Dales ESAs.

SYSTEM DEVELOPMENT

The volume and nature of the data involved have been an important factor in the choice of a computer based GIS approach. Data accumulates over time and individual grassland fields in the Pennine Dales ESA having been under agreement since 1987 for example. There are now some 15,000 plus individual fields under agreement. Most of the data is spatial in that it can be related to a location; either an individual field or a farm. Much ESA data exists in digital format in for example, databases or digital maps. In addition to these data related requirements, analysis demands have also evolved. There is an increased requirement to take a more targeted approach to ESA agreements and to include spatial considerations in scheme evaluation. At its simplest level this means answering the question 'where are ESA agreements?' rather than simply 'how many ESA agreements?'

These factors all indicated that a GIS based approach would provide advantages. This would allow large volumes of digital data to be related to a common underlying geography and the spatial aspects of the data to be utilised in analysis. In addition recent technological advances and falling real costs of hardware have made the provision of relatively simple PC based GIS based systems an increasingly realistic option.

SYSTEM DESCRIPTION

The ESA system was developed using ESRI's ArcView software; a desktop viewing and GIS package. The system is generally run on PCs with at least a P133 processor and 24 mb of RAM under Windows '95. The system uses inbuilt ArcView functions and also customised ESA query routines.

The core data used is ESA agreement information over an Ordnance Survey map base. ESA agreement maps for each holding are created digitally which allows them to be readily converted for use within the GIS. This information includes agreement holder details, field numbers and areas, ESA options and details of other environmental features such as stockproof walls. In addition information on other relevant designations such as SSSIs are also stored on the system. Environmental survey data collected by FRCA are also stored by site; for example botanical monitoring fields.

Also, where relevant environmental data is available from other bodies these are also incorporated. For example, grassland inventory data from English Nature indicating known grasslands of interest and breeding wader survey records from RSPB.

EXAMPLE APPLICATIONS

The system can be used to answer queries from a wide range of people involved in ESA management including Project Officers, ecologists and MAFF. Two specific examples are described.

Combining ESA agreement data with external data sources allows a comprehensive assessment of ESA uptake. As well as quantifying and describing overall uptake within an ESA the system also allows uptake to be assessed against specific features. Table 1 gives an example of uptake figures in the Pennine Dales ESA generated by the system.

Table 1.   Features under agreement in the Pennine Dales ESA by March 1997.

	% under agreement	
	1992	1996
ESA (area)	50	59
SSSIs (area)	63	74
EN grassland sites (number)	57	69
EN calcareous sites on inventory (number)	31	35

These figures indicate a disproportionately high uptake of SSSI designated land and conversely relatively lower uptake of calcareous grassland.

An example from the Lake District ESA involved the identification of land under Tier II wetland agreement within 10 km of 4 recorded marsh fritillary breeding sites. This information is being fed back to the Project Officer to ensure where possible, appropriate management of wetland sites within the target areas.

CONCLUSIONS

Pilot systems for two ESAs have been set up and the potential for this type of approach demonstrated. These systems will have an increasing role to play in the complex task of ESA management where access to information is a pre-requisite to effective management.

The Effects of Raising Water Levels on Invertebrate Food Supply for Breeding Waders on Lowland Wet Grassland

M. AUSDEN

RSPB, The Lodge, Sandy, Bedfordshire, SG19 2DL

INTRODUCTION

Research on the ecology of breeding waders on lowland wet grassland has indicated that raising water levels benefits breeding waders, primarily by increasing food supply (e.g. Green, 1986 and 1988). As a result of this, management prescriptions to raise water levels have been incorporated within several Environmentally Sensitive Areas to benefit breeding waders. This paper summarises research on the effects of raising water levels, and in particular introducing winter flooding, on soil, terrestrial and aquatic invertebrate prey for breeding waders on lowland wet grassland.

METHODS

Soil macroinvertebrates were sampled by digging soil samples. The ability of earthworms to withstand immersion was tested by flooding buried, sealed, intact soil samples. Relative preferences of earthworms for flooded and unflooded soil were determined by immersing one half of sealed intact soil samples. Macroinvertebrates were removed from the soil by hand sorting and wet sieving, preserved in 3% formaldehyde, blotted dry and weighed on a top pan balance to give formaldehyde preserved weight.

Terrestrial arthropods were sampled using pitfall traps. Benthic invertebrates were sampled by taking cores and wet sieving them through stacked sieves. Full details of methods are given in Ausden (1996).

RESULTS

Grasslands subject to regular winter flooding over a long period (>300 years) contained a distinctly different soil macroinvertebrate fauna to unflooded parts of sites where water levels have been raised during the last 14 years to benefit breeding waders. The fauna of sites subject to regular flooding over a long period was mainly composed of the earthworm species *Octolasion tyrtaeum*, *Allolobophora chlorotica* (green morph), *Lumbricus rubellus* and *Eiseniella tetraedra* which together comprised on average 85% of the macroinvertebrate biomass at these sites. All of these species had survived periods of between 150 and 270 days continual flooding prior to sampling in early spring. The fauna of unflooded parts of fields where water levels have recently been raised was dominated by the earthworm species *Aporrectodea caliginosa*, *A. longa*, *A. rosea*, *Allolobophora chlorotica* (both unpigmented and green morphs), *Lumbricus rubellus*, *L. terrestris* and *Tipula* species. At these sites, total soil macroinvertebrate biomass was highly significantly lower in winter flooded (for 20-120 days) than in unflooded parts of the same field (mean$_{un}$ = 74.1g/m^2, se = 13.5 g/m^2; mean$_{fl}$ = 6.6g/m^2, se = 2.7g/m^2, paired t = 8.47, n = 14, $P<0.0001$) as was that of the five most abundant earthworm species in the unflooded grassland. No invertebrate taxa were significantly more abundant in the flooded areas. Soil macroinvertebrate biomass remained low in winter flooded parts of fields throughout the wader breeding season. The results of experiments suggested that the main reason for the low biomass in winter flooded parts of fields was because most earthworm species of unflooded grassland actively avoided flooded soil. However, if forced to remain in flooded soil, all of the species tested *Allolobophora chlorotica* (green morph), *Aporrectodea caliginosa*, *A. longa* and *L. castaneus* were able to survive for at least 120 days from the beginning of January until the beginning of May.

Mean pitfall traps catch rates (number caught per 10 trap days) of terrestrial invertebrates were significantly lower in winter flooded parts of fields compared to unflooded parts of the same field (mean$_{un}$ = 44.8, se = 5.9; mean$_{fl}$ = 25.5, se = 2.5, paired t = 3.28, n = 7, P = 0.0169). Mean vegetation height was also significantly lower in the winter flooded grassland throughout the wader breeding season, due to the replacement of MG6 *Lolium perenne - Cynosurus cristatus* grassland with MG13 *Agrostis stolonifera - Alopecurus geniculatus* grassland (Rodwell, 1992), the difference in height increasing as the wader breeding season progressed. Since pitfall trap catch efficiency decreases with vegetation height (e.g. Greenslade, 1964), terrestrial arthropod abundance must have been lower in the winter flooded grassland. The results of experiments showed that this was in part due to arthropods being expelled from the soil during the first few days of flooding.

Surface water provided an additional prey source in the form of aquatic Diptera and Coleoptera larvae and adult Coleoptera. Temporarily flooded grassland and permanent pools only contained low biomasses (mean dry weight = 1.10g/m^2, se 0.31g/m^2, n = 12) of benthic invertebrates during the first half of April, but higher biomasses (mean dry weight = 2.91g/m^2, se 0.66g/m^2, n = 11) by the first half of June, mainly Chironomid larvae.

DISCUSSION

Breeding lapwings *Vanellus vanellus* and redshank *Tringa totanus* on lowland wet grassland feed on soil, terrestrial and aquatic invertebrates (Green, 1986; Ausden, 1996). Winter flooding increases the physical availability of soil and terrestrial invertebrate prey for lapwings and redshank by reducing vegetation height, but also decreases prey abundance. Surface water provides an additional prey source, which becomes increasingly important for feeding waders as the breeding season progresses, and as grass height increases. Breeding snipe *Gallinago gallinago* feed almost exclusively by probing for macroinvertebrates in soft soil (Green, 1986 and 1988). Surface flooding will increase the likelihood of the soil remaining wet and therefore soft enough for snipe to probe, but will also greatly reduce prey biomass in these areas.

ACKNOWLEDGEMENTS
This work was funded by the RSPB and the Broads Authority.

REFERENCES

AUSDEN M. (1996) *The effects of raised water levels on food supply for breeding waders on lowland wet grassland*. PhD thesis. University of East Anglia.

GREEN R.E. (1986) *The management of lowland wet grassland for breeding waders*. Unpublished report. Sandy: RSPB.

GREEN R.E. (1988) Effects of environmental factors on the timing and success of breeding common snipe *Gallinago gallinago* (Aves: Scolopacidae). *Journal of Applied Ecology*, 25, 79-93.

GREENSLADE P.J.M. (1964) Pitfall trapping as a method for studying populations of Carabidae. *Journal of Animal Ecology*, 33, 301-310.

RODWELL J.S. (ed.) 1992 *British Plant Communities. Vol. 3. Grasslands and Montane communities*. Cambridge: Cambridge University Press.

The Usage of Lowland Wet Grassland by Wetland Birds: The Importance of Site Wetness

R. CALDOW[1], B. PEARSON[1] and S. ROSE[2]

[1]Institute of Terrestrial Ecology, Furzebrook Research Station, Furzebrook Road, Wareham, Dorset. BH20 5AS

[2]ADAS, Gleadthorpe Research Centre, Meden Vale, Mansfield, Notts. NG20 9PF

INTRODUCTION

One of the major factors in the process of agricultural intensification has been improvements in drainage. Drainage has led to dramatic changes in the agricultural landscape; the loss of wet grassland between 1930 and the mid-1980s exceeded 40% (Williams and Bowers, 1987). Such changes are believed to have led, amongst many other deleterious ecological effects, to a reduction in numbers and a contraction of the distribution of several species of waterfowl and wading birds that are dependent upon this habitat. Consequently, wet grassland, with its associated floral and faunal communities, has been identified by the Ministry of Agriculture, Fisheries and Food (MAFF) as one of a suite of habitats, which the Environmentally Sensitive Areas (ESA) scheme seeks to restore. This study seeks to establish whether wet conditions on lowland grasslands within ESAs are attractive to breeding and wintering wetland birds, and whether the implementation of higher Tiers has been of any benefit to wetland bird communities.

METHODS

The breeding and wintering populations of wetland birds have been monitored at six sites within the Somerset Levels and Moors, Broads, and Upper Thames Tributaries ESAs since 1992. Surveys have been carried out in line with standard methodology (Bibby *et al.*, 1992; O'Brien and Smith, 1992).

To establish whether wet conditions on lowland grasslands within ESAs are attractive to breeding and wintering wetland birds, the strength of the correlations between measures of 'on the ground' wetness and the densities of breeding waders, and the density of wintering wetland birds in each month, on each site in each year were calculated. 'On the ground' wetness of each field was quantified by scoring surface wetness on a nine point scale ranging from 0 (completely dry) to 8 (more than 75% flooded). The wetness conditions across each site on each visit during the breeding season was expressed as the proportion of fields showing any surface wetness (scores of 1 or more), and during the winter months, as the average wetness score.

The wetness guidelines for each Tier in each ESA were ranked on a scale from 0 for the driest management (non-ESA) to 8 for the wettest (Somerset Levels and Moors ESA Tier 3). Each field in each year was then assigned a score to characterise the intensity and duration of its management for wet conditions by multiplying its wetness rank by the duration of that level of management. These scores were then averaged across all fields within a site. The strength of the correlation between these average scores and the densities of breeding and wintering wetland birds were calculated to establish whether the implementation of higher Tiers has been of benefit to wetland bird communities.

RESULTS

The total density of breeding pairs of waders (snipe *Gallinago gallinago*, redshank *Tringa totanus*, lapwing *Vanellus vanellus* and curlew *Numenius arquata*) on a site was positively correlated to the proportion of that site classified as wet in June (r_s=0.68 df=13 P<0.01). Moreover, there was a positive correlation between the density of breeding pairs of waders on a site and its average wetness management rank score (r_s=0.71 df=17 P<0.001). On sites where the average wetness rank was high (a high proportion of fields in higher Tiers), the density of breeding waders generally increased over the years while it decreased on those sites with low average wetness ranks. With the exception of the two sites in the Broads ESA, all sites in all years exhibited a dramatic decline in the extent of surface wetness between April and June. This coincided with a decrease in the number of waders, particularly snipe, seen over these months. Consequently, with the exception of the two sites in the Broads ESA, the densities of breeding waders at all sites, in all years were extremely low; less than 10 pairs /100 ha. The total density of wetland birds on each site on each monthly winter visit was positively correlated with the average wetness score of the site (r_s=0.49 df=27 P<0.01), as was the monthly count of wetland species seen (r_s=0.63 df=27 P<0.01). However, preliminary correlations between mean overwinter wetland bird densities and species richness, and wetness management levels were not significant.

CONCLUSIONS

The extent of surface wetness at a site is a major factor in determining its attractiveness to breeding waders. Moreover,the association between higher wetness Tiers and relatively high and increasing densities of waders suggests that the implementation of higher Tiers has been of benefit to breeding waders. However, the densities of breeding waders on virtually all sites were extremely low. Sites' potentials, as assessed by the numbers of waders seen in April, are still not being achieved. Current results suggest that if ESA prescriptions are modified to lengthen the time that the soil surface is kept moist in spring and early summer, densities of breeding waders are likely to increase.

In winter too, wet conditions clearly attract greater numbers of individuals and species of wetland birds. However, preliminary analysis leads to the conclusion that widespread implementation of raised water-level management across a site has not been of any clear benefit to wintering wetland bird populations. This may be because, within winters, sites with a preponderance of fields in the higher Tiers have not necessarily been wetter than other sites. The variation in species richness and bird density between winter visits to every site indicates that all sites in all ESAs have a potential that is often not realised. Current results suggest that if ESA prescriptions can be modified to bring about more consistently wet conditions throughout the winter, the mean overwinter density and species richness of wetland bird communities are likely to increase.

ACKNOWLEDGEMENT
This work was funded by the Ministry of Agriculture, Fisheries and Food.

REFERENCES
BIBBY C.J., BURGESS N.D. and HILL D.A. (1992) *Bird Census Techniques*. London: Academic Press.
O'BRIEN M. and SMITH K.W. (1992) Changes in the status of waders breeding on wet lowland grasslands in England and Wales between 1982 and 1989. *Bird Study*, 39, 165-176.
WILLIAMS G. and BOWERS J.K. (1987) Land drainage and birds in England and Wales. *RSPB Conservation Review*, 1, 25-30.

Soil Nutrient Status and Botanical Composition of Grassland in Environmentally Sensitive Areas

B. J. CHAMBERS[1], S. C. ROSE[1] AND C. N. R. CRITCHLEY[2]

[1]ADAS Land Research Centre, Gleadthorpe, Meden Vale, Mansfield, Notts
NG20 9PF

[2]ADAS Newcastle, Kenton Bar, Newcastle-upon-Tyne, Tyne and Wear NE1 2YA

INTRODUCTION

The botanical composition of grasslands within Environmentally Sensitive Areas (ESAs) is regularly assessed to evaluate the performance of the schemes in maintaining or enhancing botanical quality. Whilst it is generally accepted that grasslands of the highest conservation value are associated with low soil fertility, relationships between different grassland types and nutrient status may be more complex. A MAFF funded research project was set up in 1995 to establish more precisely the relationships between grassland types and soil parameters so that ESA prescriptions can be optimised.

MATERIALS AND METHODS

The first tranche of ESAs designated in England, contained four (South Downs, Broads, Pennine Dales and Somerset Levels and Moors) that were predominantly grasslands. From each of these, a stratified sample of fields was selected for botanical monitoring, enabling important grassland types to be targeted.

Botanical survey

Permanent grassland. For the ESA monitoring programme, five 1 m x 1 m fixed quadrats per field were positioned along a transect. All vascular plants rooted within the quadrats were recorded, along with estimates of ground cover for each species. Plant communities were described according to the National Vegetation Classification (NVC) (Rodwell, 1991 *et seq.*). For this project, a sub-sample of quadrats was selected (usually, one per field) for soil sampling.

Grassland in raised water level areas (RWLAs). At two sites managed as RWLAs in the Somerset Levels and Moors ESA, botanical data were collected from 8 m x 4 m stands and the plant communities described as above.

Soil samples

Twenty soil cores (0-7.5 cm depth) per quadrat/stand were collected in 1995. These cores were then bulked prior to analysis by standard methods for pH, extractable phosphorus (P), potassium (K), magnesium (Mg) and sodium (Na), total nitrogen (N), organic matter (OM) and conductivity (MAFF, 1986).

RESULTS AND DISCUSSION

Soil P status was generally low to moderate (ADAS Index 0-2) (MAFF, 1994) for all the study fields which had not undergone significant agricultural improvement. As many of the fields were permanent grasslands they had organic matter levels $>10\%$ and total N levels $>0.5\%$. Soil K status was in the ADAS Index range 0-4 and Mg in the ADAS Index range 1-7, with the Pennine Dales generally having a much lower Mg status than the other ESAs.

In the South Downs arable reversion grasslands, ADAS soil P and K Indices of >2 were associated with swards dominated by perennial ryegrass (*Lolium perenne*) (NVC community MG7), which may persist for many years. These recently converted fields also had the lowest OM contents (7-10 %) indicating losses due to oxidation during arable production. Most fields had low Mg levels (ADAS Index 0-2), but in some fields higher Mg (ADAS Index 4-6) levels were found to be associated with semi-improved neutral grasslands (NVC communities MG6/MG10b).

In the Broads ESA, soils with elevated Na (>200mg/l) and conductivity levels (ADAS Index >2) were associated with plant communities containing species typical of coastal sites, such as hairy buttercup (*Ranunculus sardous*). These fields also had elevated concentrations of K (ADAS Index 2-4) and Mg (ADAS Index 4-7). Improved grasslands had ADAS Indices >2 for K and Mg contents, OM $<15\%$, total N $<1\%$, and were dominated by NVC community MG7a.

Fields in the Pennine Dales ESA which had been agriculturally improved tended to have ADAS Indices of 2-4 for P and K contents, and ADAS Index >3 for Mg content. Samples from distinctive acidic (NVC community U4) or calcareous pastures (NVC communities CG2c/MG5) had lower P (ADAS Index 0-1), K (ADAS Index 1-2) and Mg (ADAS Index <3) levels.

Most of the soils from the Somerset Levels ESA were organic or peaty in texture ($>10\%$ OM), with very few showing evidence of recent salt water inundation. The P and K contents of the soils were generally low to moderate (ADAS Indices 0-2), with Mg indices greater than 4 for almost all samples.

Formal relationships between botanical composition of the swards and soil nutrients are being analysed using multivariate and regression techniques.

REFERENCES

MAFF (1986) *Analysis of Agricultural Materials. Reference Book 427*. HMSO, London.

MAFF (1994) *Fertiliser Recommendations for Agricultural and Horticultural Crops. Reference Book 209*. Sixth Edition. HMSO, London.

RODWELL, J. S. [Ed] (1991 *et seq.*) *British Plant Communities*. Cambridge University Press, Cambridge.

Management of Semi-Natural Rough Grazing in the Cambrian Mountains Environmentally Sensitive Area

A. P. M. COWDY

ADAS, Yr Hen Ysgol Gymraeg, Ffordd Alexandra, Aberystwyth, Ceredigion
SY23 1LF

INTRODUCTION

The Cambrian Mountains ESA is a scenically attractive area of hills and uplands in the central part of Wales. One of the main objectives of the ESA is to encourage farmers to protect and enhance SNRG with a consequent benefit to upland birds including the nationally rare Red Kite, and upland landscape. Under the scheme, agricultural improvement of SNRG by cultivation or use of fertiliser is prohibited, and grazing levels, winter feeding, and the use of pesticides are controlled.

PROCEDURE FOR SETTING TIER 1A STOCKING LEVELS

Prior to entry of SNRG into the scheme, a vegetation survey is undertaken and an appropriate grazing density to avoid environmental damage is calculated based on the following vegetation types:

Vegetation Type	Range (Hill sheep/ha)	
	Minimum	Maximum
Agrostis/Festuca	2	5
Molinia	2	3.5
Nardus	1	3
Calluna/Erica/Vaccinium	0.5	1.3
Tricophorum/Eriophorum	0	1

The position within the range depends on the mixture and level of different species in the sward, along with physical factors such as exposure of site. The stocking figure is normally expressed as hill sheep per hectare, as the majority of holdings in the ESA are sheep farms. In this context a sheep is defined as one ewe plus her lamb(s) until weaned. Maximum stocking levels and payments under Tier 1A are as follows:

	LU/ha	Sheep/ha	Payment £/ha
SNRG	0.375	2.5	25
SNRG with Heather	0.22	1.5	35

These payments are in addition to a payment on the whole farm of £3-£20 per hectare.

TIER 2 STOCKING LEVELS

Degraded heather can be restored under a voluntary Tier 2, where additional payments are offered for further stock reductions. An extra £20/ha is offered in return for a lower maximum annual average stocking rate of 0.15LU/ha (1 sheep/ha), reducing to 0.1LU/ha (0.66 sheep/ha) from 1 September to 31 March. The lower winter stocking rate is designed to give further protection to the heather during this particularly sensitive period when it would otherwise be preferentially grazed by stock. Around 60% of eligible land coming under agreement is being entered into this higher tier.

ASSOCIATED RESEARCH

Research has been undertaken at ADAS Pwllpeiran to investigate the effects of grazing densities on SNRG within the Cambrian Mountains ESA. The effects on livestock production have also been measured. Results to date are summarised in a paper by Griffiths *et al.,* (1997), included in these proceedings.

PROGRESS UP TO FEBRUARY 1997

Uptake of the scheme has been high, with around three-quarters of the eligible SNRG other than common land now under agreement, and further areas under negotiation. Uptake of the scheme on common land has been low on multiple grazier commons due to problems in reaching agreement on apportionment of stock reduction.

Where heather is overgrown, or regeneration of heather is apparent due to the lower stocking rates, farmers are being encouraged to consider management by cutting or burning. Grant aid is available for this work, along with other beneficial activities such as bracken control.

REFERENCES

GRIFFITHS J.B., HENMAN D., JONES D.L., WILDIG J., RUSHTON S.P. and SANDERSON R. (1997) Stocking Rate Comparisons on Semi Natural Rough Grazings in The Cambrian Mountains ESA. *Proceedings of the 1997 British Grassland Society Conference.*

Grassland Monitoring in the South Downs ESA

I. A. DIACK

ADAS, Wharf House, Wharf Road, Guildford, Surrey GU1 4RP

INTRODUCTION

The South Downs is one of the most important chalk landscapes in the UK. The remaining areas of semi-natural calcareous grassland are of extremely high wildlife conservation value, supporting a great diversity of plants and associated invertebrates. The ESA was designated in 1987 to protect the landscape as a whole, and in particular, the semi-natural calcareous grassland, from further agricultural intensification. One of the principal objectives of the ESA was to maintain and enhance the wildlife conservation value of the grassland. The effectiveness of the scheme in achieving this was evaluated on the basis of a botanical monitoring programme. The results of the monitoring can also be used to refine management prescriptions.

METHODS

A total of 37 fields was objectively sampled, and five permanent quadrats were objectively positioned within each field. These were first surveyed in 1987, and subsequently in 1990 and 1994. Full details of site selection, field methods and data recording are described in ADAS (1996). Management information was obtained from farmers, and meteorological data were also obtained. Quadrats were grouped by applying TWINSPAN (Hill, 1979) to the 1987 quadrat data and the resultant endgroups were described using the National Vegetation Classification (NVC) (Rodwell, 1992). In order to achieve the relevant objective, farmers were required to follow management prescriptions set to maintain or create the environmental conditions which are necessary to sustain grassland of high conservation value. On the South Downs, favourable conditions should occur where grassland is managed under a moderate grazing regime on soils of low nutrient status. Rules were defined to select plant species which were suited to the environmental conditions linked to the ESA objective and management prescriptions (Critchley *et al.*, 1996). The relative abundance of the selected species was calculated for each endgroup and changes in their scores between years were analysed. Analysis procedures are described in Critchley *et al.* (1996).

RESULTS AND DISCUSSION

Five vegetation types were identified from the TWINSPAN output (Table 1). In general, little change was detected between 1987 and 1994. Maintenance of the community of highest ecological value (well-grazed unimproved grassland) was expected and generally achieved. However, a trend for mesophytic species, in particular Yorkshire fog (*Holcus lanatus*) and creeping bent (*Agrostis stolonifera*), to increase was apparent within this vegetation type. This may be a result of a long-term shift from sheep to cattle-grazing, and a slight reduction in stocking intensity on some sites. In the coarser undergrazed unimproved grassland, which had grown rank prior to the establishment of the ESA, no significant changes were detected. Those species which had attained dominance in this community, such as upright brome (*Bromus erectus*) and tor grass (*Brachypodium pinnatum*) were able to maintain their pre-ESA cover under the low–moderate grazing intensity imposed. In the three more agriculturally improved communities, the ESA management prescriptions were expected to bring about enhancement in terms of an increase in vegetation characteristic of semi-natural calcareous grassland. In particular, the ban on fertiliser use was expected to reduce soil fertility levels, thereby disadvantaging species such as rye-grass (*Lolium perenne*), and allowing the spread of less-nutrient demanding species typical of less-improved grassland. Also, it was expected that the prescribed stocking rates would maintain the swards at optimal heights and facilitate the creation of germination sites for colonising species. Beneficial change was only detected in the species-rich semi-improved grassland where there was a trend for species suited to low nutrient status to increase and those suited to high nutrient status to decrease. No change in the other two vegetation types was detected, and this was probably a result of the high residual fertility maintaining the species-poor grass-dominated swards. Also, the scarcity or absence of desirable species in the sward and the distance of many sites from other sources of propagules prevented their spread into, or colonisation of, these low diversity grasslands.

Table 1.   NVC communities present in each endgroup when first surveyed (1987) and the number of quadrats in each endgroup.

Vegetation type	NVC community	No. of quadrats
Well-grazed unimproved grassland	CG2/CG3	43
Under-grazed unimproved grassland	CG3/CG4/MG1/CG2c	13
Species-rich semi-improved grassland	MG5b/CG2c	41
Species-poor semi-improved grassland	MG6/MG5b/MG1	61
Improved grassland	MG7/MG6	25

CONCLUSIONS

The ESA scheme has been generally successful in maintaining the quality of grassland. However, results from the vegetation type of greatest ecological value and the absence of enhancement in low diversity grassland indicate that the ESA objective was not met in full. Up until 1996, the same management guidelines applied to all types of grassland; the results suggested that more specific management guidelines should be applied to different types of grassland. In order to meet the ESA aim, revised prescriptions, which will be operational from April 1997, will require site specific grassland management plans to be be drawn up for all grassland coming into the scheme.

ACKNOWLEDGEMENT
This work was funded by the Ministry of Agriculture, Fisheries and Food.

REFERENCES

ADAS (1996) *Botanical Monitoring of Grassland in the South Downs ESA, 1987–1995.* Unpublished report to MAFF, ADAS Oxford.

CRITCHLEY C.N.R., SMART S.M., POULTON S.M.C. and MYERS G.M. (1996) Monitoring the consequences of vegetation management in Environmentally Sensitive Areas. *Aspects of Applied Biology*, 44, 193-201.

HILL M.O. (1979) *TWINSPAN - a FORTRAN program for arranging multivariate data in an ordered two-way table by classification of individuals and attributes.* Cornell University, New York.

RODWELL J.S. (ed.) (1992) British Plant Communities: Vol 3 - *Grasslands and Montane Communities*. Cambridge University Press: Cambridge.

Theory into Practice: The ESA Project Officer Perspective

M. EDWARDS
Project Officer, FRCA Penrith

INTRODUCTION

The Lake District ESA was launched in 1993, aimed at protecting and enhancing the unique environment of the area. It is the largest and most diverse English ESA covering valley wetlands and meadows to mountain heaths.

The ESA's are administered by MAFF locally, through a Regional Service Centre. The field work is done by four FRCA Project Officers who are key personnel on the ground. They are the vital link between the farming community and MAFF, other bodies such as the Lake District National Park and English Nature, and FRCA Specialists (ecologists and landscape architects). Their duties cover stimulating interest in the scheme at the outset leading to the securing of individual agreements, followed by on-going management of these agreements. This paper provides details of the Lake District ESA Scheme, practical aspects of the work of the Project Officers and overall impact of the scheme to date.

THE LAKE DISTRICT ESA SCHEME

The scheme is voluntary and invites farmers to enter into a ten year land management agreement. Applicants are obliged to enter all their land that lies within the ESA. This is then surveyed to produce two sets of maps. One shows the various categories of land type, stockproof walls and hedges, and location of weatherproof traditional buildings. The other shows the location of historic and archaeological features. Agreement holders undertake to comply with a set of rules related to each type of land in return for compensatory payments. The minimum requirement is to apply the basic set of rules (tier 1) which are designed to at least maintain the quality of the various environmental features. A further set of rules designed to protect and enhance areas of high ecological value can also be applied (tier 2). Entry of tier 2 land is optional and discretionary.

The management agreement provides the option of supplementary payments for enhancing ghylls (small wooded valleys), rebuilding stone walls and work under Conservation Plans. The latter provides grant-aid for various environmental projects including hedge planting, hedge laying, bracken control, renovation of traditional farm buildings and regeneration of wildlife habitats.

ESA PROJECT OFFICERS - RESPONSIBILITIES

Project Officers promote the scheme, brief prospective applicants, assist with applications, survey the land and draw-up agreements on behalf of MAFF, liaising with Statutory Agencies and other interested bodies. Securing agreements on multiple occupancy grazing (common land) is a particular challenge. The value of agreements are enhanced by entry of tier 2 land, walling programmes, new public access routes and ghylls. The value of agreements also depend on setting an appropriate level of stocking

223

for mountain grazing within the prescribed limit in order to prevent overgrazing. The value of tier 2 wetland within the ESA agreement depends on drawing-up an appropriate management plan tailored for the type and quality of wetland entered. The contribution of FRCA ecologists (and English Nature ecologists in the case of SSSI's) is a vital component in producing the agreements.

Follow-on management of the agreements includes amendments to allow for changes in area of land, up-grading areas to tier 2 and extending walling programmes. Also, to agree on the management of woodland, bracken, scrub and heather. Furthermore, there are ongoing requests for derogations and queries by MAFF regarding compliance and accuracy of agreements following visits by inspecting officers.

The impact of the scheme depends on uptake, quality of agreements and number of conservation plans. These are influenced by levels of compensatory payments and grant-aid but progress also depends on the ability of Project Officers to sell the scheme and obtain the best agreements according to the farmers attitude and characteristics of the holding. Project Officers attempt to maintain a cordial working relationship with the farming community, by applying a pragmatic approach without undermining the integrity of the scheme. This ensures that land under agreement is managed in such a way that the environment is maintained or improved within a viable farming system.

CONCLUSIONS

The number of secure agreements at the end of the fourth year of the scheme (March 1997) totalled 1,032 representing 57% of total number of holdings in the ESA. These include the entry of 108,661 ha under tier 1 and 5,698 under tier 2 which, together with non-payment areas, cover 56% of eligible area. The total length of walling to be renovated is 106,006m, total length of hedges to be planted and laid is 139,893m and number of buildings for renovation amount to 251. In addition there are 13 access agreements and 13 ghylls protected.

Environmentally Responsible Grassland Management - The Northern Ireland Experience

J. FULTON and C. A. MILLSOPP
Countryside Management Division, Department of Agriculture, Annex D,
Dundonald House, Upper Newtownards Road, Belfast. BT4 3SB

The Environmentally Sensitive Area (ESA) scheme was launched by the Department of Agriculture in Northern Ireland (DANI) in 1988 and five ESAs, covering 20% of agricultural land have now been designated. Within the ESAs a wide variety of semi-natural grassland habitats exist, such as limestone grassland, hay meadows and wet grassland. These habitats are of a high wildlife, landscape and historical value, for example, the lowland wet grasslands of the West Fermanagh and Erne Lakeland ESA have gained international significance in their support of large numbers of breeding waders. DANI plays a vital role in safeguarding the future of these habitats through encouraging positive management by providing financial incentives for participating in environmentally friendly farming practices.

The ESA scheme is voluntary and helps strike a balance between running a successful farm business and the care and protection of the countryside. Farmers within the designated areas are offered a ten year agreement (but may opt out after five years) and given financial incentives for maintaining and enhancing the landscape, wildlife and historic features on their farms. The benefits and opportunities offered by the scheme are reflected in the considerable support already shown by farming communities in the ESAs. Approximately 60% of the eligible land area within the designated areas is now under the protection of the ESA scheme. Education and training forms an important component of the implementation of the scheme, aimed at raising awareness of environmental issues and changing attitudes to conservation.

Each ESA has various tiers which set out the agricultural practices (prescriptions) that must be followed. Every grassland habitat has a specific set of prescriptions covering grazing, cutting, nutrient management and use of herbicides. The higher the tier, the greater the environmental benefits and the more restrictive in terms of farming practices. In return for following the prescriptions, the farmer receives an annual payment. In addition participants are offered the opportunity to undertake enhancement works on their farm such as hedge planting and regeneration, tree planting, control of bracken and heather regeneration.

ESA prescriptions aim to protect and enhance the species diversity of semi-natural habitats. Protection is provided primarily through Tier 1 prescriptions, which include restrictions on reclamation, drainage, reseeding and the use of herbicides. Tier 2 prescriptions which must be followed by ESA participants if these habitats are present on the farm, requires positive management of such sites, for example, grazing management (density and timing), application of nutrients (fertilisers, slurry and farmyard manure) and cutting dates, in the case of hay meadows. Proposals have now been accepted for the inclusion of a species rich grassland category, at a higher Tier, with restrictions on application of fertiliser, lime, grazing and cutting regimes, to provide more protection for these important habitats.

The aim of the ESA scheme, by application of these management prescriptions is to maintain or enhance the wildlife diversity of these habitats. The long term monitoring programme, established by DANI in 1992 (McAdam *et al.*, 1994;1995) evaluates the effectiveness of the ESA scheme by biological, landscape, historical and socio-economic monitoring, providing information on the implementation of the ESA management prescriptions on the wildlife and landscape value of each ESA. This provides a mechanism for identifying opportunities to refine prescriptions, to maximise the environmental benefit achieved under the scheme. Appropriate research is encouraged, for example on wet pastures (Mallon *et al.*, in press) and hay meadows (Hoppe *et al.*, in press) to enable the refinement and effectiveness of prescriptions. DANI liaises with other interested bodies to ensure a co-ordinated and integrated approach is taken to deliver an accurate and appropriate assessment of the effectiveness of the scheme.

REFERENCES

HOPPE G., McADAM J.H. and MULHOLLAND F. (in press). Hay meadow grassland types in the West Fermanagh and Erne Lakeland ESA. *Grassland Management in the ESAs*. Ed. R.Sheldrick. British Grassland Society. 23-25 September 1997.

MALLON E., McADAM J.H. and MONTGOMERY W.I. (in press). Grazing management of lowland wet grasslands in the West Fermanagh and Erne Lakeland ESA. *Grassland Management in the ESAs*. Ed. R.Sheldrick. British Grassland Society. 23-25 September 1997.

McADAM J.H., HEGARTY C.A., McFERRAN D., CAMERON A. and MULHOLLAND F. (1994) Environmentally Sensitive Areas in Northern Ireland. Biological Monitoring Report Year One - 1993.

McADAM J.H., HEGARTY C.A., McFERRAN D., CAMERON A. and MULHOLLAND F. (1995) Environmentally Sensitive Areas in Northern Ireland. Biological Monitoring Report Year Two - 1994.

ESA Monitoring in Scotland - Grasslands

J. H. GAULD[1], R. CUMMINS[2] and D. A. ELSTON[3]

[1]Macaulay Land Use Research Institute, Craigiebuckler, Aberdeen AB15 8QH;
[2]Institute of Terrestrial Ecology, Banchory Research Station, Hill of Brathens, Glassel, Kincardineshire AB31 4BY
[3]Biomathematics & Statistics Scotland, Environmental Modelling Unit, Macaulay Land Use Research Institute, Craigiebuckler, Aberdeen AB15 8QH

INTRODUCTION

The Scottish Office Agriculture, Environment and Fisheries Department, (SOAEFD) requires to undertake a monitoring programme within the designated ESAs in order to demonstrate whether or not the specified environmentally friendly farming practices are achieving the desired objectives. Early monitoring work, between 1989 and 1994, was completed by staff at the Macaulay Land Use Research Institute and focused on the first tranche of 5 ESAs. Since 1994, the number of ESAs has doubled to cover approximately 20% of the Scottish landmass and farmers are permitted to remain within the scheme for 10 years, with a possible break at year 5. A second contract has been commissioned by SOAEFD for the period 1994-2004 and has been awarded to a Consortium including the Institute of Terrestrial Ecology (ITE) and the Macaulay Land Use Research Institute (MLURI) (landscape and biological monitoring), AOC Scotland Ltd (archaeological work), with all statistical work undertaken by Biomathematics & Statistics Scotland (BioSS, formerly SASS).

THE SYSTEMATIC MONITORING OF ESAs IN SCOTLAND - OVERALL STRATEGY

The grassland monitoring scheme created for the Scottish ESAs operates at two distinct levels:-

Background Monitoring

Designed to provide information for the whole of the ESA regardless of uptake of the scheme. Such information will be used to:-

a)   place the grassland component within the ESA in a national context and allow comparison of trends of change shown by national datasets, for example Countryside Surveys undertaken by ITE and The Land Cover of Scotland data compiled at MLURI.

b)   examine on-going trends taking place within ESAs as a whole.

Prescription Monitoring

Designed to determine trends on land that has been entered into the scheme for comparison with 'whole ESA' and national figures.

THE SYSTEMATIC MONITORING OF ESA GRASSLANDS - GENERAL METHODOLOGY

The methodology has been developed to assess possible change within key vegetation types, which, besides grassland, will include woodland, moorland, wetland and water margin sites. Procedures for monitoring habitats include broadscale mapping and detailed fixed point sampling in relation to:-

Background Monitoring

Involves a random selection of about 26 1 km squares in each ESA, regardless of whether the land is within the Scheme or not. Using robust statistical techniques, the sample squares have been stratified by ITE land class groups with the number of squares sampled in each stratum being proportional to the cover of that stratum in the ESA. Within each 1 km square, the distribution and composition of all habitats, including grassland, across each ESA has been mapped using techniques used in the ITE Countryside Survey 1990 (Barr et al., 1990). The minimum mapping area is 400 m2 and grassland communities are mapped as separate units wherever they differ by a single code from adjacent units e.g. changes in a dominant species, even in the same field. For grassland, the species composition is based on visual estimates of the cover of major species i.e. those with 25% or more cover, recorded in 25% classes. In each 1 km square, a 2 x 2 m quadrat is recorded for key vegetation types, for example herb-rich grassland. Key vegetation types are based on the habitats detailed on the SOAEFD explanatory leaflet relevant to each ESA.

Prescription Monitoring

Involves specific targeting of Tier 2 habitats on in-scheme farms with the sampling unit represented by the management block in the conservation plan submitted to SOAEFD by the farmer. Species within a 2 x 2 m fixed quadrat have been recorded for 30 grassland sites in ESAs where grassland represents a key vegetation type.

CONCLUSION

A grassland monitoring scheme, which incorporates strict quality control measures, has been created for the Scottish ESAs and field data is currently being collected. Results will be published initially in Year 5 (2000).

ACKNOWLEDGEMENTS

This work was commissioned by The Scottish Office Agricultural Environment, and Fisheries Department.

REFERENCE

BARR C.J., BUNCE R.G.H., CLARKE R.T., RULLER R.M., FURSE M.T., GILLESPIE M.K., GROOM G.B., HALLAM C.J., HORNUNG M., HOWARD D.C. and NESS M.J. (1993). Countryside Survey 1990: main report. Countryside 1990 Vol. 2. London: Department of the Environment.

The Use of Ditches to Maximise the Benefits of ESA Water Level Prescriptions to both Agricultural Grazing and Conservation

J. GILBERT, D. GOWING and G. SPOOR

Silsoe College, Cranfield University, Silsoe, Bedford. MK45 4DT

INTRODUCTION

Field water tables in lowland wet grassland ESAs are currently regulated by means of water level prescriptions for ditches. There is a great deal of latitude within a given prescription because in-field water regimes are largely governed by ditch spacing and geometry. Hydrological models can redesign ditch systems to improve the water regime for a given area, suiting both agricultural and conservation interests. The tier 2 and tier 3 water level prescriptions for the Somerset Levels and Moors ESA have been modelled for five ditch spacing scenarios and the results analysed in terms of the limitations each regime places on grazing, breeding waders and botanical interest. The smallest spacing of 20 m represents water management using sub-irrigation channels.

METHOD AND ASSUMPTIONS

A hydrological model (Youngs et al., 1989) was used to estimate water table height within a deep peat soil over a period of ten years. It has been assumed that grazing is restricted when the water table lies within the top 0.25 m of the field surface at this site, since soil would be at risk of poaching. Feeding waders require a soft soil surface to enable penetration of their beaks into the soil (Spoor and Chapman, 1992). The average number of weeks per year between April and October for which grazing is limited and during the breeding season for which wader penetration is limited have been calculated over a ten year period for each ditch spacing scenario (Table 1). Gowing et al. (1994) show plant tolerances can be given in terms of Sum Exceedence Values (SEVs): a measure of water table variation throughout the season. An SEV has been calculated for each scenario and used to evaluate which plant species tolerate the different regimes.

Table 1 The effect that ditch spacing has on agricultural and conservation conditions.

Ditch spacing	Tier 2				Tier 3			
(m)	1	2	3	4	1	2	3	4
20	1.8	4.4	0.1	2.3	7.3	0.2	0	5.6
30	3.4	4.2	0.1	2.2	8.4	0	0	5.5
50	6.4	8.7	0.1	1.7	12.1	2	0.1	5.2
100	6.7	8.2	2.0	1.9	13	2	1.1	5.1
150	7.6	7	2.7	2.7	14.5	1.5	1.5	5.6

1	Weeks when grazing is limited,	2	when wader feeding is limited
3	Drought SEV in metre.weeks	4	Aeration SEV in metre.weeks

DISCUSSION

The number of weeks between April and October when grazing is limited increases with the spacing of the ditches, because widely spaced ditches are less able to drain excess rainfall from the field centre. The same effect is seen for both tiers, with tier 3 having a larger number of weeks limited since the ditch water levels are held higher in the spring. The number of weeks when feeding of waders is limited generally increases with ditch spacing since wider spacing limits the amount of sub-irrigation in summer and hence gives drier conditions. The results of the evaluation of SEVs show that under tier 2, drought stress is only limiting to a few plant species (*e.g. Caltha palustris*) when the spacing exceeds 100 m. Drought stress is not limiting to wet grassland plant species under tier 3 management. Aeration stress in tier 2 is not limiting to wet grassland plant species for ditch spacings of up to 100 m but above this it becomes too wet for some (*e.g. Lathyrus pratensis*). Under tier 3, aeration stress is too high for species-rich wet grassland whatever the ditch spacing. Each of the scenarios was ranked for their effect on the limitation of grazing, wader feeding and grassland diversity. The total score for each scenario is given as the sum of the ranks. The various scenarios have then been listed in ascending order with the smallest representing the scenario which most closely satisfies the goal of the ESA to combine agriculture and conservation (Table 2).

Table 2   The total score given to each scenario for its combined effect on agriculture and conservation.

		Spacing (m)	Grazing	Birds	Plants	Score
Best	Tier 2	20	1	7	1	9
	Tier 2	30	2	6	1	9
	Tier 3	20	5	2	6	13
	Tier 3	30	7	1	6	14
	Tier 2	50	3	10	1	14
	Tier 2	100	4	9	1	14
	Tier 3	50	8	4	6	18
	Tier 3	100	9	4	6	19
	Tier 2	150	6	8	5	19
Worst	Tier 3	150	10	3	6	19

CONCLUSIONS

Ditch spacing is an important factor influencing in-field water table positions. Tier 2 appears to be of greater overall suitability than tier 3. Narrow ditch spacings under tier 3, however, can give conditions that are of comparable suitability. Installing new ditches or sub-irrigation channels can help to achieve the desired water regime. Narrower ditch spacings give greater control over in-field water tables. The ditch water management regime can then be used more effectively to achieve the requirements of agriculture and conservation. If in addition to consideration of ditch spacing, more flexibility were given to ditch level control based on in-field conditions, then it should be possible to satisfy all interests on one site.

REFERENCES
GOWING D.J.G., SPOOR G., MOUNTFORD J.O. and YOUNGS E.G (1994) *The water-regime requirements of lowland wet grassland plants.* Report to MAFF.
SPOOR G. and CHAPMAN J.M. (1992) *Comparison of hydrological conditions on reserves in relation to their suitability for breeding waders.* Report to RSPB.
YOUNGS E.G., LEEDS-HARRISON P.B. and CHAPMAN J.M. (1989) Modelling water-table movement in flat low-lying lands. *Hydrological Processes,* 3, 301-315.

Stocking Rate Comparisons on Semi-Natural Rough Grazings in The Cambrian Mountains

J. B. GRIFFITHS[1], D. HENMAN[1], D. L. JONES[1], J. WILDIG[1] and
S. P. RUSHTON[2] and R. SANDERSON[2]

[1]ADAS Pwllpeiran, Cwmystwyth, Aberystwyth, SY23 4AB
[2]Centre for Land Use and Water Research, University of Newcastle upon Tyne,
Newcastle upon Tyne NE1 7RU

INTRODUCTION

The Cambrian Mountains ESA was designated in 1987 as government policy moved to redress the adverse environmental effects of post war production orientated agriculture. It was set up to safeguard the remaining areas of semi- natural rough grazings (SNRG) in the Cambrian Mountains which were under threat from overgrazing, land improvement and afforestation. From 1989 in support of its ESA policies, MAFF has funded a fully integrated comparison of Cambrian Mountains ESA Tier 1 and Tier 2 stocking rates on SNRG, on both a farm scale and 2 ha grazing paddock level at ADAS Pwllpeiran.

The farm scale comparison started in 1989/90 and involves some 300 ha of land between 300 and 500 m a.s.l., and over 500 Welsh ewes and followers, with both land and livestock resources being split to create two similar units, both having limited in-bye land. The SNRG of the two units is typical of the vegetation types found in the ESA, ranging from overgrazed dry grassy heath, to rank heather (*Calluna vulgaris*) dominated wet and dry heath.

SUMMARY OF RESULTS TO DATE

Effects on overall *Calluna* cover, Dwarf Shrub Heath species and communities.
Aerial photographic records of the experimental area of some 254 ha SNRG, date back to 1957 and the areas of dominant *Calluna* has been estimated for each set of prints. This revealed a marked decline in the area of dominant *Calluna* cover from 61% in 1957 to 47% in 1987. Thereafter there has been encouraging signs of a slow recovery with the area of dominant *Calluna* reaching 50% in 1992 and 53% in 1995.

Even on an area of dry grassy heath where Calluna was grazed out in the early 1960s, there has been a marked increase in the cover of *Vaccinium myrtillus*, but as yet heather cover is not recordable.

Vegetation has been closely monitored on two large grazing paddocks and analysis and modelling of the data from 1990 to 1995 suggests that:-

- *Calluna* cover has remained relatively constant at the Tier 1 stocking rate.
- *Calluna* cover has increased on the Tier 2 stocking rate with *Vaccinium* and *Nardus stricta* cover falling slightly.
- Ordination and modelling of the botanical data, using the techniques of Rushton *et al*. (1996) suggest that the Tier 2 paddock is moving slowly and steadily towards a more desirable *Calluna* rich mix of species.

Livestock production and Financial Results.

Throughout the period of the experiment, production overall has been in line with what would be expected from an exposed mountain unit and is well illustrated by the data presented in Table 1. However, on the ESA Tier 2 unit, although less lambs have been weaned off the SNRG, their weaning weight has increased and this is illustrated by data from four paddocks of dry grassy heath in Table 2.

Table 1.   Overall Physical Performance 1995/96 (kg).

	ESA Tier 1	ESA Tier 2
Ewe liveweight at tupping	36.5	38.0
Weaning percentage	99.6%	98.8%
Lamb weaning weight	25.8	27.4
kg of weaned lamb/ha	44.9	45.2
% Barren ewes	2.6%	5.2%
% Ewe deaths	1.8%	2.0%

Table 2.   Mean Weaning Weights of lambs (kg) off paddocks of dry grassy heath.

Year	1990	1991	1992	1993	1994	1995	1996
Lambs off Tier 1 paddocks	21.0	22.8	21.7	23.0	22.4	24.9	25.2
Lambs off Tier 2 paddocks	22.6	24.3	25.4	25.4	28.5	28.4	28.4

With both units having limited middle hill land which is not subject to ESA grazing prescription and which can be managed relatively intensively, analysis of the financial data shows that Gross Margin/ewe and Gross Margin/ha in recent years have been similar at around £53/ewe and £100/ha with Gross Output from both units being heavily dependant on agricultural support payments.

REFERENCES
RUSHTON S.P., SANDERSON R.A., WILDIG J. and BYRNE J.P. (1996) The effects of grazing management on moorland vegetation; a comparison of farm unit, grazing paddock and plot experiments using a community modelling approach. *Aspects of Applied Biology* 44, 211-219.

The Effects of ESA Management Guidelines on the Machair Grasslands of the Uists and Benbecula, Outer Hebrides

D. J. HENDERSON, G. HUDSON and W. TOWERS

Macaulay Land Use Research Institute, Craigiebuckler, Aberdeen, AB15 8QH

INTRODUCTION

The machair lands of the Hebrides of Scotland represent a valuable but fragile ecosystem with a unique assemblage of agricultural, ornithological and geomorphological features. A comprehensive account of the natural environment of the Outer Hebrides is published in Boyd (1979) and detailed botanical records are given in the National Sand Dune Vegetation Site Survey Reports (e.g. Crawford, 1988). Machairs are most extensive on the Atlantic seaboard of the Outer Hebrides where dunes fringe the coastline and level or gently undulating plains are found further inland. These areas are composed of windblown shell sand which either fade out eastwards or end abruptly in wetlands, and thereafter the land becomes more typical of the Western Isles as a whole, with rocky knolls and peatland interspersed with lochans.

The light calcareous soils of the machair provide the main opportunities for crofters to grow crops and grass for winter feed. Traditionally only a small proportion of the machair grasslands is cropped each year using natural fertilisers, and under the rotation practised the land is then left fallow to permit rapid reversion to semi-natural pasture. During the 1980s, however, as cultivation expanded and intensified, there was an increasing risk of wind erosion and loss of habitat. As well as having a rich flora, the machairs areas provide an important breeding ground for a variety of waders and also form one of the main strongholds of the corncrake (*Crex crex*). In recognition of the importance of this vulnerable habitat, the Machair Lands of the Uists and Benbecula, Barra and Vatersay Environmentally Sensitive Area (ESA) was established in 1988. The aim of this designation was to maintain, and where possible to enhance, the landscape, soil fertility and wildlife diversity. To achieve these objectives, guidelines (Department of Agriculture and Fisheries for Scotland (DAFS), 1988) were issued to all farmers and crofters voluntarily entering the ESA Scheme for the first five years, and those particularly relevant to the machair grassland areas were: 1) to retain a rotational pattern of cultivation; 2) to apply seaweed, dung or peat to cropped areas of machair annually; 3) to avoid overgrazing.

In 1989 a monitoring programme was initiated to investigate the effects of the management guidelines, particularly with regard to changes in the extent of rotational cultivation, plant species composition and soil fertility.

METHODS

From over 100 crofts which entered the Scheme during the initial monitoring year, 60 sites were randomly selected. On each croft the area of cultivated land was mapped and a 1m x 1m permanent quadrat for botanical study randomly sited; adjacent topsoils from a subsample of 21 quadrat positions were sampled for analysis. Baseline data were obtained for all sites in 1989 (mid-June), with a subsample of sites (44) completed in 1991 (late July) and a survey of all sites repeated in 1993 (early July).

RESULTS AND DISCUSSION
Cultivation patterns
Of the three main vegetation types occurring in the permanent quadrats — crops, ley pasture and dune pasture, there were no significant differences in the overall numbers of quadrats in each category from year to year, and in total, around one third of the quadrats were under cultivation in each year. However, the vegetation type in many of the individual quadrats varied from year to year, in line with the desired objective of maintaining rotation. Of the 44 quadrats recorded on all three visits, 30 had been cultivated in at least one of the three years while the remaining 14 quadrats were under dune pasture on each visit; none of the quadrats were cultivated in all three years.

Within the townships monitored the amount of cropped land did not change significantly between 1989 and 1993. In 1989, 14% of the total eligible area was under cultivation, and 15% in 1993.

Species composition
According to the National Vegetation Classification (NVC), the uncultivated machair grasslands consist of *Festuca rubra - Galium verum* dune grassland (SD8), principally the *Ranunculus acris - Bellis perennis* sub-community (SD8d). No significant changes in species composition or percentage cover were noted for quadrats which had remained as dune pasture between 1989 and 1993.

Soil analyses
Mean topsoil levels of organic matter (%), nitrogen (%), exchangeable calcium (me/100g) and pH (in water) were very similar in each monitoring year (11.9, 0.2, 35.4 and 7.6 respectively in 1993). No differences were detected in mean values for the above variables between cropped and dune pasture samples in any year.

CONCLUSIONS
The results indicate that the application of ESA management guidelines maintained the rotational cultivation patterns, species composition and soil properties of the machair grasslands between 1989 and 1993.

ACKNOWLEDGEMENTS
This work was commissioned by DAFS [now the Scottish Office Agriculture, Environment and Fisheries Department (SOAEFD)].

REFERENCES
BOYD J.M. (1979) The natural environment of Outer Hebrides. *Proceedings of the Royal Society of Edinburgh*, 77B.

CRAWFORD, I.C. (1989) *Stilligarry, South Uist*. National Sand Dune Vegetation Survey, Site Report No. 65. Peterborough: Nature Conservancy Council.

DEPARTMENT OF AGRICULTURE AND FISHERIES FOR SCOTLAND (1988) *Guidelines for Farmers: Machair of the Uists and Benbecula, Barra and Vatersay Environmentally Sensitive Area.*

The Way Forward for ESAs in Delivering Real Environmental Benefits

S. HOOPER[1] and J. DWYER[2]

[1]Uplands Team, English Nature, Northminster House, Peterborough, PE1 1UA
[2]Land Use Branch, Countryside Commission, John Dower House, Crescent Place, Cheltenham, Glos., GL50 3RA

INTRODUCTION

English Nature is the Government's statutory adviser on nature conservation in England. The Countryside Commission advises on the countryside and landscape. As such, they advise MAFF on the priorities for ESA designation, the setting of environmental objectives, the development of management prescriptions and monitoring frameworks, provision of training and areas for policy development within the context of the Agri-Environment Programme and reform of the Common Agricultural Policy.

ESAs are, by definition, areas of high nature conservation, landscape and archaeological interest. They are designed to assist in the introduction and maintenance of low intensity farming practices which have helped create many of our valuable wildlife habitats and landscapes in areas where these are under threat. This poster paper presents principles which relate to all habitats covered by ESA designations and to the current review process. It is based on English Nature and Countryside Commission submissions to the House of Commons Agriculture Committee Inquiry on Environmentally Sensitive Areas and Other Agri-Environment Schemes and to the ESA review.

EFFECTIVENESS

In general, ESAs have been effective in stemming further loss of wildlife habitats and in maintaining the broader character of the countryside. However, degradation of the countryside has occurred due to a combination of feature neglect, over-management and the continuing loss of non-agricultural land categories (eg, fens, osier beds, traditional orchards, etc.). So that the higher, more demanding tiers, which are often dependent on the survival of a wider farming system, are underpinned, it is important that tier 1 is a success.

ESAs have been less successful in promoting enhancement and re-creation of the natural environment; higher tiers have significantly lower uptake rates. There is even evidence of habitats declining in ecological quality as a result of prescriptions insufficiently related to the biodiversity interest (eg. hay meadows in the Pennine Dales). The value of field boundaries and other habitats in maintaining the overall biodiversity and landscape interest of ESAs has also been underplayed. The Conservation Plan could have a stronger role in addressing both these issues.

FUTURE DEVELOPMENT

The Countryside Agencies recognise that schemes such as ESAs can make a valuable contribution to achieving a broad range of environmental priorities including biodiversity, landscape, historic, amenity and resource protection.

Habitat and Species Action Plans arising from the UK Biodiversity Action Plan (BAP) identify Agri-Environment Schemes as mechanisms to deliver national and local BAP targets. Realisation of the UK's obligations to manage Natura 2000 sites under the Habitats and Birds Directives, and Natural Area and Character Area objectives also rely on agri-environment schemes including the ESA approach.

Ultimately, the appropriate management of habitats and landscapes on special sites and in the wider countryside requires wholescale reform of the Common Agricultural Policy away from support based on agricultural production and towards support for environmentally sustainable agricultural practices and environmental 'products'. Both English Nature and the Countryside Commission are engaged in dialogue with the Ministry of Agriculture and the Department of the Environment on approaches to an Integrated Rural Policy and this remains a long-term goal.

In the shorter term, there are important opportunities, such as the ESA reviews, for improving delivery of conservation benefits through ESAs. Future developments of the ESA approach could hinge upon:

- incorporation of UK Biodiversity Action Plan, Natural Area and Character Area targets and objectives into ESA environmental objectives with prescriptions, etc. being closely allied to these;

- designation of further ESAs, or similar area-based schemes, to conserve remaining extensive semi-natural habitats and landscapes or targeted at fragmented or more general farmland habitats;

- increased flexibility allowing for local circumstances;

- links to the experimental approach of English Nature's Wildlife Enhancement Scheme and Countryside Commission local-area projects;

- development of ESAs as a 'model' for future support mechanisms in delivering environmental benefits.

MAFF's current review of ESAs has addressed some of these issues and English Nature and the Countryside Commission along with the other statutory agencies and voluntary conservation bodies will continue to work with MAFF to ensure that the ESA scheme continues to develop and improve in its effective delivery of environmental benefits.

An Investigation into the Ecological Efficacy of Downland Turf Creation Schemes (in Particular the South Wessex Downs Environmentally Sensitive Area), Using Invertebrates as Indicators

A. HOARE

Bournemouth University, Centre for Land Based Studies, The Lindens, East Lulworth, Wareham, Dorset, BH20 5QT

Butterfly Conservation, PO Box 444, Wareham, Dorset, BH20 5YA

INTRODUCTION

In 1993 the South Wessex Downs Environmentally Sensitive Area (SWD ESA) was designated by the UK Government. This area, consisting of Cretaceous chalk overlain in places by clay/flint drift and encompassing Cranborne Chase and the Vale of Waldour in Dorset and also the West Wiltshire Downs, is one of 22 such areas designated in the last ten years as part of the government's agri-environment programme. The South Wessex Downs ESA has several Tiers of entry, including one for downland turf creation where arable land is taken out of production and reseeded with a downland mix.

Within the ESA monitoring and research is carried out to look at a number of issues, from how downland birds have responded to the changes in management to how the scheme has affected public awareness of the countryside. This research complements this work by looking at inter-related aspects of the ESA scheme, and this poster reports aspects of the first year's work. In particular it looks at two related questions; are butterflies using created downland turf in preference to arable fields, and, is the created downland turf of use to invertebrates given that many species sown are of non-native provenance.

METHODS AND RESULTS

Butterfly Transects

Transects were carried out once fortnightly on eight sites within the SWD ESA, in accordance with the National Butterfly Monitoring Scheme methodology (Pollard, 1977; Hall, 1981) and a more recent adaptation (Feber, 1995). This allowed the comparison of butterfly numbers at different sites and habitats. The sites were chosen to satisfy three criteria; they contained areas of downland turf creation, areas of established downland and fields under arable production adjacent to these. Each transect had four sections, within which all butterflies seen were counted. Although each section was longer than 100m, the butterflies seen on the first 100m of each section were recorded separately from the section. The sections walked were; arable field edge, downland turf creation field edge, downland turf creation field mid-habitat and downland turf mid-habitat. This meant that butterfly numbers could be compared by looking at edge areas and mid-habitat areas.

Analysis of the results showed that there was a significant difference (df = 3, $P<0.05$) in overall number of butterfly species found on downland turf creation field edges and arable edges. This remained significant when only those species classified as non-mobile and selective were looked at; an average of 6 selective species were seen on downland turf creation field edges, compared to an average of 3.29 species seen on arable field edges.

Seed Provenance

Sixty plants each of three varieties of bird's foot trefoil (*Lotus corniculatus*), one native and two agricultural cultivars (Leo and Maitland), were grown under standardized conditions until they had reached a suitable size for harvesting. They were then used to feed common blue butterfly (*Polyommatus icarus*) larvae arranged in individual trays on a randomized grid, to investigate the affect on invertebrates of sowing non-native provenance seed on the downland turf creation areas instead of native provenance seed.

It was found that larvae fed on the native *L. corniculatus* showed a large weight gain over a relatively short time period, whereas larvae fed on one of the non-native varieties showed a large weight gain over a relatively longer time period. In addition, when the imagos hatched and were mated, keeping those fed on the different varieties separate from each other, it was found that there was variation in egg batch size; the largest egg batch belonged to the *P. icarus* fed native variety *L. corniculatus*.

DISCUSSION

Butterflies are seen as a representative species group with regards to ecological changes in habitat. As such, the work carried out so far indicates that invertebrates are using three year old downland turf creation fields significantly more than they are using arable fields. However, what is not known is how they are using these fields. Future work (1997/8) will investigate this, using emergence traps to find out if butterflies are using the creation fields to breed on and also doing observational work to discover whether nectaring or sheltering are the main activities.

As yet there is little research investigating the effects of invertebrates feeding on non-native variety plants, but if the effects are similar to those shown in this study then they will be subtle but pervasive, especially in years with marginal weather, putting time constraints on breeding cycles. In the long run this may affect the usefulness of downland turf creation for invertebrates.

REFERENCES

HALL M.L. (1981) *Butterfly Monitoring Scheme, Instructions for Independent Recorders*. Cambridge: Institute of Terrestrial Ecology (Monks Wood).
FEBER R. (1995) *The effects of organic and conventional farming systems on the abundance of butterflies*. WWF (UK) Project 95/93 - Plants and Butterflies: Organic Farms.
POLLARD E. (1977) A method for assessing changes in the abundance of butterflies. *Biological Conservation*, 12, 115-134.

The Importance of Wildflower Seed Origin in the Restoration of Diverse Grassland

A. T. JONES and M. J. HAYES
Biodiversity Group, Institute of Grassland and Environmental Research,
Plas Gogerddan, Aberystwyth, Ceredigion SY23 3EB

INTRODUCTION

With the huge losses of wildflower grassland since the 1950's, there has recently been a focus on methods for their restoration. Many of the approaches involved in meadow creation have in essence been inherited from agriculture as have the targets *i.e.* visually appealing crops of wildflowers established to a given recipe and flowering in the first year. These well intentioned methodologies have attempted to create new conservation areas but there has often been complete ignorance of the need to consider genetic variation in wildflower species. Furthermore, certain seed companies had offered seed-mixtures containing non-native, imported seed and also seed from crop grown wildflowers without sufficient regulation and hence populations of non-British varieties of native wildflowers and even completely non-native species have become established.

More and more evidence is being uncovered that our native wildflower species are genetically highly variable with these differences linked to soil type, climate, geographical location and history of habitat. In considering the importance of our meadows at a global level, we have no endemic higher plant flora, nearly all our higher plant species being shared with continental Europe, however, the evolution of and the combinations of species that have developed under our hyper-oceanic climate are unique. It is precisely the protection and enhancement of this very richness in genetic diversity that should be the main target of future restoration and conservation efforts.

METHODS FOR GRASSLAND RESTORATION

There are parallels in grassland restoration with the restoration of works of art. Where damage has occurred to a painting, then the recreation of an original detail is based strictly on the tints and pattern surrounding those damaged areas. Similarly, where diverse grasslands have been lost through agricultural intensification then we should base restoration on the surviving genetic resources of the surrounding areas.

Given that financial resources will always be limiting, such techniques relying on donor sources of biodiversity in the vicinity of a new restoration sites, may be economically more viable rather than bringing in new material from completely different districts in a *laissez faire* fashion. Already in ESA's, which are being extended to the general countryside in the form of the countryside stewardship scheme, there is scope for farmers who conserve wildflowers to receive income from the harvesting of wildflower seed. This seed can be used in grassland restoration programmes concerning other farmers within the same district, once factors such as soil type and ecological factors are matched. This approach would be much cheaper than buying in expensive and inappropriate commercial wildflower seed mixtures. Within ESA areas there could be donors and recipients of diversity, funded by the ESA grants towards conserving biodiversity that are currently in place.

REDEFINING OUR OBJECTIVES

Very often in grassland restoration, conservation resources are directed towards the creation of artificial combinations of species and the quest for diversity to the *n*th level. Such a target, alone, is a misguided one and I believe objectives should be directed at the finer detail of ecological and genetic structure and relationships with other biota.

Two common and to some extent mutually exclusive reasons are often voiced for writing off the importance of the conservation of genetic diversity in the general countryside:

1. *Nothing worth saving* - any patterns of genetic variation in grassland have been lost through a history of agricultural and industrial damage or past widespread movement of plant material.
2. *The environmental sieve* - whatever mistakes we make in habitat restoration, for instance, in introducing alien plant material, selection forces will automatically weed them out and the natives will reassert themselves.

To the first point, a system of nature reserves argues that there is much that has survived and also wildflower species have managed to move to 'new' habitats, *e.g.* railway cuttings, and roadverges. From a casual glance through publications of the Botanical Society of the British Isles and old floras, it can be seen that many very old populations of certain species survive despite agricultural intensification.

To the second point, this is simply not the case and in many native vegetation types around the world the main threat is of the spread of exotic, introduced aliens. With sufficient resources, it would be quite easy to obliterate natural patterns of genetic variation in populations of many wildflower species by widespread, indiscriminate sowing of inappropriate wildflower seed mixtures.

At the intraspecific level it can be a relatively easy task to introduce non-native strains of a particular species to an non-native area. Recent research at Aberystwyth (Jones and Hayes, unpublished) has shown that in some cases non-native material can even outperform native material in a grassland situation.

Table 1.   Flowering frequency score for alien and native genotypes of wildflower species introduced into a extensive sward.

	Plantago lanceolata	*Prunella vulgaris*	*Centaurea nigra*
native	0.260	0.084	0.018
alien	0.362	0.137	0.144
s.e.d.			0.0225**

242

If we cannot within ESA's, manage and restore our own remaining grasslands to sufficiently rigorous standards, then why should we expect those in other countries, responsible for much richer floras, to adequately conserve their indigenous habitats?

Increasing the Wildflower Diversity of a Lowland Sward

A. T. JONES and M. J. HAYES

Institute of Grassland and Environmental Research, Plas Gogerddan, Aberystwyth, Ceredigion, SY23 3EB

INTRODUCTION

A current priority within grassland ESA's is the restoration of floristic diversity. In agriculturally improved, moderately fertile lowland pastures where wildflowers have been lost, it is known that reducing soil macronutrient availability is a prerequisite for increasing diversity. There is a need to identify sward managements that will quickly reduce this residual soil fertility and allow a concomitant increase in diversity by allowing wildflower colonization from both surviving sward populations and from adjacent refugia. Initial results are presented from a field study initiated in 1992 designed to evaluate a range of cutting and grazing treatments, under nil fertiliser inputs, in terms of their success at increasing diversity.

METHODS

The study was carried out within a 9-year old, *Lolium perenne*-dominated, lowland reseed at Trawsgoed Research Farm, Aberystwyth, Ceredigion. The 4 ha pasture had received regular annual fertilizer applications of 150 kg N, 75 kg P and 75 kg K/ha and had been grazed continually by sheep. In Spring 1992, 18 separate plots (each 50 x 30m) were fenced and arranged as three replicated blocks of six management treatments. Each treatment consisted of different combinations of cutting and grazing regimes with all receiving nil fertilizer inputs, except a control treatment which had normal inputs (Table 1). All treatments received lime inputs as necessary to maintain a soil pH of 6 to 6.5, except Treatment 2 which was left unlimed. Treatments were applied annually between 1992 and 1996.

Table 1.   Summary of management treatments.

Treatment	Fertilizer	Lime	Cutting	Grazing
T1. (Control)	+	+	Nil	Continuous
T2.	-	-	June & August	Autumn/Winter
T3.	-	+	June & August	Autumn/Winter
T4.	-	+	June & August	Nil
T5.	-	+	July	Autumn/Winter
T6.	-	+	Nil	Continuous

Treatments were assessed annually for soil nutrient status, soil pH and herbage yields. Botanical changes were monitored in May of each year by assessing 12 (1 m^2) permanent inclined point quadrats randomly located within each plot with percentage cover being derived for all species from 36 points. In addition, the total number of species present in each plot was regularly assessed to give a measure of total species richness.

RESULTS AND DISCUSSION

Between 1992 and 1996 there were progressive decreases in soil macronutrient concentrations, herbage yields and the *Lolium perenne* content of all the unfertilized treatments compared with the fertilized control, together with an corresponding increase in both the percentage contribution of other grasses and forbs and in total species richness. By 1996 all unfertilized treatments, and particularly those receiving two hay cuts followed by aftermath grazing (T2 and T3), had shown significant increases in the percentage cover of forbs when compared with the fertilized control (Table 2). The non-limed treatment (T2) had a mean species richness of 31 (compared with 19 in the control treatment) and had the greatest percentage of forbs, many of which were desirable wildflowers including *Hypochaeris radicata*, *Veronica chamaedrys* and *Lathyrus pratensis*. Future survival of these desirable perennial species appears to be dependent on lime inputs (T3), and in the absence of this (T2) colonizing species are more typically biennials or ruderals. Treatment 5, with a single cut in July and aftermath grazing, had the next highest proportion of forbs and also showed a large increase in *Holcus lanatus* cover. The grazed-only treatment (T6) remained reasonably fertile with a higher *Lolium* content together with a relatively large *Cirsium vulgare* population (6.4% cover). The cut-only treatment (T4) showed poorer results than expected and implies that where infrequent cutting is the only management the result could be a lack of increase of diversity and dominance by coarse grasses.

Table 2. Botanical composition (% cover) of the main sward components and mean species richness for the six management treatments-May 1996.

Management Treatment	T1	T2	T3	T4	T5	T6	s.e.d.
Lolium perenne	52.5	23.7	24.7	21.3	20.8	32.6	1.96
Poa spp.	24.8	12.5	17.3	33.3	15.7	24.2	1.70
Agrostis spp.	5.5	15.6	15.1	19.5	3.5	12.0	2.58
Holcus lanatus	1.3	1.1	0.3	3.0	23.6	0.9	1.37
Other grasses	0.4	4.7	2.6	3.2	4.0	1.7	1.54
Forbs	13.6	42.2	39.5	19.6	31.7	26.1	2.71
Mean species richness	19.0	31.0	27.0	24.0	21.0	23.0	3.30

Results so far have demonstrated that in the case of swards overlying soils of low to moderate fertility and near wildflower refugia, it is possible to produce a reasonable facsimile of a wildflower meadow within a few years and without recourse to seed introduction. Results suggest that there is potential for introducing a two-phase programme for increasing the species diversity of such pastures within ESA's. For the first year or two at least two cuts per season would reduce residual soil fertility and optimize ingress and colonization of new species by reducing competition to wildflower seedlings. Then a second phase would involve a traditional summer hay-cut followed by aftermath grazing allowing the seeding and dispersal of colonizing species.

ACKNOWLEDGMENT

This project is being funded by the Ministry of Agriculture, Fisheries and Food.

Positive Management of Wetlands in the Ynys Môn ESA

D. L. JONES

FRCA Aberystwyth, Yr Hen Ysgol Gymraeg, Ffordd Alexandra, Aberystwyth,
Ceredigion, SY23 1LF

INTRODUCTION

The Ynys Môn ESA Scheme (covering the whole of the Island of Anglesey in North Wales) has been operational since August 1993. The Scheme aims to protect three main elements, namely wildlife habitats, landscape and archaeological features. Wetlands form one of the most important habitats for wildlife on the Island, and the Scheme has been designed to encourage farmers to protect and enhance these areas through development of wetland management plans.

THE VALUE OF WETLANDS IN THE ESA

Wet areas comprise a suite of shallow lakes with fringing reedbeds, rich fens, basin mires, and wet/marshy pastures scattered throughout the intensive agricultural landscape. These areas support many species and communities which are rare in Wales and also provide refuge for a high concentration of breeding wildfowl. Many farmland birds are attracted to the Island for winter feeding, but the numbers that remain to breed in the spring are limited. The creation of suitable breeding habitat for birds such as lapwing, curlew and snipe is one of the main objectives of ESA wetland management programmes.

THE THREAT TO THE WETLANDS OF YNYS MÔN

During the late '70's and '80's intensive drainage and reseeding programmes were undertaken by farmers which resulted in wholescale destruction and loss of wetland habitat. These land improvements have to a large extent ceased, but drainage operations are still attempted periodically. However, the value of wetland habitat is now threatened by insensitive grazing management (predominantly by sheep) or to a lesser extent by abandonment and consequent dereliction.

THE STRUCTURE OF THE YNYS MÔN ESA SCHEME

The ESA Scheme has adopted a tiered structure coupled with capital payments for positive works and a public access element. Tier 1 aims to retain all features that are of environmental significance. Annual payments are made on a per hectare basis depending on farm size ranging from £10/ha to £25/ha. Additional payments are made under Tier 1A for retaining areas of wildlife habitat. These include Wetlands (£45/ha). Further payments for enhancement of habitats through positive management are offered under Tier 2A which is optional but often negotiated by Project Officers. Wetlands are included in this tier and an additional payment £20/ha is given for agreeing a positive management programme. The site specific management plan approach is exclusive to ESA's in Wales. Within the optional tier there is also the facility to offer payments for recreation of habitat from agriculturally improved land. The wetland reversion payment is £80/ha. Farmers are

247

therefore encouraged to manage wetlands through the Tier 1A and 2A payments (total £65/ha) and on large farms a significant commitment to wetland management often justifies the Tier 1 payment.

COMMONLY ADOPTED WETLAND MANAGEMENT TECHNIQUES

- Continuation of a high water table into spring and early summer
- Livestock reduction (or exclusion) during bird nesting season
- Cutting *Juncus* sp. in late summer
- Removal of encroaching scrub
- Profiling of ditches
- Laying/coppicing adjacent overgrown hedges (which can be funded separately within the Scheme).

TAKE UP OF THE WETLAND MANAGEMENT ELEMENT OF THE SCHEME

As of 4 February 1997 1,200 ha of Wetland had been committed to Tier 1A (retention) with 870 ha of this area entered for positive management in Tier 2A. This gave a total payment level of £71,400 per annum for Wetlands in the ESA (£53,990 for retention and £17,410 for management).

CASE STUDY

A holding of 55 ha containing 9.3 ha wetland in Tier 1A and Tier 2A. Total ESA payment is £1,675/annum of which £606 is for wetland retention and management. Under Tier 1A the Agreement Holder has an obligation not to intensify agricultural production on the wetland (no ploughing, reseeding, application of fertilizer/lime/agro-chemicals, overgrazing/poaching, supplementary feeding, modifying of drainage systems).

At the outset of the Agreement, the wetland was severely undergrazed, with rank vegetation (*Molinia caerulea and Juncus effusus*) becoming dominant. The objective of the Tier 2A management plan was to restore the area so as to encourage a greater diversity of plant species and create a sward structure that would encourage curlew and snipe. This involved grazing in the first year at a level that would remove excess rank growth by mass stocking with 25 cattle or ponies mainly during the period May to August and then in following years maintaining the more open sward with 9 cattle or ponies during spring and summer and 15 cattle or ponies during autumn and winter. Other prescriptions included topping of *Juncus effusus* in September of each year and not maintaining drainage.

Initial results have been encouraging with a much more open sward being created and the Agreement Holder reporting an increased numbers of birds utilising the site for feeding and breeding.

Conserving British Varieties of Wildflower Species

M. KING

Plantlife, Natural History Museum, Cromwell Road, London SW7 5BD

THE USE OF NON-NATIVE WILD-FLOWER SEED

Native plant species are increasingly being demanded for habitat creation and restoration schemes such as Environmentally Sensitive Areas (ESAs) and Countryside Stewardship. However, much of the seed used in these schemes is not native to Britain, let alone to the locality of the scheme. As a result, non-native variants of native wild plants are being widely introduced to the countryside. This has serious implications for our native vegetation.

WHY SHOULD WE BE CONCERNED ABOUT THE INTRODUCTION OF NON-NATIVE VARIANTS OF NATIVE WILD PLANTS?

There are very significant problems resulting from the introduction of non-native varieties of native plant species. One of the most serious threats is the competition between native plants and non-native variants of the same species. These non-native variants may displace the native strains, leading eventually to the loss of distinctive variants of some British wild plants altogether. Similarly, crossing between native and introduced plants will lead to an erosion of native genetic variation. Because many of our native plants are now confined to small and isolated habitat fragments, they are particularly vulnerable to these threats. Furthermore, any changes in British wild flower varieties will also have largely unknown knock-on effects for other wildlife.

A more subtle and insidious danger is the loss of diversity in the countryside and a trend towards uniformity in our vegetation. The introduction of non-native wild flower varieties is leading to an increasingly artificial countryside. The British countryside and its vegetation has evolved over thousands of years into a complex pattern. Native plants all have a distribution which reflects upon the climate, soil conditions and the long history of traditional farming practices. Each plant 'tells us' something about the ecological conditions and land-use history of its location. The widespread introduction of non-native variants of wild plants is destroying this meaning in the landscape.

WHO IS RESPONSIBLE FOR THESE PROBLEMS?

The use of non-native variants of native wild plants in habitat creation and restoration schemes occurs for a number of reasons and illustrates a series of problems which need to be addressed. These include:

1) A lack of commitment to the establishment of native wild flowers in ESA/ Countryside Stewardship schemes. This stems from both a lack of clear policy guidance and a lack of sufficient awareness amongst project advisors and within ADAS.
2) Seed merchants who supply material of continental origin, whilst claiming that it is native.

3) Absence of means by which farmers may determine whether truly native seed has been supplied.

4) A lack of appropriate policies within MAFF and other agricultural departments/ agencies on the use of native seed in habitat creation and restoration schemes.

5) Lack of legislation which would allow for compensation if seeds sold as native varieties turn out to be non-native.

These problems are compounded by the lack of availability of native wild flower seed and the relative abundance and low cost of continental varieties and agricultural fodder crops.

WHAT IS BEING DONE TO ADDRESS THESE PROBLEMS?

Plantlife in conjunction with the Nature Conservation Bureau have established 'Flora Locale', a project which aims to address the problem of non-native wild flower seed. The project aims to adopt a range of approaches including:

1) Consultation with all relevant organisations such as conservation organisations, forestry agencies, the DoE, agricultural agencies, the highways agency, horticulturists, landscape architects, local authorities, ecologists, and many others.

2) Promotion of good practice and provision of technical guidance for habitat restoration and wild flower seed production.

3) Research into the genetic diversity of British wild plants.

4) Establishment of an accreditation and certification scheme for nurseries and seed merchants who are able to provide material of known native origin.

FURTHER ACTION NEEDED

Much work still needs to be done to reduce the widespread introduction of non-native varieties of native plants into the countryside. In addition to initiatives outlined above, the following action is also desperately needed:

1) The appointment of more professional ecologists to agricultural advisory groups.

2) The development of more rigorous policies within MAFF and other agricultural departments and agencies on the use of native seed in habitat creation and restoration schemes.

3) Reduction of the cost differential between continental and British provenance seeds.

4) Continual and independent assessment of government funded schemes. Many of these do not meet their objectives regarding the plant material used *e.g.* non-native seed is usually used in the creation of 'native' grasslands within ESAs.

5) The development of legislation which would allow for compensation if seeds sold as 'native' varieties turn out to be non-native.

The Effect of Cutting Date on Seed Rain in Hay Meadows Within the Somerset Levels and Moors ESA

F. W. KIRKHAM

University of Plymouth, Drake Circus, Plymouth PL4 8AA

INTRODUCTION

Regulations within the Somerset Moors and Levels ESA preclude cutting before the 1 July in Tier 2 and before 8 July in Tier 3. One purpose of this rule is to allow a wide variety of plants to set seed. In the Pennine Dales, occasional cutting in August or even later is needed to allow maximal ripe seed production by the majority of species present (Smith and Jones, 1991). The present work investigated the influence of cutting date on seed return in plant communities on a Somerset peat moor.

METHODS

The effects on 'seed rain' of cutting on one of 4 dates (see Table 1) were examined in a randomized block experiment with 72 plots, each 8 m^2 in area, in meadows which had either previously received inorganic fertilizers (200 kg N/ha with replacement rates of P and K for five years) or which had never been fertilized. Vegetation cut in May was wilted for 24 hours before removal, but hay was made at later cutting dates. Five 13.5 cm diameter compost-filled dishes were set into the ground on each plot in early spring, removed after harvest of the vegetation and then watered in a poly-tunnel for 18 months. Emerging seedlings were identified and the numbers grouped into various categories. Linear and quadratic effects of cutting date (days after 1 April) and the interaction with previous fertilizer treatment were tested by analysis of variance for polynomial contrasts.

RESULTS

Of the 73 species recorded altogether, 29 produced viable seeds with cutting in late May, 51 with July cutting and 63 with cutting in early August. Most species showed a peak in seedlings following harvesting in July or August, with lower numbers in September (Table 1). This pattern was most marked for species which have no seed dormancy (seed bank Type I, Grime *et al.*, 1988) and those which had increased in abundance with regular fertilizer application. The number of seedlings of species which contribute to the long-term seed bank (Type IV) increased sharply with lateness of cutting.

DISCUSSION

Cutting in July is clearly too early to allow many species to set seed. Since many later flowering plants are Type IV species, July cutting will deplete the seed bank if repeated continually. Type I species have little or no seed dormancy and most can germinate beneath a closed canopy. Many of these flower relatively early but appear to be susceptible to late cutting, either through seed predation or because they are unable to survive as seedlings during the prolonged period until the canopy is removed. Year-to-year variations in cutting date are therefore important for the maintenace of a wide range of species in these meadows and ESA regulations ensuring at least occasional cutting in August or later are needed.

Table 1.   Number of seedlings/m^2 produced from seed shed up to and during harvesting on 4 cutting dates in 1991

Species group	Previous fertilizer	22 May	17 July	9 Aug.	4 Sep.	Significance of response
Grasses	-F	7	4561	9249	12233	(F*, L***, Q***)
	+F	16	14493	19782	16166	
Dicots.	-F	2997	4753	8989	8806	L***, Q***, F x Q**
	+F	3815	10452	14802	11211	
Cyperaceae	-F	5	13	18	16	None
	+F	1	1	1	3	
Juncaceae	-F	4	43	168	63	(L***, Q***)
	+F	5	10	44	23	
Seed bank Type I	-F	2823	5467	9286	8276	F*, L***, Q***,
	+F	3681	13824	11882	7907	F x Q***
Seed bank Type IV	-F	15	413	1239	5458	L***, Q*
	+F	18	1025	1155	4871	
Total of all species	-F	3012	9370	18424	21119	L***, Q**,
	+F	3837	24957	34629	27402	F x Q***

Asterisks denote significance of effects (* $P<0.05$, ** $P<0.01$ and *** $P<0.001$): F = previous fertilizer, L = linear and Q = quadratic response to cutting date. Bracketed symbols refer to analyses performed on square-root transformed data

ACKNOWLEDGEMENTS
This work was carried out in collaboration with IGER, North Wyke. Current financial support from ADAS is acknowledged.

REFERENCES
GRIME J.P., HODGSON J.G. and HUNT R. (1988) *Comparative Plant Ecology: a Functional Approach to Common British Species*. London: Unwin Hyman.
SMITH R.S. and JONES L. (1991) The phenology of mesotrophic grassland in the Pennine Dales, Northern England: historic hay cutting dates, vegetation variation and plant species phenologies. *Journal of Applied Ecology*, 28, 42-59.

The Influence of Hay Making Operations on Seed Rain in Hay Meadows Within the Somerset Levels and Moors ESA

F. W. KIRKHAM

University of Plymouth, Drake Circus, Plymouth PL4 8AA

INTRODUCTION

An accompanying paper described the influence of cutting date on seed rain in meadows on a Somerset peat moor (Kirkham, 1997). The present paper describes studies of the number and species of viable seeds shed during the various phases of cutting and hay making in the same meadows.

METHODS

Data were obtained from two studies on unfertilized meadows. In the first, a subset of the plots described in the accompanying paper were used to record the number of seedlings emerging from seed shed between 22 May and cutting on each of three dates (17 July, 9 August - 2 plots each, or 4 September - 4 plots) and during subsequent hay making. Five 13.5 cm diameter compost-filled dishes were set into the ground on each plot on 22 May and removed before cutting. Dishes were replaced immediately before cutting by fresh ones which were subsequently removed after hay had been made and harvested from the plots. The number of seedlings already present on removal from the plots, and those subsequently emerging over a period of 18 months with daily watering in a poly-tunnel, were recorded. This procedure allowed seedlings produced from seed shed prior to cutting to be differentiated from those shed during hay making. A similar technique was used in the second study, where 10 dishes were laid out in a 2m x 19m area immediately before cutting on 9 August and replaced with fresh ones after cutting. This procedure was repeated to capture seeds shed during drying and turning and during rowing and baling.

RESULTS

Only 22% of the total number of seedlings resulting from seed captured both prior to and during hay making in July came from seeds shed before cutting, increasing to 24% with harvesting in August and 58% in September. These proportions were notably lower for dicotyledonous species than for grasses (19%, 24% and 38% compared with 22%, 24% and 64%). *Juncaceae* showed a similar pattern to dicots, but very few viable seeds of *Cyperaceae* were shed before cutting.

Drying and turning accounted for 53% of the total number of seedlings produced during hay making in August, with only 37% from seed shed during cutting (Table 1). This effect was more pronounced with dicots than grasses, but was reversed for *Juncaceae*.

DISCUSSION

The hay making process is clearly important for stimulating seed shedding, even with harvesting in August or later. Moreover, removal of herbage soon after cutting (as in silage making) will not only be less effective in stimulating seed rain but will also favour grasses at the expense of dicots and *Cyperaceae*. In further studies with selected dicot species, drying for 72 hours (as in hay making) stimulated seed shedding significantly compared to wilting for 24 hours, even with late cutting (Kirkham, 1996). It is therefore important that ESA regulations should stipulate that vegetation should be made into hay rather than allowing silage making, even where the latter involves wilting.

Table 1.   Number of seedlings/m^2 produced from seed shed during three phases of hay making in early August.

Species/group	Hay making operation			Total
	Cutting	Drying//turning	Rowing/baling	
Grasses	6155 ± 639.6	9237 ± 1460.1	1055 ± 650.9	16447 ± 1527. 9
Dicots.	1152 ± 344.3	2878 ± 824.2	452 ± 299.1	4482 ± 771.5
Cyperaceae	0 ±! 0.0	60 ± 27.1	8 ± 7.5	68 ± 26.4
Juncaceae	1771 ± 1130.1	595 ± 162.7	889 ± 375.2	3255 ± 1231.1
Total of all species	9079 ± 2682.1	12770 ± 1893.3	2403 ± 1106.8	24252 ± 2447.1

± values are standard errors (s.e.), n=10

ACKNOWLEDGEMENTS
This work was carried out in collaboration with IGER, North Wyke. Current financial support from ADAS is acknowledged.

REFERENCES
KIRKHAM F.W. (1997) The effect of cutting date on seed rain in hay meadows within the Somerset Levels and Moors ESA. In: Sheldrick R.D. (ed) *Grassland Management in the ESAs*. Occ. Symp. 32, British Grassland Society, Reading.
KIRKHAM F.W. (1996) *The Agricultural Ecology Of Hay Meadows Within The Somerset Levels And Moors Environmentally Sensitive Area*. Ph.D. thesis, University of Plymouth.

Botanical Composition and its Impact on Digestibility, Nutritive Value and Roughage Intake

H. KOREVAAR and C. VAN DER WEL[1]

Research Institute for Agrobiology and Soil Fertility (AB-DLO), P.O. Box 14, 6700 AA
Wageningen, The Netherlands

[1] Research Station for Cattle, Sheep and Horse Husbandry, Lelystad, The Netherlands

INTRODUCTION

During the last 20 years the Dutch government offered management agreements to individual farmers to conserve the most valuable and vulnerable parts of the countryside. Some 6,000 farmers have already signed such an agreement for a total of 40,000 ha. Grassland utilization according to these agreements in general leads to a greater variation of grass species and herbs in the sward. Most roughage from these species-rich grasslands is used on intensive dairy farms. Therefore it is important to have information on the nutritive value of roughage from these grasslands and the roughage intake and animal production by the stock (Korevaar *et al.*, 1988, Nösberger *et al.*, 1994).

MATERIALS AND METHODS

Herbage samples were taken from grasslands on wet peaty soils at regular intervals during the year 1990 (experiment 1). At each sampling date tufts of 25 cm^2 herbage were taken from approximately 40 spots and pooled. Earlier sampled spots were avoided. Depending on the length of the herbage, 1 or more composite samples were completely separated into species until enough material (at least 10 g DM per species) was collected for further analyses. For individual species as well as the mixed herbage organic matter digestibility (OMD) was determined in vitro by incubation with rumen fluid followed by pepsin-HCl. The in vitro results were corrected for the differences between in vivo and in vitro with in vitro samples of known in vivo digestibility (Steg *et al.*, 1990).

During three years (1989-1991) a comparison (experiment 2) was made of silage quality and roughage intake from fields dominated (> 80%) by *Lolium perenne* (good botanical composition) and from fields with mixed swards of mainly *Agrostis stolonifera*, *Lolium perenne*, *Poa trivialis* and *Alopecurus geniculatus* (moderate botanical composition). One half of each field was fertilized with 80 kg N/ha and cut mid of May. The other halves received no nitrogen fertilizer and silage making was delayed to mid of June. After prewilting, the grass was ensiled into clamp-silos. In winter the silages were fed to low productive cows at the end of their lactation cycle. The roughage intake and daily milk production were measured.

RESULTS

In May and June, during primary growth, all grass species showed a strong decline in digestibility (Table 1). At all sampling dates considerable differences occurred in digestibility between the species. At most sampling dates *Lolium perenne* had the highest and *Alopecurus geniculatus* the lowest digestibility. *Holcus lanatus* started with a high digestibility, but at the end of May its digestibility declined sharply. *Agrostis stolonifera* on the other hand started at a relative low level and ended in the mid of June at about the same level of digestibility as *Lolium*.

In previous experiments (Korevaar, 1986) we found that, when the number of growing days was the same, the level of N-application had no impact on the digestibility. Also for these grass species there is no relation between N-level and OMD (Table 1).

Table 1.   OMD (%) of some species during primary growth (Experiment 1).

Date	N/ha	1-5	8-5	15-5	21-5	29-5	5-6	12-6	18-6
Lolium perenne	80	85.3	80.7	78.7	76.5	74.2	70.3	69.0	69.0
	0	-	81.9	-	77.4	-	67.9	-	70.5
Poa trivialis	80	83.4	77.6	73.6	71.7	71.1	68.2	67.1	68.1
	0	-	78.1	-	71.6	-	66.5	-	65.3
Agrostis stolonifera	80	79.9	74.9	74.2	73.2	74.8	70.1	67.6	68.2
	0	-	76.9	-	74.7	-	72.4	-	69.2
Holcus lanatus	80	84.5	80.4	76.5	73.7	70.5	65.1	65.4	66.5
	0	-	76.8	-	72.5	-	70.1	-	65.3
A. geniculatus	80	81.7	76.6	75.1	71.5	70.7	68.0	64.4	66.7
	0	-	76.9	-	71.7	-	71.2	-	68.5

Table 2.   OMD, net energy content, intake and milk production per cow of silages made from different swards and at two stages of maturing. Average figures for 1989-1991 (Experiment 2).

Date	Botanical composition	N (kg/ha)	OMD (%)	Net energy (MJ/kg DM)	intake (kgDM/day)	milk (kg/day)
May	good	80	77.4	6.29	14.5	14.7
	moderate	80	73.5	5.95	14.1	14.4
June	good	0	68.5	5.39	11.8	10.7
	moderate	0	59.8	4.64	10.3	10.3

For the silages made in May the impact of botanical composition on digestibility, energy content, roughage intake and milk production was limited. When silage making was delayed till mid June the difference between silage from *Lolium* swards and from the mixed sward with a moderate botanical composition was substantial: in net energy -0.75 MJ/kg DM, in roughage intake -1.5 kg DM/cow/day. The impact on milk production was rather small (-0.4 kg milk/cow/day) and not significant.

However, the differences between silages made in May and in June overrulled the differences between botanical composition.

CONCLUSION

Botanical composition has, just like stage of growth, a great impact on digestibility and net energy content of the herbage. A lower digestibility causes a lower intake of roughage. In combination with the lower energy content this means a smaller energy intake by the animal, which leads to a lower animal production.

REFERENCES

KOREVAAR H. (1986) *Production and feeding value of grass from grassland with restrictions in use and fertilization for nature conservation*. Ph.D thesis (in Dutch with English summary and translation of Tables and Figures). Report 101. Research and Advisory Institute for Cattle, Sheep and Horse Husbandry, Lelystad, The Netherlands.

KOREVAAR H., DEN BOER D.J. and VELLINGA T. V. (1988) Intensive and extensive grassland systems: implications of restrictions. *Proceedings of the 12th General Meeting of the European Grassland Federation*, Dublin, pp. 98-115.

NÖSBERGER J., LEHMANN J., JEANGROS B., DIETL W., KESSLER W., BASSETTI P. and MITCHLEY J. (1994) Grassland production systems and nature conservation. *Proceedings of the 15th General Meeting of the European Grassland Federation*, Wageningen, pp. 255-265.

STEG A., SPOELSTRA S.F., VAN DE MEER J.M. and HINDLE V.A. (1990) Digestibility of grass silage. *Netherlands Journal of Agricultural Science*, 38, 407-422.

Grazing Management of Lowland Wet Grassland in the West Fermanagh and Erne Lakeland Environmentally Sensitive Area

E. D. MALLON *[1], J. H. MCADAM [1] and W. I. MONTGOMERY [2]

[1]Applied Plant Science, Queen's University, Newforge Lane, Belfast, BT9 5PX UK
[2]School of Biology and Biochemistry, Queen's University, Belfast, BT7 1NN UK

INTRODUCTION

Lowland wet grassland can be defined as managed grassland situated at less than 200 metres above sea-level subject to periodic inundation with freshwater and having a diverse flora and fauna. The extent and quality of this habitat has declined in recent years. The West Fermanagh and Erne Lakeland ESA provides an opportunity to maintain and where possible enhance this habitat and its internationally important populations of breeding waders, through appropriate management regimes. The research described here, aims to investigate those characteristics of lowland wet grassland which make them particularly attractive to waders and, enhance and refine some of the ESA management prescriptions in order to improve the botanical and ornithological value of lowland wet grassland.

MATERIALS AND METHODS

Twelve lowland wet grassland sites around Upper Lough Erne were selected, using the Royal Society for the Protection of Birds (RSPB) grading system (Partridge, 1992), which grades sites according to the number of key breeding wader pairs present: grade I: >20 pairs, grade II: 19-10 pairs and grade III: <10 pairs. Four sites (two grade I and two grade III) were chosen from the original twelve to establish grazing trials. Four grazing trials were established by subdividing each field into three plots, in a ratio by area of 2:1:2 and grazed at one of three grazing densities i.e. 0, 1.5, or 3 cows/ha. The vegetation of each field was systematically mapped, classifying it into 3 vegetation zones along a soil moisture gradient, V1 (dry), V2 (marshy) and V3 (waterlogged) for practical and experimental purposes.

RESULTS

TWINSPAN classification separated vegetation samples into a range of groups of plant species from those indicative of relatively free-draining, improved/semi-improved grassland, V1 to those indicative of wet and often waterlogged grassland, V3. Rush tussocks tended to be taller, wider, larger and most dense on grade III sites and in the V1 vegetation zone.

Soils of grade I sites were consistently easier to penetrate than grade III sites on all recording dates and soil profile depths during 1994 and 1995 with the exception of two occasions in 1995. The degree of soil poaching differed significantly between vegetation zones with V3 being poached significantly more than V1 and V2, this relationship was evident to a greater extent in grade I sites than in grade III.

Table 1.   Summary of two way analyses of variance indicating the effect of site grade on mean soil penetrability during the 1994 field season. Variance ratios are presented with significance denoted by bold type and * $P<0.005$, **$P<0.01$, ***$P<0.001$.

Date	10/6	28/6	12/7	24/8	18/10
Site d.f. (1,2)	22.46*	24.22*	20.31*	458.99***	127.40**

DISCUSSION

Rush tussocks are used by waders to provide cover from predators and as a nesting site. The ideal rush density is one which provides sufficient cover for camouflage and sufficient visibility of approaching predators. Grade III wet pastures tend to have taller, wider and more dense rush tussocks than those found in grade I pastures. The structure and distribution of the rush tussocks may, along with several other variables, be a contributory factor to the lower breeding wader density in Grade III pastures.

Penetrability is a measure of soil strength and as soil strength is highly dependent on soil moisture. it is not surprising that soil from grade I sites were easier to penetrate than soils from grade III soils. Soil poaching is also dependent on soil moisture content. V3 vegetation zone was found to have a higher soil water content than V1 and V2, due to its proximity to a watercourse and, as expected, the degree of poaching in V3 was greater than in V1 and V2. Light soil poaching is beneficial as it provides germination niches, bare ground for probing by waders and a tussocky sward structure which can be used by waders for nesting and camouflage from predators.

Grazing management cannot be considered in isolation as numerous, diverse factors affect the population and breeding success of waders in any given area such as climate, predation and food availability. All these factors and their interactions must be taken into account in the management of wet grassland, to achieve the maximum benefit for the habitat.

REFERENCES

PARTRIDGE K. (1992). *1992 Re-survey of Northern Ireland breeding wader sites.* Royal Society for the Protection of Birds. Sandy.

GREEN R.E. (1985). *The management of lowland wet grassland for breeding waders.* Royal Society for the Protection of Birds. Sandy.

The Success of Nurse Crops in the Establishment of Species-Rich Lowland Wet Grassland

S.J. MANCHESTER, J.R. TREWEEK, J.O. MOUNTFORD and R.F. PYWELL

NERC Institute of Terrestrial Ecology, Monks Wood, Abbots Ripton,

Huntingdon, PE17 2LS

INTRODUCTION

Historically, 'nurse' or 'cover' crops have often been used to promote the germination and establishment of agricultural crops and grasslands. Indeed, within the Upper Thames Tributaries Environmentally Sensitive Area (ESA), the traditional method for establishment of grass leys on ex-arable sites was to undersow spring barley crops or to sow with a nurse crop of annual ryegrass (R.Lambourne, personal communication). The advantages of using a nurse crop to promote grassland establishment include: i) quick germination and establishment of green vegetation; ii) suppression of excessive annual weed growth, and iii) amelioration of harsh conditions and provision of shelter for slower germinating/establishing forb species (Wells, 1989).

This paper reports partial findings of a MAFF-commissioned field experiment designed primarily to investigate techniques for the recreation of lowland wet grassland upon ex-arable land, focussing on the deliberate introduction of potential colonising species as seed. Within the experiment itself, treatments were repeated both with and without a nurse crop of Westerwolds annual ryegrass (*Lolium multiflorum*), thus allowing sward establishment and performance to be compared with and without the nurse. Experimental treatments were sown in September 1993 and monitored for three subsequent years. The work was carried out within the River Ray catchment of the Upper Thames Tributaries ESA.

RESULTS AND DISCUSSION

Species considered appropriate for inclusion in lowland wet grassland swards ('desirable' or 'target' species) were classified as either Class I (species indicative of lowland wet grassland) or Class II (wider grassland species). Results were thus considered in terms of total species numbers, numbers of target species, establishment of sown species, and percentage ground cover of species. Effects attributable to the nurse crop were observed over all treatments, and thus individual treatment results are not discussed in detail.

The experimental site suffered from an excess of *Lolium multiflorum*, sown as a nurse crop but also already present within the pre-existing vegetation and soil seed bank (contributing 21% of all recorded seedlings). Early within the experiment, it became apparent that the nurse crop was not actually beneficial, but was instead having adverse effects on species establishment, total species numbers and ground cover of target species.

One year after sowing the nurse crop had suppressed the germination of sown species. Throughout the duration of the experiment there were consistently greater numbers of target species, and a higher ground cover of Class I species, in the absence of the nurse crop. In 1994, the ground cover of non-target species (not including *L. multiflorum*) was also suppressed by the presence of the nurse crop, and such a reduction in potential weeds may have some benefits for the re-creation of habitats. However, the suppression of target and sown species is obviously undesirable.

In this instance, the nurse crop appeared to have a generally detrimental effect on the establishment of the target vegetation. The failure of the nurse crop to promote establishment of other species may be attributed in part to the fact that the field already contained *Lolium multiflorum*, and thus the sowing of more *L. multiflorum* increased abundances beyond levels desirable in a companion crop.

Nurse crops may be beneficial on some sites to establish ground cover, protect soil from erosion and provide a sheltered environment for the germination and establishment of sown wild flowers. It should be remembered that the main aim of this experiment was to re-establish species-rich grassland of conservation value, and not to create an agriculturally valuable sward for which nurse crops may be more appropriate. Suitable nurse crops should be short-lived, not persistent or troublesome to eradicate, and should not inhibit establishment of other sown species by shading or competition. Westerwolds Ryegrass is often recommended for use as a nurse crop but does tend to produce dense growth and lodges if allowed to grow unchecked.

This study illustrates that preliminary investigation of pre-existing vegetation, and the composition of the soil seed bank, may be essential in determining whether a nurse crop is necessary for grassland establishment.

REFERENCES
WELLS T.C.E. (1989). The recreation of grassland habitats. *The Entomologist*, 108(1-2): 97-108.

Tier 2 Wetland in the Lake District ESA

D. MARTIN

FRCA, Otley Road, Lawnswood, Leeds, LS16 5QT

INTRODUCTION

Wetland has proved the most popular Tier 2 option on inbye land within MAFF's Lake District ESA scheme. Wetland sites represent a range of semi-natural habitats often surrounded by more agriculturally intensive grassland. Management agreements are aimed at maintaining and enhancing the nature conservation interest of these sites. Sites entered into this option up to and including 1996 total 491 covering 1600 ha.

Before accepting land into Tier 2 a reconnaissance field survey is carried out with summary botanical information recorded. In order to monitor the range of sites under agreement and as an aid to management this information has been analysed and used to form the basis of a wetland management database.

METHOD

Since most botanical site reports consist of an inexhaustive list of species, and vary in detail, the approach has been to create botanical groups. These consist of either single, often dominant, species which will usually be recorded in the field, such as soft rush (*Juncus effusus*) (Group 1) and purple moor grass (*Molinia caerulea*) (Group 5), or broad ecological or structural groups, for example base rich sedges (Group 8) and tall reeds (Group 13). Twenty botanical groups in total have been used in the database.

The analysis package TWINSPAN has been used to classify wetland sites based on these botanical groups. Groups are treated as species, on a presence or absence basis. The resulting TWINSPAN end classes are described in terms of broad vegetation types represented. In addition, several sites have been surveyed in detail using the ESA grassland monitoring method (Critchley & Poulton, in preparation) as part of the Lake District ESA monitoring programme (ADAS, 1997). Where possible these have been used to suggest typical National Vegetation Classification (NVC) (Rodwell, 1991) types within end classes.

RESULTS

A total of 348 sites have been classified into eight end classes, the remainder lacking sufficient botanical information. The frequency of sites within each end class is shown in Figure 1. The initial split of the data is between those sites of broadly mesotrophic conditions, often with a rush component and fragmented within relatively intensively managed land, and sites of more nutrient poor, often acidic conditions, which may be quite extensive and relatively undisturbed.

Four end classes A, B, C and D represent the former, including rush pasture with NVC communities M23 *Juncus effusus/acutiflorus - Galium palustre* rush pasture, and MG10 *Holcus lanatus - Juncus effusus* rush pasture (Class C), tall reed and sedge communities fringing rivers or tarns (Class D), sites with mosaics of remnant wet heath and raised mire (Class B) and sites with sedge flushes and wetter elements of Sphagnum mire, such as M6 *Carex echinata -*

Sphagnum recurvum/auriculatum mire.

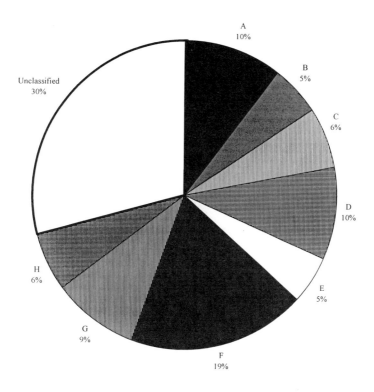

Figure 1. Frequency of sites within TWINSPAN end classes

Less detailed botanical monitoring information exists for the nutrient poor classes E, F, G and H. Vegetation ranges from lowland mires with purple moor grass, dwarf shrub and carr woodland (Class E), remnant wet heath (Class G) such as M15 *Scirpus cespitosus - Erica tetralix* wet heath similar to Class B but in mosaics with less improved acidic grassland, and relatively species poor acidic grassland often with sedge flushes (Class H), some examples of which may be included for ornithological interest. A large class (F) contains sites with a range of nutrient poor acidic lowland mire of cotton grasses, dwarf shrubs and *Sphagnum* spp often in mosaics with mesotrophic vegetation. This class may be sub-divided as more detailed information becomes available.

FURTHER DEVELOPMENT AND APPLICATIONS
It is intended to examine the distribution of the classes using the Geographical Information System (GIS) ArcView. The relationship with landcover classes and landscape types, also held on GIS, can be examined.

The GIS may be used for a range of applications, such as targeting of specific habitats for conservation. For example potential habitats for the marsh fritillary butterfly may be identified within buffer zones of known populations. The management information held on the database could be used to co-ordinate a consistent approach to management of similar sites. Results from ESA monitoring may be extrapolated to a wider range of sites with similar vegetation and management.

CONCLUSIONS

The wetland database has been developed from botanical and management information. An attempt has been made to classify sites based on often limited botanical information. The database may be used to target habitats for conservation and biodiversity purposes, and aid in the management of the Lake District ESA wetland resources.

REFERENCES

ADAS (1997) Environmental monitoring in the Lake District ESA 1993-1996.

CRITCHLEY C.N.R. and POULTON S.M.C. (in preparation) A method to optimise precision and scale in vegetation monitoring and survey.

RODWELL J.S. (Ed) (1991) *British plant communities Vol 2, Mires and Heaths*. Cambridge University Press.

Re-creation of Chalk Downland from Arable Land

S. E. McKENZIE[1] and S. PEEL[2]

[1]ADAS SE, Wharf House, Wharf Road, Guildford, Surrey GU1 4RP

[2]ADAS Bridgets, Martyr Worthy, Winchester, Hampshire SO21 1AP

INTRODUCTION

Monitoring of the South Downs ESA has shown that conversion from arable to grassland using perennial ryegrass and clover resulted in species-poor swards, despite no fertiliser or herbicide use for eight years. A new option was introduced in 1992 to encourage species more typical of chalk downland, using at least 5 grass species from a list of 10. The project described supports this by identifying appropriate mixtures to sow on soils of initially high P and K status, which will produce a sward resembling chalk downland under sheep grazing.

METHODS

Plots 4.2 x 10m were sown on 27 August 1992 within a field with a long arable history and high nutrient status (P index 2/3 and K index 4). The plots were unfenced and grazed by sheep. Mixtures were sown at two rates; 15 and 30 kg/ha:

1. Chewings fescue *(Festuca rubra* ssp. *commutata* cv. Banner)
2. Strong creeping red fescue *(F. rubra ssp rubra* cv. Boreal)
3. Equal parts (1) and (2)
4. "Commercial mix" (30% *F. rubra* ssp. *commutata*; 30% *Cynosurus cristatus*; 30% *Poa pratensis*, 5% *F. ovina*, 5% *Phleum pratense*)
5. "Commercial with legumes" (as (4) but reduce each main grass to 25% and add 7.5% *Lotus corniculatus* cv. Empire, 7.5% *Medicago lupulina* cv. Virgo Pajberg.
6. " Diverse mix" (Equal seed numbers of all 10 of the permitted grass species*)
7. "Diverse with wildflowers' (as (6), replacing 20% with six flower species**)
8. No seeds sown

* The 10 grass species are: *F. rubra* ssp. *commutata*; *F. ovina*; *C cristatus*; *P. pratensis*; *Phleum pratense* ssp. *bertolonii*, *Agrostis capillaris*, *Anthoxanthum odoratum*, *Trisetum flavescens*; *Briza media*; *Bromus erectus*.
** The 6 wildflower species are: *Galium verum*; *Plantago lanceolata*; *Prunella vulgaris*; *Sanguisorba minor*; *Scabiosa columbaria*; *Daucus carota*.

There were three replicates. Botanical assessments were made in June/July from 1993 to 1996. Exclosure cages were placed in March on a number of plots, with herbage being cut on c. 15 June and 15 July. In addition to the plot experiment, detailed monitoring was carried out on seven whole fields, sown in 1992 mainly to grass-only mixtures.

RESULTS

Despite high soil nutrient status all sown species established and persisted over four years, although *Cynosurus, Poa pratensis* and *Briza media* were particularly slow to develop. Sowing rate had no significant effect, representing a substantial cost saving. The "Diverse" mixes contained significantly more unsown species than other mixtures. Many of these were ruderals but these mixtures may favour colonisation of desirable species either from the seed bank or from an adjacent seed source. Assessments of whole fields reveal that species characteristic of chalk downland will begin to colonise even within three years.

Peel *et al.* (1994) showed that in the first harvest year of this experiment the addition of legumes tended to increase yield, and nutritive value. By the 3rd and 4th harvest years the proportion of legumes, particularly *M.lupulina,* had declined. Nevertheless table 1 shows that benefits in herbage yield and nutritive value were still apparent.

Table 1. Herbage production and nutritive value at the mid-June out. Mean data for 3rd and 4th harvest years (1995 and 1996)

		Herbage Yield kg DM/ha	Digestibility NCGD	Nitrogen (%)	Ash (%)
mix 4	Grasses only	1310	45.6	1.25	5.0
mix 5	Grasses plus legumes	1789	53.4	1.79	6.2
SED		322.2	2.80	0.180	0.42

The legumes significantly increased ash %, signifying a greater content of nutritionally valuable minerals such as phosphorus and magnesium. They also increased nitrogen %, indicative of a greater protein content. The addition of wildflowers (mix 7) also tended to increase nutritive value. The addition of legumes to the "commercial mix" did not significantly reduce the ingress of unsown species, suggesting that this may be a valuable means of increasing the attractiveness of this option to farmers without compromising diversity.

CONCLUSIONS
1. On chalk soils of high nutrient status, a wide range of grass and forb species can establish even from low seed rates, and persist for at least 4 years under hard sheep grazing.
2. Even after many years arable cropping, species typical of chalk downland can start to colonise within 3 years.
3. Sowing commercial cultivars of native legume species increases productivity and nutritive value, and may not threaten ingress of other species.

ACKNOWLEDGEMENTS
We are very grateful to MAFF for funding this work. We also thank Gill Swash (FRCA), Ben Benatt and Bob Antonini for botanical assessments.

REFERENCES
PEEL S., SWASH G. and McKENZIE S.E. (1994) Seeds mixtures for chalk downland. In: Haggar R.J. and Peel S. (Eds) *Grassland Management and Nature conservation.* Occ. Symp 28, British Grassland Society, 310-311.

Landscape Monitoring in Environmentally Sensitive Areas in Northern Ireland

C. A. MILLSOPP, A. CAMERON and J. H. McADAM
Department of Applied Plant Sciences, The Queen's University, Newforge Lane, Belfast
BT9 5PX

INTRODUCTION

Landscape monitoring involves providing an overview of the landscape character of each ESA, as soon as possible after designation and forms an important link with biological, historical and management monitoring to assess the effectiveness of the ESA scheme. Landscape monitoring over time will enable broad changes in the character of the ESA to be recorded and assess the impact of ESA management practices on the character and quality of the landscape. This will involve quantifying the change in quality of field boundaries and other habitats subject to ESA prescriptions and enhancement plans and comparing with habitats on farms which have not participated in the ESA scheme. In 1995 a baseline landscape monitoring programme was carried out in all of Northern Ireland's ESAs to evaluate the impact of the ESA scheme on the character and the quality of the landscape.

MONITORING STRATEGY

Sampling strategy

Stratified random sampling method using the Northern Ireland land classification (Cooper, 1986) provided a greater dispersion and representation of samples and potentially more precise estimates than simple random sampling. A sampling intensity of 1.5%-2.0% by ESA area was chosen to give a reasonable estimate of common land cover types, and on the basis of time and financial constraints. All five ESAs were surveyed between May and September 1995, mapping a total of 183 sample 25 hectare squares.

Recording land cover

Land cover features such as grasslands, woodland, field boundaries, heather moorland, buildings and historical monuments were recorded onto 1:10 000 Ordnance Survey maps. Habitats were classified according to guidelines issued by the Department of Agriculture. This enables the landscape monitoring programme to be fully integral with biological monitoring (Cameron *et al.*, 1997). Farm ownership boundaries were added to assess the effectiveness of the ESA scheme, by analysing land cover differences between participants and non-participants.

Data storage, access and retrieval

The geographic information system PC ARC/INFO in conjunction with ArcView was used to store, process and display all map data information. The ratio estimate method was used to calculate land cover estimates, standard errors (se) and coefficient of variation (CV) were used to describe the precision of the estimate (Cochran, 1977; Murray *et al.*, 1992).

RESULTS

An extensive map-based database has been completed for each ESA, accessed and processed using ArcView. This enables areas of the major habitats in each ESA to be predicted and estimates made of land under an ESA agreement at the time of sampling. Grassland was the major habitat in each ESA. Improved grassland was most prevalent in the Mournes and Slieve Croob ESA (56% of total area) and the Antrim Coast, Glens and Rathlin ESA (42% of total area). Species-rich unimproved grassland, typified by a high plant species diversity and indicators such as sedge species, was most frequent in the West Fermanagh and Erne Lakeland ESA (16397 hectares) and common in the Sperrins (8777 hectares) and the Antrim Coast, Glens and Rathlin (4199 hectares). In the West Fermanagh and Erne Lakeland ESA, grasslands were classified into the habitat types wet grasslands, hay meadows and limestone grasslands. Woodland eligible for the ESA scheme was most common in the Antrim Coast, Glens and Rathlin ESA (9% of total area) and in the West Fermanagh and Erne Lakeland ESA and in the Slieve Gullion ESA (6% of total area). This compares with a NI total of 5.5-6%. The estimations of areas under agreement are comparable with actual figures of areas under ESA agreement.

CONCLUSIONS

Predictions of the areas of habitats targeted by the ESA scheme are valuable to both the ESA scheme promoters, planners and monitoring team. The landscape monitoring of all five ESAs will be repeated in 1998. This will provide the initial broad evaluation of the ESA scheme, after three years. Whilst the overall changes in the landscape may occur at a slow rate, the changes brought about by ESA enhancement grants, such as hedge and dry stone wall restoration can be estimated. Landscape monitoring in conjunction with the biological, socio-economic and historical monitoring results will help assess the overall effectiveness of the ESA scheme and where necessary help redefine management prescriptions.

REFERENCES

CAMERON A., MILLSOPP C.A. and McADAM J.H. (1997) Biological monitoring of grasslands in the West Fermanagh and Erne Lakeland Environmentally Sensitive Area. In:Sheldrick, R. (ed) *Grassland Management in the ESAs*. British Grassland Society.

COCHRAN W.G. (1977) *Sampling Techniques*. 3rd edition, Wiley, New York.

COOPER A. (1986) *The Northern Ireland Land Classification*. University of Ulster.

MURRAY R., McCANN T. and COOPER A. (1992) *A Land Classification and Landscape Ecological Study of Northern Ireland*. Contract Report to Environment Service, DoE (NI), University of Ulster.

The Effects of Liming Upland Grassland in a Northern Ireland ESA

F. P. MULHOLLAND, G. M. HOPPÉ and J. H. MCADAM

Applied Plant Science Division, Department of Agriculture for Northern Ireland, Newforge Lane, Belfast BT9 5PX

INTRODUCTION

The introduction of ESA schemes into Northern Ireland has encouraged farmers to use less intensive practices to retain or enhance the traditional farmed landscape. There are 5 ESAs in NI, all with broadly similar aims and prescriptions. Whilst grasslands can be limed, no application of lime is permitted on rough grazing (DANI, 1993). Unimproved grassland cannot be ploughed, levelled or reseeded and there can be no new drainage or reclamation works, nor any increase in fertiliser application rates for any land on the farm.

Much grassland is traditionally limed once in 10-15 years, depending on suitable autumn weather. Liming encourages the growth of grasses and many herbs and can assist in mineral uptake, thereby enhancing sward palatability and nutritive value (Larcher, 1995).

This study aims to evaluate the effects of autumn liming on upland vegetation and soil nutrient status, and some changes in grassland output, species composition and quality related to soil nutrient status are outlined in this paper.

METHODS

The experimental site (310-340m) is on a commercial sheep and beef upland farm in the Antrim Coast, Glens and Rathlin ESA, and managed within the farm's normal framework. Eight vegetationally paired plots - each 6m x 5m - were marked out permanently on each of 2 vegetation types (unimproved grassland and rough grazing). Limed plots (applied at 5 t/ha) and unlimed plots were established in September/October 1993.

Initial vegetation assessments were made at the time of application in 1993, with records of botanical composition - species presence and abundance in 1m x 1m permanent quadrats, plus the occurrence of additional species in the whole plot - being collected in 1994. Herbage was clipped to ground level in two 1m x 0.1m quadrats per plot in 1994 and 1996 and assessed for biomass, botanical composition and nutritive value. One bulked soil sample per plot was collected in February 1993, September 1993, 1994, 1995 and 1996, and analysed for pH, P, K, Mg.

RESULTS and DISCUSSION

The two sward types are characterised by their vegetation, with *Festuca rubra* and *Anthoxanthum odoratum* occurring in most plots. Rough grazing contained *Nardus stricta*, *Deschampsia flexuosa*, *Juncus squarrosus*, *Carex* spp and *Potentilla erecta*, whilst the unimproved grassland was dominated by *Festuca ovina*, *Agrostis capillaris*, *Cynosurus cristatus*, *Trifolium repens* and *Cardamine fontanum*. No obvious effect of lime application on species composition has yet been noted.

In three years since the lime application, there have been no significant changes in soil analyses (Table 1), although limed plots are consistently higher for pH and phosphate than unlimed for both vegetation types. The effects of an application of super phosphate in spring 1995 can be seen in that year but was disappearing by the following year.

Herbage yields (around 2-2.5 t/ha) were similar for both sward types and lime treatment. This would be expected as the experimental plots are not enclosed and are subject to similar stocking densities. Herbage digestibility and nutrient analyses show an increase in herbage quality between 1994 and 1996, but no significant effect of liming (Table 2). Quality might be expected to improve with liming, especially on the more acid rough grazing, because of better uptake of minerals by the sward (Larcher, 1995). The effect here may be masked by the lack of a marked change in pH of either sward after liming, or because different species occur in the 2 sward types.

Further work is required to see if the present small differences continue over time and if any species change does occur as a result of this one application of lime. A lack of change in the botanical composition of upland rough grazing after liming would suggest modifications of the ESA prescription on liming may be possible.

Table 1.   Soil pH and P changes with liming of rough grazing and unimproved grassland

			pre treat		post treatment		
Nutrient	Sward Type		1993	1993	1994	1995	1996
pH	Rough Grazing	Limed	5.08	5.36	5.16	5.23	5.37
		Unlimed	5.08	4.97	5.02	5.00	5.20
	Unimproved	Limed	5.70	6.32	6.14	6.15	6.15
	Grassland	Unlimed	5.70	6.02	5.90	5.98	5.90
P mg/l	Rough Grazing	Limed	9.3	7.2	8.0	12.2	11.0
		Unlimed	9.3	6.8	7.6	12.2	8.1
	Unimproved	Limed	9.8	8.7	6.6	12.8	6.3
	Grassland	Unlimed	9.8	7.1	6.6	12.8	7.5

Table 2.   Response of herbage quality to liming rough grazing and unimproved grassland

		%DOMD		N g/kg		P g/kg		K g/kg	
Sward Type		1994	1996	1994	1996	1994	1996	1994	1996
Rough Grazing	Limed	60.0	64.5	13.4	18.4	1.44	2.99	6.92	9.68
	Unlimed	60.3	63.9	14.9	7.8	1.81	2.98	8.52	10.1
Unimproved	Limed	67.7	71.1	21.8	19.4	2.51	3.06	16.1	14.7
Grassland	Unlimed	66.7	70.4	19.2	20.6	2.59	3.12	13.6	15.9

REFERENCES

DANI (1993) *Antrim Coast, Glens and Rathlin Environmentally Sensitive Area Guidelines for Farmers (ESA/2)*.

LARCHER W. (1995) (Ed). *Physiological Plant Ecology* (3rd edn). Springer.

Botanical Changes in Unimproved Enclosed Grasslands of the Breadalbane ESA, Scotland, 1989-1993

A. J. NOLAN, M. J. STILL, J. S. BELL and J. H. GAULD

Macaulay Land Use Research Institute, Craigiebuckler, Aberdeen AB15 8QH, UK

INTRODUCTION

The Breadalbane Environmentally Sensitive Area (ESA) lies at the southern edge of the Central Highlands in Perthshire, occupying an area (113 500 ha) of outstanding ecological value with a great diversity of landscapes and natural habitats. These include the arable farmland, stone wall-enclosed pastures and broadleaved woodlands of Strath Tay and Strathardle in the east, and the more rugged terrain with mountains, moorlands and lochs in the west, typified by Glen Lyon, Ben Lawers, Loch Rannoch and Loch Tay. The underlying geology consists of metamorphic rocks of the Dalradian and Moinian Assemblages, principally schists and gneisses, but including bands of limestone, notably in the Ben Lawers area.

The ESA has many small mixed farms on marginal land where traditional forms of management are practiced. Of particular interest are the areas of unimproved pasture towards the upper limit of enclosed agricultural land. Many of these fields receive little or no artificial fertiliser and are noted for their floristic diversity, with species such as lady's mantle (*Alchemilla vulgaris* agg.), quaking grass (*Briza media*), greater butterfly orchid (*Platanthera chlorantha*), yellow rattle (*Rhinanthus minor*) and globe flower (*Trollius europaeus*). In response to concern about the deterioration and loss of such semi-natural habitats through agricultural intensification, the Breadalbane ESA was one of the first to be designated in Scotland in 1987, with the aim of maintaining, and where possible enhancing, the conservation value of the land. Financial incentives were available to achieve these objectives, and guidelines were issued to all farmers voluntarily entering the ESA Scheme (Department of Agriculture and Fisheries for Scotland (DAFS), 1987). Unimproved enclosed grassland was one of a number of features of conservation interest targetted for support. The management prescriptions precluded the application of lime, fertiliser or herbicides (with certain exceptions) and specified that grazing should be controlled.

In 1989 a programme was initiated to monitor the effects of the management guidelines and compare these with trends occurring on similar land outwith the ESA.

METHODS

By the end of March 1989, a total of 326 fields (1964 ha) had been entered into the Scheme. A number of sites were indicated on the conservation plans as being especially herb-rich, and sites were selected randomly from the unimproved and herb-rich unimproved groups to give a total of 30 fields within the ESA for monitoring. A further 10 fields outwith the ESA were selected for comparison. At each site, five permanent 2 m x 2 m quadrats were established at equal spacings along the longest field diagonal. Records for species, percentage cover and heights of the grass, forb and ground layers were made for all sites in June-July of 1989, 1991 and 1993.

RESULTS AND DISCUSSION
Mean numbers of species
Significant increases in mean numbers of species per quadrat were recorded between 1989 and 1993 at both groups of sites within the ESA, and at sites overall outwith the ESA. These ranged from 21.6 to 24.4 for unimproved grasslands, 22.5 to 25.9 for herb-rich unimproved grasslands, and 20.5 to 24.4 for those sites outwith the ESA. The lower numbers of species recorded at most sites in the baseline year may have been the result of a summer drought in 1989, causing the early senescence or non-appearance of some species. The trends in species numbers were similar in the three groups, in that each showed a highly significant change between 1989 and 1991, and no significant change thereafter, giving rise to the significant overall differences between 1989 and 1993. No significant decrease was recorded at any individual site either within or outwith the ESA between 1989 and 1993.

Indicator species
The presence of indicator species (Nolan *et al.*, 1994, after R.A.H. Smith, SNH, pers. comm.), considered to be characteristic of unimproved grasslands in the Breadalbane area, was investigated. Overall, the mean number of indicator species per quadrat increased significantly between 1989 and 1993 at herb-rich sites within the ESA (4.1 to 5.0) but no significant changes were detected at the remaining unimproved grassland sites within the ESA, or at sites outwith the ESA (4.1 to 4.6, and 4.1 to 4.4 respectively).

Sward height
There were no significant differences in mean heights of the forb and grass layers in 1993 between sites within the ESA and those outwith, though both were consistently taller within the ESA. At herb-rich sites within the ESA, grasses and forbs were significantly taller in 1993 compared to 1991, which may have resulted from more carefully controlled grazing in the early part of the summer at these sites. There was no change in heights at the remaining group of unimproved sites within the ESA, or at sites outwith the ESA.

CONCLUSIONS
The prescriptions have sucessfully maintained, and at some sites enhanced, the botanical composition and diversity of unimproved enclosed grasslands within the ESA. However, as similar trends were recorded at analogous sites outwith the ESA, it is likely that other factors, notably climate, may have exerted the dominant influence during the monitoring period.

ACKNOWLEDGEMENTS
This work was commissioned by DAFS [now the Scottish Office Agriculture, Environment and Fisheries Department (SOAEFD)].

REFERENCES
DEPARTMENT OF AGRICULTURE AND FISHERIES FOR SCOTLAND (1987). *Guidelines for Farmers: Breadalbane Environmentally Sensitive Area.*

NOLAN A.J., STILL M.J., BELL J.S. and GAULD J.H. (1994). *The Environmentally Sensitive Areas Designated in Scotland. The Breadalbane ESA - Biological Monitoring Report, years one to five, 1989-1993.* The Macaulay Land Use Research Institute, Aberdeen.

A Hierarchical Modelling Strategy for Monitoring and Predicting Spatial Change in the Composition of Upland Pasture: Case Studies in the Cambrian Mountains ESA and Northumberland National Park

D. E.OATWAY[1], R.KEATINGE[2] and J.WILDIG[3]

[1]Centre for Land Use and Water Resources Research, Porter Building, The University, Newcastle-upon-Tyne, NE1 7RU
[2]ADAS Redesdale, Rochester, Otterburn, Newcastle-upon-Tyne, NE19 1SB
[3]ADAS Pwllpeiran, Cwmystwyth, Aberystwyth, Dyfed, SY23 4AB

INTRODUCTION

Hierarchy theory (Allen and Starr, 1982) provides a framework for understanding the structures and behaviour of upland pasture systems. These systems exhibit responses to environmental conditions and management regimes at several spatial and temporal scales. The hierarchical levels of most interest to land managers and policy makers, are those associated with the dynamics of plant species and communities. Processes in natural systems result in complex spatio-temporal behaviour (Itami, 1994) and studies intending to understand system dynamics should account for this. Observation of the upland pasture system at several spatial and temporal scales affords a larger window of perception and therefore better definition of the whole system. This can indicate trends in behaviour otherwise missed by a single observation point at a single scale.

This study describes a modelling system to predict the spatial composition and dynamics of upland pasture systems, which can be used to interpret the effects of management regime on such communities.

THE MODEL

The model is being developed using data from two sites: Redesdale experimental husbandry farm, Northumberland and Tyr Emrys, Cambrian mountains ESA. The site in Redesdale has been converted to organic livestock production in the last five years, and the effects of the subsequent changes in management are being monitored alongside a conventionally run unit at the site. The Tyr Emrys site comprises a paddock experiment investigating the effects of different grazing intensities on the plant community. The sites are monitored at fixed time intervals by aerial photography and permanent $1m^2$ quadrats. The quadrat data record the dominant species in each cell of a lattice.

Two cellular automata (CA) models are constructed as discrete sub-units of the overall modelling system. The first CA predicts the spatial distribution of species in quadrats and the second CA plant communities in landscapes. The output of these sub-models are linked to produce the model of system behaviour across the scales.

The CA models are generated assuming that the ecological changes observed are Markovian (Usher, 1979); in that future states of the system can be predicted with knowledge of past and present states. Events in discrete time are predicted by application of a rule base to site data, predicting the future state of a unit of space (cell) based on the present state of that cell and of neighbouring cells. The choice of future state is probabilistic, based on the suite of states present in the neighbourhood. The rule base is generated from spatially referenced time series data.

INITIAL OUTPUTS AND DISCUSSION

The modelling system developed using the quadrat data will be applied to data abstracted from aerial photographs. Initial outputs are discussed here.

One hundred simulations of the model using empirically based transition rules predicted the future state of cells better than a neutral model using rules generated from the same cover of species randomly distributed in space. This suggests that spatially referenced time series data contains signals which indicate that local interactions between plants explains some of the behaviour of the system. The mechanisms implicated in this are vegetative expansion and local seed dispersal.

The model is a weaker predictor for species whose spatial arrangement is manifested at a scale finer than the grid size used to collect the data. This emphasises the importance of a multi-scale approach to studying such systems, as many of the components of the system will exhibit dynamics which are detected in a different spatial or temporal frame.

The accuracy of the rule base in the CA models is dependent on the quality and quantity of data used in its generation. The sensitivity of the model to data used in generation of the rule base is indicative of the importance of collecting appropriate data. Extremely large amounts of good data would generate a rule base which could even predict the composition (if not the exact location) of infrequently occurring states whose dynamics are not dependent on local seed dispersal and vegetative spread. Smaller amounts of data will predict the most frequent and abundant species. This approach to modelling upland pasture is most suited to species or communities which exhibit high inertia at these scales of observation. These are the functional types of species such as Ericaceous shrubs and tussock forming grasses and mosses, and the communities in which they are dominant.

REFERENCES

ALLEN T.F.H and STARR T.B. (1982) *Hierarchy*. Chicago: University of Chicago Press
ITAMI R.M. (1994) Simulating spatial dynamics: cellular automata theory. *Landscape and Urban Planning*, 30, 27-47.
USHER M.B. (1979) Markovian approaches to ecological succession. *Journal of Animal Ecology*, 48, 413-426.

Control of Creeping Thistle on an Ancient Grazed Common

S. PEEL[1] and A. T. JONES[2]

[1] ADAS Bridgets, Martyr Worthy, Winchester, SO21 1AP
[2] IGER, Aberystwyth, Dyfed, SY23 3EB

INTRODUCTION

Creeping thistle (*Cirsium arvense*) is a widespread problem in permanent grassland, particularly that managed by grazing with moderate or low fertilizer inputs (Hopkins & Peel, 1985). It is classified as injurious under the Weeds Act 1959 and is difficult to control even with herbicides. An experiment was initiated in 1994 on Port Meadow, Oxford; an ancient pasture scheduled as an SSSI which is within the Upper Thames ESA. The meadow has full public access, rights of common grazing for cattle and horses 365 days per year, and has had a large population of thistle for many years. The main objective was to examine the effect of control treatments, judged feasible on an SSSI grazed common, on the thistle population and on the vegetation as a whole.

METHODS

A split-plot experiment was established with the following treatments:

Grazing rest period (main plots)	i)	None
	ii)	1 December - 15 April
Weed control (sub-plots)	i)	None
	ii)	Herbicide weed-wipe
	iii)	Mechanical topping

There were 6 treatment combinations, with 4 replicates. Plots were each 4m x 20m. The winter rest period was achieved by fencing each main plot. Weed wiping was carried out on 30 June and 18 August 1994, and 26 July 1995 using a Rotowiper with the herbicide Dow Shield (active ingredient clopyralid) at a dilution of 1:27, with Agral 90 wetter and a marker dye. Topping was carried out with a flail mower concurrently with weed wiping in 1994, with toppings removed. In 1995 and 1996 topping dates were 13 July and 18 July respectively; there was almost no regrowth so no second topping was necessary.

RESULTS AND DISCUSSION

Soil analysis in May 1994 showed that pH was neutral at 7.1, available (Olsen) phosphorus was low at 9 mg/l, and available potassium was moderate at 151 mg/l. Species diversity was 16 species of higher plant per 0.25 x 0.25m area, and remained at this level in 1995 and 1996 even on plots subject to herbicide weed-wiping. Greater abundance of thistles was negatively correlated with species diversity ($P < 0.05$). In late June 1994, immediately prior to treatments, there were 18.2 thistles/m². Assessments in July 1995 showed that both weed-wiping and topping had significantly ($P < 0.05$) reduced thistle numbers. By July 1996 (Table 1) the effect of weed control was not quite significant ($P = 0.064$). Winter resting had no significant effect and there was no significant interaction with weed control treatment.

Table 1. Number of thistles /m^2 in July 1996 (adjusted for covariate).

Rest period	Weed Control treatment			
	None	Weed-wipe	Topping	Mean
Not rested	7.5	2.6	2.6	4.4
Rested Dec-April	9.4	4.5	2.7	5.5
Mean	8.5	3.6	2.7	
Standard error of means:	1.54 (weed control)			
	1.62 (rest period)			

Even on the control plots thistles had declined to half their former density. This reflects observations on the meadow as a whole and is attributed to a combination of dry summers, wet winters and heavy grazing. Sward height was measured monthly on all plots; it showed a declining trend throughout the experiment, being 8.6 cm in June 1994 and only 4.0 cm in June 1995. On winter grazed plots it fell to 2.0 cm. The experiment is continuing through 1997 and 1998.

INTERIM CONCLUSIONS
1. Creeping thistle is negatively correlated with botanical diversity.
2. Thistle numbers can be reduced by either topping, or weed-wiping with clopyralid.
3. Topping is more effective than anticipated, possibly because of extra stress imposed by weather conditions and heavy grazing
4. Weed-wiping is less effective than anticipated, probably because of the wide range of maturities of thistle 'plants'.
5. Winter resting has so far had no effect on number of thistles.
6. None of the treatments has reduced botanical diversity.

ACKNOWLEDGMENTS
We are very grateful to Oxford City Council for funding this work.

REFERENCES
HOPKINS A. and PEEL S. (1985). Incidence of weeds in permanent grassland. In: Brockman, J.S. (Ed): *Weeds, pests and diseases of grassland and herbage legumes*. Occ. Symp. 18. British Grassland Society: Hurley.

Organic Farming in The Cambrian Mountains ESA

T. L. POWELL and D. E. EVANS
ADAS Pwllpeiran, Cwmystwyth, Aberystwyth, SY23 4AB

Large areas of the hills and uplands in the UK are included in Schemes which provide financial assistance for following management prescriptions leading to more environmentally conscious farming. If compliance with such prescriptions can be allied with organic production then the income arising could provide the stimulus for the uptake of a farming system giving both environmental benefits and higher prices for livestock sales.

Pwllpeiran is a 1120 ha hill farm in the heart of The Cambrian Mountains ESA in mid-Wales and conversion of 111 ha to an organic unit commenced in May 1993. The objective is to develop a beef cow and sheep system complying with both UKROFS standards and ESA management prescriptions covering

1)   Semi-natural rough grazings (SNRG)
2)   Hay meadows and
3)   Enclosed, partially improved grassland

No "conventionally" farmed unit has been created alongside the organic area. Production and financial results from the Pwllpeiran resource have been recorded for many years and provide the information for any comparison which may be required.

RESOURCES

There are three categories of pasture within the unit: SNRG (47.1 ha) Partially improved grassland or "Mosaics" (39.9 ha) and Fields (24.5 ha - 9.1 ha for silage). The ratio of SNRG to improved grassland is the same as the conventionally farmed area. Both SNRG and Mosaics are on organic soils above 450 m. The SNRG has 50% heather (*Calluna vulgaris*) cover. Mosaics were created in the 1970s from SNRG after liming, surface disturbance and reseeding of those areas accessible to machinery. The three fields are between 300 and 400 m altitude and on mineral soil. Two are used for forage conservation, the larger being reseeded during the conversion period.

Herd and flock numbers were originally chosen so that approaching 95% of the annual feed supply should come from grassland within the unit. The stocking rate arrived at was 60% of that which would be carried under the conventional system at Pwllpeiran. The ratio of cows to ewes is narrower than on comparable commercial farms and should help reduce nematode worm problems.

The beef herd comprises 10 Welsh Black cows (plus replacements) bred pure for April calving. The herd is winter housed and calves weaned at the end of January. There are 160 Hardy Speckled Face ewes, plus replacements, with one third bred to Texel. Lambing commences in mid April. Twin bearing ewes are inwintered for 8 weeks prior to lambing. Mixed grazing of the cattle and sheep occurs. There is no commercially acceptable means of devising "clean" or "safe" grazing. The SNRG is not used between mid November and early April and is primarily grazed by dry stock. In order to receive an annual payment of £35/ha, the SNRG must not carry an average daily stocking rate in excess of 1.5 ewes/ha.

Silage is made as big bales at the end of July. After harvesting, the conservation fields receive FYM and slurry produced on the unit. The smaller silage field, which had not been reseeded since 1987, qualifies for a "hay meadow" payment of £75/ha provided no artificial fertiliser is used and cutting is delayed until after 15 July.

RESULTS

Improved grassland under a "grazed-only" regime had a mean sward height range of 5.3 to 7.6 cm between early May and late September. Assessments of "% cover" showed an increase of from 10 to 15% in white clover in the main grazing field between Years 1 and 3. During the same period, total species recorded in this long term ley increased from 19 to 35.

The highest yield of silage DM (3.2 t/ha) was obtained in the fourth year and was largely attributable to a combination of favourable weather conditions and the main silage field having been reseeded 2 years previously. The unit is self sufficient for silage at a yield of 3.0 t/ha. The low index (1) is a cause for concern about the potash status of the 10 year old silage field, but white clover content is increasing and silage yields remain good.

Calf and lamb performance has generally been similar to that obtained under conventional management. However, in Years 3 and 4, 90% of the wether lambs from the organic unit were sold finished before the end of October which is at least 30% higher than expected. The improvement coincided with the re-seeding of the main silage field which developed into a white clover rich sward (40% cover in summer 1996).

The cattle do not receive any pharmaceuticals for disease prevention. Twin lambs have always needed an early July anthelmintic drench, largely because of Nematodirus incidence. The singles graze separately and "flock treatment" is confined to fly strike and scab prevention. Ewes receive pre-lambing Clostridial vaccination.

Financial results expressed as Gross Margin/ha have shown a 15% improvement for organic compared with conventional farming receiving no ESA payments and seeking to maximise production. Further improvement would require a higher stocking rate but, to date, the present system does not appear to allow any increase.

Impact of Inorganic Fertiliser on Soil Seed Bank of Species-rich Meadows on the Somerset Levels and Moors ESA

R. E. N. SMITH, BEKKER, R. M. and J. R. B. TALLOWIN
Institute of Grassland and Environmental Research, North Wyke Research Station,
Okehampton, Devon, EX20 2SB, UK

INTRODUCTION

The effects of inorganic fertilisers on plant communities are well established; grasses become dominant and floristic diversity is reduced (*e.g.* Brenchley and Warington 1958). The effect of fertilizers on the seed bank of such sites is less well documented. This study examined the effect of fertilizer N on the seed bank of a species-rich *Centaureo-Cynosuretum* grassland in the Somerset levels.

METHODS

Seed bank was sampled at two depths, 0-5 and 5-10cm, from two replicates of an experiment which had received 0 (control), 25, 50 and 100kg N/ha per year and from one replicate receiving 200kg N/ha per year from 1986 to 1993. Sampling for seed bank was completed following the methodology of ter Heerdt *et al.* (1996). The effects of the treatments on the seed bank was examined using regression analysis to compare the seed bank of both species and functional groups with N level and the vegetation cover in both 1986 and 1993.

RESULTS AND DISCUSSION

There was a significant decline of the numbers of species in the soil seed bank in the 0-5cm horizon for both species with a short term persistency ($f=0.047$)and the total number of species with increasing level of nitrogen input ($f=0.002$). No such decline was observed in the in the lower 5-10cm horizon. Nitrogen inputs had a positive effect on the number of seeds/m^2 of individual species at 0-5cm: timothy (*Phleum pratense*), $f=0.022$ and cuckoo flower (*Cardamine pratensis*), $f=0.008$, at 5-10cm. Most relationships tended to be quadratic rather than linear. Sorrel (*Rumex acetosa*) and dandelions (*Taraxacum officinale* agg), at 0-5cm, and Yorkshire fog *(Holcus lanatus)*, at both horizons, increased with nitrogen application up to 100kg/ha but then declined on the 200kg/ha plot. Hardhead (*Centaurea nigra*) declined quadratically, $f=0.046$. There were also a number of trends showing correlations of the number of seeds of individual species/m^2 with the vegetation cover, as it had been at the onset of the experiment and at its conclusion eight years later. Within the upper horizon bents (*Agrostis* spp.), $f=0.030$, rushes (*Juncus* spp), $f=0.041$, ragged robin *(Lychnis flos-cuculi)*, $f=<0.001$ and lesser stitchwort (*Stellaria graminea*), $f=0.017$, showed a significant linear relation with vegetation cover as it had been in 1986. In the 5-10cm horizon two rushes (J. *articulatus* and J. *inflexus*), $f=0.009$ and $f=0.006$, were quadratically related to the vegetation cover as it was in 1986. Comparing the number of seed/m^2 with the vegetation as it had become by 1993 *Agrostis* spp. at 0-5cm were still, quadratically, related to the vegetation cover, $f=<0.001$. Also at 0-5cm sweet vernal grass (*Anthoxanthum odoratum*), $f=0.007$, C.

nigra, f=0.007, and red clover (*Trifolium pratense*), f=0.009, all showed positive linear relationships with vegetation cover and *H. lanatus*, f=0.015, ribwort plantain (*Plantago lanceolata*), f= <0.001, and selfheal (*Prunella vulgaris*), f= <0.001, positive, quadratic relationships. Within the 5-10cm horizon *H.lanatus*, f=0.015, had a positive relationship with the vegetation.

Species-richness of the established vegetation at this site was reduced significantly by the addition of fertilizer N, (Mountford *et al.*, 1993). This was reflected in the seed bank in the upper but not in the lower horizon. These differences between the seed bank and the established vegetation were probably due to changes in the seed rain rather than a direct influence of nitrogen fertiliser on the seed bank. The numbers of seeds of both *P. lanceolata* and *T. pratense* were correlated significantly with the vegetation cover in 1993 although the abundance of both species was reduced in vegetation by nitrogen input. A number of species known to have been encouraged by nitrogen application, *e.g. H. lanatus* and *R. acetosa*, showed a corresponding positive relationship in the seed bank. These relationships were generally reflected by similar trends in the lower horizon. None of these species showed any relationship with the vegetation cover as it was in 1986. Interestingly, these four species all have seed banks with short term persistence. By contrast, species which disappeared from the vegetation following nitrogen application, *e.g. Juncus* species which are known to have a persistent seed bank, showed a close relationship with the vegetation cover as it was in 1986 but none with the cover in 1993. Indeed some species which showed a relationship with the vegetation as it was in 1986 did so at both soil horizons suggesting that they are unaffected by soil nitrogen levels.

It appeared that soil seed bank at this site was closely related to the vegetation, either as it was in 1986 or as it had become by 1993. Those species which have been lost from the vegetation may still persist in the seed bank. Nevertheless, had the nitrogen treatment been continued, a limited number of grasses would have continued to dominate both the vegetation and the seed bank. Additional losses of species from the seed bank would probably have occurred as the sward became more impoverished in both species-richness or the abundance of individual species. Since recruitment to the vegetation is more likely to take place from seed in the upper horizons the opportunities for new species to colonise the site from seed bank would not be great. The opportunity for recruitment to the established vegetation from the lower horizon are in any case limited, due largely to the fact that the number and variety of species represented are lower. The chances of recovery of a species-rich vegetation from the seed bank, similar to the one which preceded nitrogen application, are therefor likely to be limited once fertilizer application ceases.

REFERENCES

BRENCHLY W.E. and WARINGTON K. (1958) *The Park Grass Plots at Rothamsted 1856-1949*. Rothamsted Experimental Station, Harpenden.

MOUNTFORD J.O., LAKHANI K.H. and KIRKHAM F.W. (1993) Experimental assessment of the effects of nitrogen addition under hay-cutting and aftermath grazing on the vegetation of meadows on a Somerset peat moor. *J. Applied Ecol.* 30, 321-332.

TER HEERDT G.N.J., VERWEIJ G.L., BEKKER R.M. and BAKKER J.P. (1996) An improved method for seed bank analysis: seedling emergence after removing the soil by sieving. *Functional Ecology* (in press).

Decrease in Potassium Availability in Species-rich Hay Meadows at Tadham on the Somerset Levels and Moors - Cause for Concern?

J. R. B. TALLOWIN[1], R. E. N. SMITH[1] and F. W. KIRKHAM[2]
[1]IGER, North Wyke Research Station, Okehampton, Devon
[2]ADAS, Wolverhampton

INTRODUCTION

For many semi-natural grasslands there is no clear definition of what constitutes a sustainable management that will ensure the long-term maintenance of the conservation interests. During the Tadham project noteable changes occurred in the botanical composition of the unfertilized species-rich "control" plots that were under traditional late hay cutting and aftermath grazing or cutting only management but with no fertilizer inputs (Kirkham et al., 1996). These species-rich meadows have no history of inorganic fertilizer use but anecdotes suggest that occasionally organic manure was applied. This study examines changes in mineral status of the unfertilized meadows and the possibility that a total lack of fertilizer input could with time become a driving factor for botanical change.

METHODS

Details of the site and experimental methods are provided in Tallowin (1996). The yields of herbage dry matter at the time of the hay harvest were measured in unfertilized plots each year, 1986-1993, in two experiments, one involved cutting for hay after 1 July followed by grazing the regrowth, the other was cut after 1 July and again in the autumn. Hay samples were analyzed for total N content using micro-Kjeldahl digestion, K content by atomic absorption spectrometry and P by content by colorimetry following wet digestion with sulphuric and nitric acids. Treatment effects on yields of N, P and K were analysed for each year separately by analysis of variance using a randomized block design and Genstat 5. Differences in weather between years affected the date of cutting, so partial influences of either cutting date or year effects on yields of the minerals were examined by multiple regression analyses.

RESULTS

When hay cutting date was delayed due to wet weather increased dry matter yields were obtained up to the first week in August. Partial regression coefficients for year and day effects on mineral yields from cut and grazed plots were:

$N_{yield} = 4055 (\pm 3356) + (-2.0 (\pm 1.69, P<0.249)$ x year$) + (0.83 (\pm 0.238, P<0.003)$ x days), percentage variance accounted for by the regression $= 36.6$,

$P_{yield} = 270 (\pm 265) + (-0.13 (\pm 0.134, P<0.331)$ x year$) + (0.066(\pm 0.0188, P<0.003)$ x days), percentage variance accounted for by the regression $= 38.4$;

$K_{yield} = 7110(\pm 1945) + (-3.56 (\pm 0.978, P<0.002)$ x year$) + (0.35 (\pm 0.138, P<0.020)$ x days), percentage variance accounted for by the regression $= 36.3$.

The partial regression coefficient "year" showed no significant influence on the yield of either N or P. There was, however, a significant effect of date of cut, with the later the cut the greater the yield. Yield of K was significantly affected by both year and date of cut, later cuts gave greater yields but, in addition, there was an overall decline in yield of K during the course of the project, as shown by the negative partial regression coefficient for year.

In unfertilized control plots that were managed by cutting only the partial regression coefficients for year and day effects on mineral yield were:

N_{yield} = -6715 ($\pm$2333) + (3.40($\pm$1.17, $P<0.009$) x year) + (0.75($\pm$0.237, $P<0.005$) x days), percentage variance accounted for by the regression = 53.9,

P_{yield} = -684 ($\pm$207) + (0.35($\pm$0.104, $P<0.003$) x year) + (0.050($\pm$0.0210, $P<0.026$) x days), percentage variance accounted for by the regression = 51.3,

K_{yield} = 1884 ($\pm$2305) + (-0.93($\pm$1.160, $P<0.430$) x year) + (0.05($\pm$0.234, $P<0.822$) x days), residual variance exceeded variance of the y variate.

The yields of N and P increased both with later date of cutting and in successive years. No apparent relationship between the yield of K and either year or date of cut was found.

The availability of K, relative to the other two minerals, as indicated by the ratios of yield of K:N or K:P showed a marked decline during the course of the project in both cut and grazed plots. In contrast the ratio of P:N yield showed no trend with time.

DISCUSSION

Changes in the yield of K relative to the yield of either N or P occurred in the hay crop of the unfertilized controls during the course of the project. In plots that were cut for hay and then grazed the yield of K declined while neither N nor P showed any significant change. In plots that were only cut the yield of K remained unchanged while both N and P showed significant increases. The changes in nutrient yield that occurred with time in both experiments, irrespective of any initial differences in availability or processes causing change, meant that the amount of K cycling within the meadow system and available for plant uptake declined in relation to the other two macro-nutrients. At the outset of the project it was established that the K status of the peat soil was low. It was therefore likely that K availability would be sensitive to continued exploitative management involving a net removal from the system. As yet it has not been established whether changes in K status, *per se*, had a direct influence on the changes that were observed in species-richness or community structure of the unfertilized meadows. This study serves to highlight an uncertainty - that the prescribed "traditional" management without any nutrient input may not sustain the conservation interests of these species-rich meadows over the long term.

ACKNOWLEDGEMENTS
The project was sponsored by the MAFF, English Nature and the DoE.

REFERENCES
KIRKHAM F.W., MOUNTFORD J.O. and WILKINS R.J. (1996) The effects of nitrogen, potassium and phosphorus addition on the vegetation of a Somerset peat moor under cutting management. *Journal of Applied Ecology*, 33, 1013-1029.
TALLOWIN J.R.B. (1996) Effects of inorganic fertilizers on flower-rich hay meadows: a review using a case study on the Somerset Levels, UK. *Grasslands and Forage Abstracts*. CAB International, Wallingford, UK.

Managing Arable Reversion Grassland to Benefit Nationally Decreasing Skylark (*Alauda arvensis* L.) Populations

A. WAKEHAM-DAWSON and N. J. AEBISCHER

The Game Conservancy Trust, Fordingbridge, Hampshire SP6 1EF

INTRODUCTION

Skylarks are a typical species of grassland and have shown a national decrease in numbers over the last 30 years. This three-year (1994-1997) research project investigated the best ways of managing arable reversion grassland to encourage breeding and over-wintering skylarks in the South Downs (established in 1987) and South Wessex Downs (established in 1993) Environmentally Sensitive Areas (ESAs). Under the schemes, arable reversion fields were converted from arable cropping to permanent grassland sown with agricultural seed mixtures (*e.g.* ryegrass *Lolium perenne* L.) (PG) or sown with traditional chalk downland seed mixtures such as fescues (*Festuca* spp) (CD).

METHODS

Breeding skylark densities were estimated by early morning counts of singing males holding territories on CD and PG arable reversion fields during two surveys (April-May and June-July) in 1994 and 1996. Counts of skylarks flocking on CD, PG and cereal stubbles were made in the winter (1995-96). Seeds lying on the ground in the winter were sampled with a portable vacuum cleaner. Based on the 1994 breeding season survey, sward height was experimentally managed on 12 5-ha PG fields (South Downs). Six fields were randomly selected for short sward management (< 10 cm) and the remaining six managed to establish a taller sward (15-25 cm). Numbers of breeding skylarks and grass seedheads were counted, and invertebrates sampled (pit-fall traps) between April and July 1995 and 1996.

RESULTS

Breeding skylark density was not significantly related to time since reversion from arable cropping or type of grazing livestock, but was significantly related to reversion type, sward height and the presence of scrub in April-May 1994 (Table 1). Trends were similar but not significant in June-July 1994 (Table 1). The effect of height was similar and significant in 1996, but type and scrub had no significant effect. Breeding skylarks deserted fields that were mown (to reduce soil fertility) during the 1994 breeding season in the South Wessex Downs ESA. Winter flock density was not significantly related to reversion type, time since reversion from arable cropping, sward height or grazing stock type in arable reversion fields, but was negatively correlated to percentage ground cover ($r_{111} = -0.66$, $P < 0.001$), with skylarks tending to forage in reversion fields with areas of open ground. Dicotyledonous seeds were recorded from cereal stubbles, were scarce in CD fields and absent from PG fields. Skylark flocks were observed foraging on cereal stubbles rather than on arable reversion fields and skylark density was positively correlated with the number of dicotyledonous seeds collected ($r_{29} = 0.66$, $P < 0.001$).

Breeding skylark density, numbers of invertebrates and numbers of grass seedheads were all significantly influenced by management of sward height in 1995 (Table 2). Results were similar in 1996.

Table 1. The effects of reversion type, grass height and presence of boundary scrub on skylarks/km^2 (means $\pm$ 1 s.e). n = no. fields; (d.f) = degrees of freedom; P (probability): **, $P < 0.01$; ***, $P < 0.001$, ns = not significant.

	April-May	n	F (d.f) P	June-July	n	F (d.f) P
Reversion type						
CD	15.9 $\pm$ 2.2	18		15.1 $\pm$ 2.8	16	
			9.52 (1,87) **			1.27(1,76) ns
PG	6.7 $\pm$ 1.3	74		9.1 $\pm$ 2.5	65	
Sward height						
< 15 cm	8.9 $\pm$ 1.1	66		6.2 $\pm$ 1.6	31	
15-25 cm	19.1 $\pm$ 3.4	24	7.43 (2,87)***	9.6 $\pm$ 1.9	37	2.74(2,76) ns
>25 cm	5.9 $\pm$ 5.4	2		20.8 $\pm$ 12.4	13	
Boundary scrub						
Absent	15.3 $\pm$ 1.5	68		16.7 $\pm$ 2.7	61	
			9.23 (1,87) **			3.47 (1,76) ns
Present	7.2 $\pm$ 1.9	24		7.6 $\pm$ 1.5	20	

Table 2. Breeding skylarks/km^2 (whole season), invertebrate numbers (July) and grass seedheads (July) (means $\pm$ 1 s.e) in arable reversion fields where sward height was controlled by grazing with sheep. n = no. fields; (d.f) = degrees of freedom; P (probability): **, $P < 0.01$;***, $P < 0.001$.

	Skylarks	Invertebrates	Seedheads
Sward < 10 cm	2.4 $\pm$ 1.3	31.6 $\pm$ 2.6	2.4 $\pm$ 0.8
(n)	(6)	(4)	(4)
Sward 15-25 cm	14.3 $\pm$ 4.0	80.7 $\pm$ 10.0	38.8 $\pm$ 5.7
(n)	(6)	(4)	(4)
F-ratios (d.f) P	14.7 (1,10)**	37.5 (1,6)***	87.5 (1,6)***

DISCUSSION

Arable reversion swards that are grazed below 10 cm in line with 1992 MAFF recommendations hold low densities of breeding skylarks, probably because of insufficient nesting cover and invertebrate chick-food. Likewise, closely-grazed arable reversion fields produce insufficient seeds to feed wintering flocks. In consequence, for this nationally decreasing bird species, less intensive grazing during the summer and over-winter cereal stubbles are an essential conservation element in downland ESAs. Both these points have been incorporated in the latest prescriptions for the South Downs ESA, which were revised in 1996.

ACKNOWLEDGEMENTS

MAFF (funding: Project BD0305); G. Norris & R. Belding (ESA Officers); Study Area farmers; Plumpton Agricultural College; K. Szoszkiewicz, K. Stern, M. Parrott & R. Hutchison (data collection).

Grassland Management Agreements in Scotland

S.D. WARD

Advisory Services, Scottish Natural Heritage, 2 Anderson Place, Edinburgh, EH6 5NP

REVIEW OF EXTANT AGREEMENTS

More than 100 grassland management agreements have been reviewed (Ward, in press), bringing together Scottish Natural Heritage's collective experience. That experience forms the basis of guidelines (Ward, 1996) to assist others reviewing or negotiating grassland management agreements.

The agreements cover lower altitude grasslands of floristic interest; those supporting birds such as chough (*Pyrrhocorax pyrrhocorax*), corncrake (*Crex crex*) and wintering wildfowl; and habitats such as machair and saltmarsh. Reasons include maintenance of the grassland; retention of essential management; control of damaging activities and restoration of a grassland type or species.

GUIDELINES TO NEW AGREEMENTS

Best practice is summarised below as a guide to others negotiating agreements.

Describing the grassland

The agreement should describe the features of *special interest* and their needs, with a simple exposition of *why* the agreement is needed, what it is intended to *achieve* and how the grassland is to be *managed*.

Good communication is the key to successful management. The description should encompass both the ecological and agricultural perspectives and explain the link.

Who does what?

The respective roles to be fulfilled by the conservation agency and the farmer should be clearly set down.

Management of the land normally falls to the farmer but an agreement may permit the conservation agency to make alternative arrangements.

Monitoring is central to an agreement. Management and its effectiveness should be recorded at the outset and at regular intervals.

Monitoring should be a joint responsibility, the farmer reporting upon management , the conservation agency assessing its effect. To ensure consistency of management records, the farmer should be provided with a proforma. As an incentive to submitting the management record annually, the agreement might make provision for a payment to be made upon its receipt.

Photographing the land at the outset and at intervals provides a useful record.

Adjusting management in the light of monitoring may be necessary and there should be provision to hold meetings to review management.

Prescribing management

If the reasons for a prescription are not given, it may be unclear whether it is there at the request of the farmer or the conservation agency. For clarity, each prescription should state its intended purpose.

The grazing prescription should specify the number of livestock units, or the type and age-group of livestock permitted; the land over which they have access and restrictions as to season or grazing days.

Livestock welfare or *safety* should include provision for their removal, e.g. in the event of flooding, to a secure place and the allocation of any costs arising, especially from failure to act promptly.

Pasture care should be defined in terms of thresholds to trigger action to prevent or arrest *poaching*, *overgrazing* or *undergrazing*.

Supplementary feeding and *mineral licks* may lead stock to congregate. To guard against damage to features of special interest, it may be necessary to specify where and when they may be deployed.

Stockproof boundaries and responsibility for their maintenance or erection should be clearly recorded. Specification may be in terms of materials (e.g. post and wire fence, dry-stane dyke, hawthorn hedge) or function (e.g. cattle-proof, provision of cover for nesting birds). Materials should be compatible with the surrounding landscape. Gates, water-troughs or routes to alternative grazing should also be specified.

Mowing prior to certain dates may prevent herbs setting seed or birds such as corncrake and partridge (*Perdix perdix*) and mammals such as brown hare (*Lepus europaeus*) rearing their young. Mowing from the centre out facilitates their escape.

Dressings and *treatments* are applied principally for farming reasons and should be the subject of precise specifications as to what may be applied where, under what circumstances and at what rate.

Vehicular use may be restricted to specified operations or routes or by permitting only light-weight vehicles.

Control of pests, pollution and other undesirable impacts should be specified.

Safeguards may be required in respect of cultivation, drainage and burning.

A managment agreement may provide opportunities for *interpretation*.

REFERENCES

WARD S.D. (1996) *Guidelines for Grassland Management Agreements*. Scottish Natural Heritage Information and Advisory Note No. 52, SNH, Battleby.

WARD S.D. (In press) *Grassland management agreements*. Scottish Natural Heritage Review No. 73, SNH, Battleby.

Establishment and Management of Grass and Wild Flower Strips at Arable Field Edges in Environmentally Sensitive Areas

T. M. WEST and E. J. P. MARSHALL

IACR - Long Ashton Research Station, Department of Agricultural Sciences, University of Bristol, Long Ashton, Bristol BS18 9AF, UK

INTRODUCTION

The objectives of this MAFF-sponsored project (BD0404) were to develop practical means of protecting existing field margin communities and enhancing wildlife habitat at the edges of arable fields in ESAs. The approach was based on the creation of field margin strips of perennial vegetation, extending the herbaceous flora of the field boundary. Increased habitat and biological diversity at field margins may satisfy environmental, amenity and agricultural objectives (Marshall, 1993), conserving species, increasing natural control of crop pests and weeds and limiting agrochemical movement and soil erosion.

METHODS

A replicated field experiment was made using 18 field sites, six in each of the Breckland, South Wessex Downs and Somerset Levels and Moors Environmentally Sensitive Areas (ESAs), to determine the best establishment methods on alkaline to acid sands, heavy clay and chalky soils, respectively. Different seed mixtures supplied by Emorsgate Seeds (grass-only; grass and wild flower mixes EM1, EM5, EM6, EM7) were tested against natural regeneration, spring versus autumn sowing, and different first and second year management treatments. One side of each field between the crop edge and the boundary (hedge, bank, shelterbelt or water course) was marked out into six plots, each 30m long and 4m wide. Each 30m plot was divided into 10m long sub-plots and during 1994 the vegetation was either left unmanaged, cut once in spring (on autumn sites) or early summer (on spring sites) or treated with the herbicide fluazifop-P-butyl (Fusilade 5, Zeneca) at 0.063 g a.i./ha on autumn sites only, to control annual grass weeds. All plots at all sites were cut in autumn. During 1995 each 10m sub-plot was further divided into two sub-sub-plots which were either cut in spring 1995 and 1996 or left unmanaged. Assessments of the developing flora were made each summer for three years to examine successional changes (Marshall *et al.*, 1994)

RESULTS

There were considerable differences between sites in the plant communities that established; the sands of the Breckland had different species to those on the chalky soils in South Wessex or the clays in Somerset. Generally, there was better establishment from autumn sowing, in terms of summer ground cover. However, plant diversity was higher on spring-sown plots for the first two years (Table 1). In the Somerset ESA, naturally regenerated and spring-sown main plots had greater plant species diversity than in the autumn-established plots in summers 1994 and 1995. In 1994, the S.Wessex ESA spring-sown plots were significantly more diverse than autumn-sown plots, while in 1995 and 1996 there was a similar trend but only spring-sown EM7 plots were statistically more diverse. In the Breckland ESA, plant species numbers were similar in each year on the spring- or autumn-sown or naturally regenerated plots.

Table 1. Numbers of plant species on autumn and spring-established margin strips, in summers 1994, 1995 and 1996. Values are means of all sub-sub plots within sites.

	autumn-established			spring-established		
Year	1994	1995	1996	1994	1995	1996
ESA						
Somerset	28.0	20.0	21.8	33.7	28.2	26.0
S.Wessex	27.6	24.8	24.3	37.0	30.8	29.1
Breckland	23.1	19.2	20.3	24.5	19.0	20.2

Plant species number on sown plots, either autumn or spring-sown, were significantly greater in 1994 compared with 1995 or 1996. The naturally regenerated plots of the autumn established sites of S. Wessex and Breckland had similar species numbers in the three years, while those in Somerset were most diverse in 1994. The naturally regenerated plots on spring-established sites in the Breckland ESA had similar numbers of species in each year, while those in Somerset were most diverse in 1994 and decreased significantly in 1995 and 1996. In contrast, plant species diversity in the unsown plots of S.Wessex was highest in 1996, significantly greater than in 1994. The effects of first-year management (single cut in September, cut in April and September or selective herbicide treatment) had only minor effects on species diversity, though there are effects on individual species, e.g. reduced annual grass weeds on herbicide-treated plots. Plots sown with grasses and wild flowers were more diverse than grass-only (least species) or natural regeneration plots, though there were only minor differences between the mixtures used. Seed mixture EM7, the most diverse mix, gave the most diverse plots, on average. Under some circumstances, natural regeneration gave reasonable results.

DISCUSSION

These results demonstrate that the creation of extended field boundary strips can be achieved on a variety of sites (West and Marshall, 1996). The strips increase available habitat for farm wildlife and act as a physical buffer to reduce drift of fertiliser and pesticide drift to adjacent habitat. Soil type and site had large effects on the results, indicating that choice of seed mixture and seed rate would need to be selected on a site-to-site basis.

REFERENCES

MARSHALL E.J.P. (1993) Exploiting semi-natural habitats as part of good agricultural practice. *Scientific basis for codes of good agricultural practice. EUR 14957* (ed. Jordan, V.W.L.), pp. 95-100. Commission for the European Communities, Luxembourg.

MARSHALL E.J.P., WEST T.M. and WINSTONE L. (1994) Extending field boundary habitats to enhance farmland wildlife and improve crop and environmental protection. *Aspects of Applied Biology No. 40. Arable Farming under CAP Reform*, pp. 387-391. Association of Applied Biologists.

WEST T.M. and MARSHALL E.J.P. (1996) Managing sown field margin strips on contrasted soil types in three Environmentally Sensitive Areas. *Aspects of Applied Biology 44. Vegetation Management in Forestry, Amenity and Conservation Areas*, pp. 269-276. Association of Applied Biologists.

INDEX OF AUTHORS